D0309427

ELECTRICITY—DIRECT AND ALTERNATING CURRENT

ELECTRICITY

DIRECT AND ALTERNATING CURRENT

CHARLES S. SISKIND, M.S.E.E.

Associate Professor, Department of Electrical Engineering
Purdue University, Lafayette, Ind.

SECOND EDITION

McGRAW-HILL BOOK COMPANY, INC.
New York Toronto London
1955

ELECTRICITY—DIRECT AND ALTERNATING CURRENT

Formerly published under the title
ELECTRICITY—PRINCIPLES, PRACTICE, EXPERIMENTS.

Library of Congress Catalog Card Number: 54-7360

VI

57743

PREFACE

This book has a threefold purpose, namely, to present the general elementary principles of direct- and alternating-current electricity, to show how these principles apply to the construction and operating characteristics of the more common types of circuits, devices, and machines, and to illustrate how these principles may be verified by the performance of simple experiments with easily obtainable and readily constructed apparatus.

Each chapter is concluded with a detailed summary of the subject matter covered and numerous questions and problems pertaining to actual electrical equipment used in practice. Much emphasis is placed upon electrical demonstrations to be performed by the instructor before student groups, in connection with which many interesting projects are outlined. Detailed instructions are also given for the calculation and construction of electromagnets and for the construction of transformers, rectifier units, and other electrical devices. The latter may serve as vocational-training projects where shop facilities are available for such work.

The book is intended for use in technical institutes, junior colleges, and short courses for non-electrical-engineering students in universities, as well as in schools conducted by or associated with industry and in many technical and vocational high schools.

To give this basic text its broad base for use in elementary as well as moderately advanced courses of study, great care was exercised in arranging the wide range of topics. It is felt, therefore, that instructors may, without disturbing the planned sequence, adapt the subject matter to several levels of instruction in electricity by including or omitting suitably selected portions of the book.

This second edition has been considerably upgraded by the addition of new material of slightly more advanced character. Chapter 4, for example, is concerned with *basic theorems and laws*, as these are applied to circuits of a more complex nature; a unique simplified treatment has, however, been given this aspect of direct-current circuit theory so that, following the chapters dealing with fundamentals, it may be studied with confidence by properly prepared students. Also, an important extension involves a discussion, Chap. 7, of direct-current electrical instruments; this appropriately follows the chapter dealing with the principles of magnetism and electromagnetism. Finally, the subject of alternating-current motors, Chap. 10, has been enlarged considerably to include most types of present-day single-phase and polyphase machines, their principles of operation, characteristics, applications, and control.

The enlarged text has also been strengthened by the inclusion of several new experiments and many additional problems of varying degrees of difficulty. These portions of the book have proved extremely worthwhile, since they emphasize the important aspect of student participation involving wiring and testing procedures and the solution of typical examples.

The mathematical treatment of the subject has been limited to simple arithmetical and algebraic operations. No attempt has been made to derive all equations given, but where it was felt that they would help to augment the proper understanding of important principles, derivations of formulas have been given rigorous treatment.

CHARLES S. SISKIND

CONTENTS

LIST OF EXPERIMENTS

CHAPTER 1

ELECTRICITY—BASIC IDEAS AND EFFECTS

Electric Current and Electrical Effects.—Electricity is now recognized as the smallest known particle of matter, the negative charge. When such negative charges are set in motion by the application of an electric force, the result is said to be an *electric current.* All substances contain large numbers of negative charges called *electrons,* most of them securely bound to their parent positive nucleuses called *protons*; those that are free, unattached, roam about lazily until forced to move in a given direction when an electric force is properly applied.

It is this motion of electrons, a current of electricity, with which this book is concerned, although attention will be centered not so much upon the electric currents themselves as upon the *effects* that they produce. To be sure, the great science of electricity is useful only through these effects, because electrical energy must be converted into some other form of energy if devices and machines of one kind or another are to function and serve. In short, an electric current by itself has absolutely no value; it is only because it develops definite, completely understandable effects, whose basic laws are well known, that numerous practical applications are possible.

There are only a few electrical effects, but, taken singly or together in various combinations, they are responsible for the proper functioning of all electrical apparatus. Fortunately, each one is rather simple to understand and to demonstrate experimentally when studied by itself, although such simplicity often seems to be obscured by what appear to be, and in fact often really are, complex machines. It is nevertheless true that any complicated device is, in reality, a combination of several simple units, each one functioning according to known laws. And it is important to note in this connection that rarely, if ever, are these laws violated.

Some of the more important electrical effects and the laws that govern them will be studied both theoretically and experimentally later, but for the present it will be sufficient to make some brief comments concerning them.

The Heating Effect of an Electric Current.—It was observed early that heat is always developed in a conductor when a current of electricity is passed through it. If the rate at which this heat is developed exceeds the rate at which it is dissipated, *i.e.*, carried off by the air or surrounding objects, then the temperature continues to rise. If, on the other hand, the rate of dissipation becomes equal to the rate at which heat is developed, the temperature levels off and becomes constant. Several factors are responsible for this heating process, the more important of which are the following: (1) the value of the current, (2) the resistance of the current-carrying conductor, (3) the time during which the current flows, (4) the kind and physical size of the heat-absorbing device, (5) the temperature, density, and motion (or lack thereof) of the surrounding air.

In many of the common heating units found in the home, such as toasters, percolators, radiant heaters, water heaters, flatirons, heating pads, incandescent lamps, electric stoves, waffle irons, and curling irons, the heating is desirable and usually under perfect control. In other cases, however, excessive heating may result in severe damage to electrical equipment unless protective measures are taken to disconnect the current before this happens. In the electric motor, for example, it is customary to use low-melting-point metal links called *fuses*, or *circuit breakers*, which function to break the current flow if for some reason the temperature should rise above safe limits. This is also true in house-wiring electric circuits where overheated wires are likely to cause serious fire hazards. In any event, it should be clear that the heating effect is a *natural* result of a flow of current, and that the extent to which such heating takes place will depend upon well-known and readily controlled factors.

The Magnetic Effect of an Electric Current.—In 1820, the great scientist Hans Christian Oersted[1] observed that a compass was deflected when placed near a wire carrying an electric current. This simple but far-reaching discovery definitely demonstrated the connection between electricity and magnetism and started a series of important investigations to advance the knowledge of the new science of *electromagnetism.* It was soon learned, for example, that the magnetic effect can be greatly strengthened by using coils of wire instead of straight conductors, by employing cores of iron or other good-quality magnetic substances, and by properly proportioning and arranging (*i.e.*, designing) the current-carrying coil and the magnetic core. Definite principles and laws were later discovered relating to electromagnetism, and these are now fundamental to the proper understanding of the operation of the great number of practical electromagnetic devices and machines. In the following chapters of this book the student will become familiar with these principles and laws through experiment and, having learned them thoroughly, will not only be able to handle electrical equipment intelligently but will be in a position to predict what will happen under known conditions. The principle of operation of such electromagnetic devices and machines as bells, telephone receivers, telegraph sounders, lifting magnets, track and elevator brakes, magnetic separators, electric meters, dynamos, transformers, and others quite as well known will be shown to depend upon the direct connection between electricity and magnetism.

The Chemical Effect of an Electric Current.—One of the greatest scientists who ever lived was Michael Faraday.[1] His many contributions were so fundamental that they have had a far-reaching influence upon the tremendous scientific progress since his time. It was he who first showed the close connection between electricity and chemical action,

[1] See Appendix, p. 520.

and this fact has resulted in such important modern processes as electroplating, electrorefining, electrotyping, the production of oxygen, hydrogen, and chlorine gases, and the manufacture of metallic sodium, potassium, and caustic soda. In this connection it is significant that electrochemical reactions are absolutely exact in the sense that they are governed by exact laws, always reproducible. This latter point has given us the basis for the accepted unit of electric current, the *international ampere*. By an act of Congress in 1894, the international ampere was defined as "*the unvarying current which, when passed through a solution of nitrate of silver in accordance with standard specifications, deposits silver at the rate of* 0.001118 *gram per second.*"

The basis for all electrochemical action is the elementary *electrolytic cell*. Essentially it consists of two dissimilar metallic plates called *electrodes*, immersed in a solution containing any salt, alkali, or acid, called the *electrolyte*. When a current of electricity is passed through such a cell from an outside source of electric power, chemical changes take place. Sometimes the metal from one plate is carried over by the electrolyte and is deposited on the other plate; in other cases gases are liberated and collected at the electrodes; in still others completely new chemical products are formed. The lead-acid storage battery is an excellent example of the practical use to which electrochemical action is put. In this valuable device the electrodes are properly *formed* by charging, *i.e.*, by sending current into the battery in a definite direction, and then are used as a *source* of electricity until the plates have been reduced. The fact that this process may be repeated many times is one good reason for the extensive use of such batteries.

The Effect of Electromagnetic Induction.—It is significant that Oersted's discovery, in 1820, of the direct connection between electricity and magnetism stimulated a good deal of scientific curiosity and enthusiasm. Michael Faraday in England was one of those brilliant men who immediately recognized its great possibilities and set about studying this strange phenomenon in his laboratory at the Royal Society in London. It must be borne in mind that in those days the only practical source of electric current was the primary battery, similar in many respects to the present-day dry cell and invented in 1801 by Alessandro Volta.[1] The more Faraday experimented with this new scientific toy, *i.e.*, magnetism produced by electric currents, the more convinced did he become that there was some way to cause a reciprocal action, which meant producing a flow of current from magnetism. In his finely kept notebook he therefore recorded a statement in the form of a question; then he proceeded to devote himself to this problem of discovering a method whereby an electrical effect would result if something was done to a magnet. He performed a great many experiments and constructed all sorts of ingenious pieces of equipment but always failed in his mission. His experiments seemed to lead him nowhere. In the light of our present knowledge, we know, of course, that Faraday was looking in the wrong place and also that he had very little background from which he could get information for his investigations. Yet he stubbornly continued in the face of his failures because he knew he was searching for a vital principle.

And then in August, 1831, he finally hit upon the solution that had evaded him for 11 years. He had constructed a sort of transformer now commonly used in all sorts of alternating-current circuits. This consisted of two separate coils of copper wire placed around an iron ring, the latter forming a common core for the two coils. To the ends of the first coil, the *primary* coil, he connected a simple battery. To the second coil, the *secondary* coil, he fastened a short length of copper wire and made it pass directly over a horizontally balanced compass needle. It was his belief that the compass needle would be deflected merely because the secondary coil was magnetically linked to the primary coil through the iron ring. Understand that the primary coil, not the secondary coil, carried a current of electricity. However, no such deflection resulted. What he did observe was something quite

[1] See Appendix, p. 519.

unexpected, something that gave him the answer to his riddle. It was this: the compass did move only when the primary circuit was either closed or opened. When the battery circuit was closed, the needle moved from its original north-south direction to a position at right angles to the wire, then, after oscillating back and forth, finally came to rest in a north-south direction. Again, upon opening the battery circuit the same action resulted. It was immediately obvious to him that a current flow resulted in the secondary circuit (the one not connected to the battery) only when a *change* took place, *i.e.*, when the primary coil was energized or de-energized. In other words, *the needle deflected only while the current was growing or decaying and at no other time.* This phenomenon is now properly known as the *principle* or *effect of electromagnetic induction* and merely indicates that the *induced* currents result from a *change* in the *magnetism* produced *electrically.* Note that the term "electromagnetic induction" is derived from three words, namely, electricity, magnetism, and induced. It is the basis of operation of all modern electrodynamic machinery such as generators, motors, and transformers. Without this important discovery we should still be using the very inefficient battery as a primary source of electricity.

Other Effects of an Electric Current.—Electricity can, of course, produce other effects than those discussed above, but since these are beyond the scope of this book they are merely mentioned here. There is, for example, the well-known *physiological effect* wherein the living body experiences strange and sometimes fatal reactions when a current of electricity is passed through it. Many of us have *felt* the muscular contractions induced by a current flow in our bodies, and still others have heard of the death of persons who came in contact with *live circuits.* Another interesting effect of a flow of electricity is the so-called *thermoelectric effect,* which is simply a heating at the junction between two dissimilar metals in an electric circuit carrying a current. Much use is made of this effect *in reverse* in connection with the measurement of electrical quantities in alternating-current circuits. Here a thermocouple, which is a junction of two dissimilar metals such as iron and copper, is placed in physical contact with an electrically heated conductor; as a result of the rise in temperature of the *couple* due to heat conduction, a current flows in a circuit consisting of the thermocouple and the measuring instrument. Since the current flow depends directly upon the rise in temperature, the deflection of the instrument needle is a true indication of the current flow and therefore the temperature. Still other electrical phenomena are the *piezoelectric effect* and the *photoelectric effect.* In the first a flow of current in a circuit results from a change in pressure upon certain crystals. This is made use of in connection with the measurements of high pressures in large guns, as well as in accurate frequency control in radio oscillators wherein precision-ground crystals are used because they have a natural period of mechanical vibration. In the second (the photoelectric effect) a current flow results when light falls upon certain light-sensitive materials. Practical examples of this important effect are talking moving pictures, television, automatic sorting machines, automatic drinking fountains, door openers, burglar-alarm systems, counting machines, and many others.

Electron Theory of Current Flow.—It was previously mentioned that a flow of current in an electric circuit is a motion of free electrons through the conducting materials that go to make up the circuit. These particles, very small indeed, exist in great numbers in all matter but are especially numerous in metals such as copper, aluminum, silver, gold, nickel, and tungsten. Before an electric potential is impressed upon the circuit (the electric potential is usually referred to as the *voltage*), the electrons roam about very slowly at random so that the actual *net* forward motion is zero. But when a voltage is applied, the electrons begin to drift at an extremely low speed toward the positive pole. Note that the *electron flow, i.e.,* the current, *is toward the positive terminal* of the source of supply, not from it. However, previous to the proposal of the electron theory, at the end of the nineteenth century, and before the performance of a great variety of experiments that have since proved it to be completely valid, it was arbitrarily assumed that the current flowed *from* (not *to*) the positive terminal of the source of supply. Understand that this is the direct opposite of the actual electron flow. Now, on the basis of that assumption several important rules were formulated so that certain electromagnetic actions could be predicted in advance. These include such well-known phenomena as the direction of the deflection of a compass when placed near a current-bearing wire or coil, the polarity of a generator when

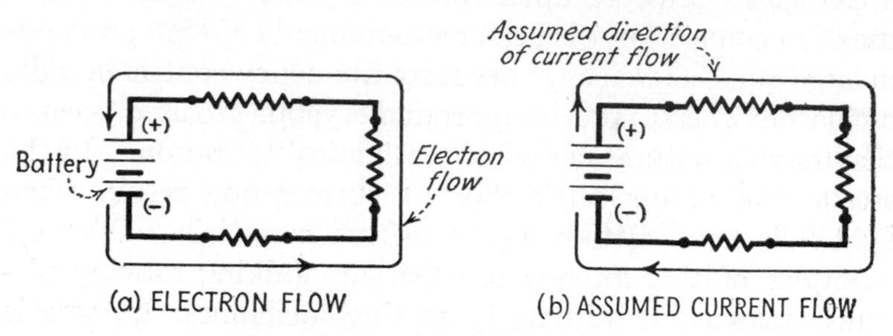

FIG. 1.—Directions of current flow.

the armature is turned in a magnetic field, the direction of rotation of a motor when its armature carries a current and is placed in a magnetic field. As will be pointed out later, these arbitrary rules are purposely worded in such a way that they merely state the results of actual experimental evidence. And since it makes absolutely no difference whether the rules are based upon the actual electron flow or upon an arbitrarily assumed current flow, so long as the rules and the actions always agree, it has been decided to retain the original statements based upon a current flow *from the positive terminal* of the source of supply (see Fig. 1*b*). It is thought, and properly so, that less confusion will result. Therefore, in all that follows in this book the student should remember that the current is assumed to flow *from* the positive terminal of the source, through the electric circuit, thence back to the negative terminal of the source.

Conductors and Insulators.—The most common of all electrical conductors is copper, which contains about 1,600,000 million million million *free electrons* in every cubic inch. (This enormous number is usually written 16×10^{23} and means 1,600,000,000,000,000,000,000,000.) As the material becomes a poorer electrical conductor, the number of free electrons decreases. For example, aluminum contains 9.8×10^{23} free electrons per cubic inch, nickel has 3.5×10^{23} free electrons per cubic inch, iron 2.2×10^{23}, German silver 3.3×10^{22}, and Nichrome 2.5×10^{22}. Silver is slightly better as a conductor of electricity than copper and contains 16.4×10^{23} free electrons per cubic inch. The fact that only the free electrons move when a voltage is applied means that the better conductors pass more current than the poorer conductors for the *same* impressed electric pressure. Or, to put it another way, the greater the number of free electrons, the better the *conductivity*.

Although the action of getting the free electrons *started* in an entire circuit is almost instantaneous when a voltage is applied, the actual speed (or drift) of the electrons toward the positive terminal is extremely low. For example, when the current in a No. 14 copper wire (a wire common to house-wiring circuits) is $8\frac{1}{2}$ amp., the average speed of the electrons will be about $\frac{1}{100}$ in. per second. Moreover, as the electric current increases (or decreases) the speed of the *same* electrons increases (or decreases) proportionately.

Materials generally regarded as insulators, *i.e.*, poor conductors, also contain some free electrons. Their number is, however, exceedingly small when compared with the metals mentioned above. For example, hard rubber contains only about 3 free electrons per cubic inch, clear mica about 14, paraffin (Parawax) about 270, paraffined mahogany wood about 670,000, and plate glass about 1,380,000.

From what has been said above, then, it should be clear that there is no such thing as a perfect electrical insulator in the sense that no electrons will move when the material is subjected to an electric pressure, *i.e.*, a voltage. All that can be said is that under ordinary circumstances the insulators will permit the flow of so few electrons that, for practical purposes, they may be considered as complete current "stoppers."

Insulating Coverings for Wires.—Most wires used in electric circuits are covered with some kind of insulating material. Its purpose is to keep the metallic conductors separated electrically and also to prevent them from touching *grounded* structures such as iron pipes, wet wood poles, railway tracks, or other bodies that can carry current back to the usually *grounded* source of supply. In motors, for example, every wire is covered with some type of insulating material that will withstand voltages much higher than those normally encountered in practice. Furthermore, to prevent insulation failure due to absorbed moisture or overheating, it is customary to dip finished coils of wire into a special insulating varnish, which, when baked at about 250°F., adds strength, stiffness, and insulating qualities far beyond those possessed by the original coatings themselves.

Among the more common insulating coverings in use today are cotton, silk, enamel, asbestos, rubber, and glass. Magnet wire, as ordinary copper wire is generally called by electrical men, may have one, two, or three layers of one or two of these materials. Until about 1910, cotton was practically the only wire insulation in use. Though still popular in single and double coverings, it is subject to deterioration under vibration and excessive heat. However, when impregnated with a baking varnish its qualities are greatly improved. To overcome the objection that cotton occupies too much space, especially when used in the winding of coils for electrical machines, silk is frequently used as a substitute. In addition to being a much better insulating material (its electrical breakdown strength is higher), it is tougher and more uniform. However, its cost is considerably higher than cotton, for which reason it is used only where it is absolutely necessary. A very common covering for wires, used extensively in connection with the windings on motors, generators, transformers, and the like, is Cottonite. This is an enameled wire with a single covering of cotton. Its insulating qualities are as good as two layers of cotton, and, in addition, it takes up much less space than the latter. Enamel and silk have also been used in limited application with good effect, but the cost has usually been found to be greater than the added value.

In recent years special high-temperature, high-mechanical-strength enamels have been developed by some manufacturers. These are usually applied in two layers and are known in the trade as Formvar and Formex. The enamels are very tough and can stand tremendous mechanical beating. Furthermore, they have a high space factor, *i.e.*, the insulation takes up very little space. The latter point is especially important in electrical machinery where the ability to perform is a direct function of the total volume of *copper* that can be put into the windings. In fact, it has been found that, when replacing other double-insulated wires, the Formvar and Formex wires may be larger because of the improved space factor. Another recent development is a spun-glass fiber, which, when manufactured in the form of tapes, can be wrapped around wires like cotton or silk. This glass wrapping is not only strong electrically and mechanically but will not absorb moisture, a very desirable characteristic indeed. In addition, it can withstand very high temperatures, so high, in fact, that it has been found practical frequently to increase the current rating of electrical machines and devices by as much as 30 per cent without subjecting them to the normal hazards due to burnout failures.

Asbestos insulation for magnet wire has only one real application, and that is where the temperatures are very high. The electric cords for toasters, flatirons, waffle irons, and the like and the wires used in motors located where the temperature is abnormally high are always covered with asbestos. It is much thicker than cotton, has poorer mechanical strength, and costs much more than cotton. For house-wiring purposes rubber-covered wire with a layer of braided cotton is standard practice. There are several grades of these wires, though they are all usually dipped in a tarlike compound to give the surface material better mechanical and weatherproof qualities.

As has been pointed out, coils of wire are usually dipped in special insulating varnishes and are baked to add stiffness, mechanical strength, and high insulation value to the finished products. This dipping and baking process may be done either before or after the complete machine or device is assembled. Dipping in varnish and baking generally serves three purposes: (1) to preserve the insulation covering, (2) to act as a partial heat conductor, and (3) to add mechanical strength to the completed coil. With regard to the first point it should be stated that the high-grade varnishes will resist water, oil, and sometimes destructive fumes. In connection with point 3, vibrations set up by magnetic fields or mechanical unbalance will usually not affect the position of the wires or coils.

There are two general kinds of varnish used by manufacturers of electrical machinery, namely, air-drying and baking varnishes. Since air-drying varnish dries rapidly, it becomes rather brittle in time and loses its mechanical strength. It is used only on coils previously treated to a dipping and baking service. Baking varnishes dry very slowly and will remain sticky and wet for several days unless properly baked. The varnishes are usually applied by submerging the whole unit in a tank containing the hot liquid until all the pores and air spaces have been penetrated. Preheating of the coils of wire generally helps drive out the air and permits better penetration. After the baking process at temperatures up to about 260°F. for several hours in gas-heated or electrically heated ovens or by applying infrared rays directly, the assembly becomes a strong, stiff mass capable of withstanding considerable mechanical abuse.

Electric Circuits.—Aside from the fact that electrical energy can be readily converted into other forms of energy, such as heating, magnetic, and chemical energy, its usefulness has been greatly extended because it may be transmitted easily and efficiently through relatively small wires. Compared with the short distances over which steam is usually sent through large pipes, the transmission of electrical energy offers the added advantage that, with the proper supplementary equipment such as transformers, enormous distances may be covered between power station and consumer. In addition to this, electrical service can be supplied to virtually any location so that its convenience is further extended. It is for these reasons, therefore, as well as others to be considered, that electrical energy has become widespread, has indeed become man's greatest servant.

The transfer of electrical energy always takes place through an *electric circuit*. Generally speaking, an electric circuit consists of six important elements: (1) the electrical source of supply, (2) the device or machine that converts the electrical energy into some other form of useful energy, (3) the device that controls the flow of the electric current, (4) the device that acts as a protective agency, (5) the instruments or meters used in measuring the various elements of electric flow, and (6) the connecting wires that properly join together those units indicated above.

Taking up each one of the elements separately, let us discuss them briefly.

1. The source of supply may be a dry cell, a storage battery, an electric generator, a photoelectric cell, or perhaps a thermocouple. It is the place where the electrical energy originates. Understand that it originates only because *some other form of energy* such as chemical energy, mechanical energy, light energy, or heat energy *has been converted into it.* This is to say that electrical energy cannot be created unless there is a definite process of conversion. In the farm lighting plant, for example, gasoline vapor is exploded in an engine which, producing mechanical rotation of the driving

and driven units, creates electrical energy in the generator. In the large steam power plant, coal is burned in a boiler, the heat of which produces steam, which in turn is made to propel the steam engine or turbine and its coupled electric generator. And in the hydroelectric plant falling water is made to revolve a water wheel, which is similarly coupled to an electric generator. Note particularly that in all these conversions the electrical energy is supplied to the electrical device only *during* the operation of the generator. When the mechanical machine is at rest, the generator is idle and has ceased to function. Electrical energy cannot be stored in a generator for future use; it must be used *during its time of manufacture*. In the case of the dry cell or the storage battery, on the other hand, chemical energy is stored in the combination of materials that go to make up the device. And when properly connected to an electrical utility such as a flashlight or a motor, the stored chemical energy is changed to the desired electrical energy. The same kinds of processes apply to the photoelectric cell and the thermocouple; in the former light energy is changed to electrical energy, and in the latter heat energy develops into electrical energy.

2. It is an interesting point that all devices and machines function usefully only when some sort of energy change takes place. The electrical devices with which we are familiar are all excellent examples of this fact. Electrical energy is converted into heat and light in the incandescent lamp, into heat in the electric furnace and the flatiron, into mechanical motion in the motor, into chemical reactions in the charging of the storage battery or in the plating of metals or in the production of useful gases and new substances in certain electrochemical operations. In short, electricity has no value whatsoever until something can be made to happen as a result of its flow. And there are literally thousands of such practical utilization devices.

3. To control the flow of electricity it is necessary to employ various kinds and types of device, depending, of course, upon the services they are expected to render. Sometimes

they are merely snap or toggle switches to turn electrical conveniences "on" and "off." In other cases they may not only "start" and "stop" the operation of such machines as electric motors but may also change the speed, produce a braking action, or reverse the direction of rotation. In still other arrangements they may act to regulate the temperature within definite limits, as, for example, in the automatic electric iron. Strictly speaking, control units are in reality *switches*, sometimes simple and sometimes complex. In some cases they operate in either of two positions, and in others in any one of a great many positions; in still other arrangements they change conditions in electric circuits from one instant to another. In any event it is always necessary to have some kind of control mechanism in an electric circuit; in fact, it is this very element of control that adds so much value to the usefulness of electrical energy.

4. Although much care is usually taken in the manufacture of all kinds of electrical equipment and the wires used to join them together, failures do occur frequently. Such failures may be the result of carelessness, lack of information concerning the installation and operation of electrical equipment, overloading beyond reasonable limits, or just plain "wearing out" due to continuous use or length of service. In any event it is always necessary to employ some kind of *protection* so that, when breakdown does occur in one part of an electric circuit, it may be localized to the extent that other parts are not affected. Many kinds of protective devices are available, taking the form of the familiar fuse, which is nothing but a low-melting-point link of metal generally inserted in one or more wires, or the more desirable electromagnetic unit known as a *circuit breaker*. In fact, electrical service is available to consumers only if proper protection is provided in accordance with rules set up by authorized agencies, such rules being devised to protect life and property.

5. When a field of knowledge reaches the place where accurate measurements can be made of the various quantities

involved, and when such measurements can yield such useful information that predictions are possible, then such a branch of knowledge becomes a science. Electricity is, in this sense, a particularly *exact science* because instruments and meters are available that will permit not only prediction of the actions of electrical devices and machines but also the operation of equipment in other sciences. In fact, design engineers depend to a large extent upon experimental evidence, obtained from accurate instruments, for the information they must have to build machines that will operate according to plan. Lord Kelvin, the eminent scientist, was speaking of this kind of *exact science* when he remarked: "I often say that when you can measure what you are speaking about, and express it in numbers, you know something about it; but when you cannot measure it, when you cannot express it in numbers, your knowledge is of a meagre and unsatisfactory kind. It may be the beginning of knowledge, but you have scarcely, in your thoughts, advanced to the stage of a *science*, whatever the matter may be." In the science of electricity there are a great many kinds and types of electrical instruments and meters. As will be pointed out in a later chapter, there are *instruments* that measure current flow (amperes), electric pressure (volts), resistance to current flow (ohms), electric power (watts), alternating-current frequency (cycles), and power factor (*P.F.*), as well as others. All of these *indicate* the quantities measured by the deflection of pointers over calibrated scales. Meters, on the other hand, are recording devices, since they register their quantities on dials and charts, as, for example, in kilowatt-hour meters, which record energy consumption on dials, or voltage and frequency recorders, which register the voltage and frequency changes on charts. In short, instruments and meters are frequently used in electric circuits for the purpose of providing useful information. Only in this way is it possible to determine precisely how much energy is consumed, how electrical quantities fluctuate, how much heating is developed, what changes should be made in existing installations, or how to design new things. To eliminate guesswork, instruments and meters must be used.

6. All parts in electric circuits must be joined together with wires. Although these are generally solid, round copper wires, this is not always the case. Wires may be square, rectangular, or even irregular in cross section and may be made up in bundles (strands) for flexibility. Furthermore, wires may be aluminum, tungsten, nickel, iron, German silver, Nichrome, or almost any other material, depending upon the circuit conditions, or may even be one metal welded right over another as in the case of steel wires coated with a thin

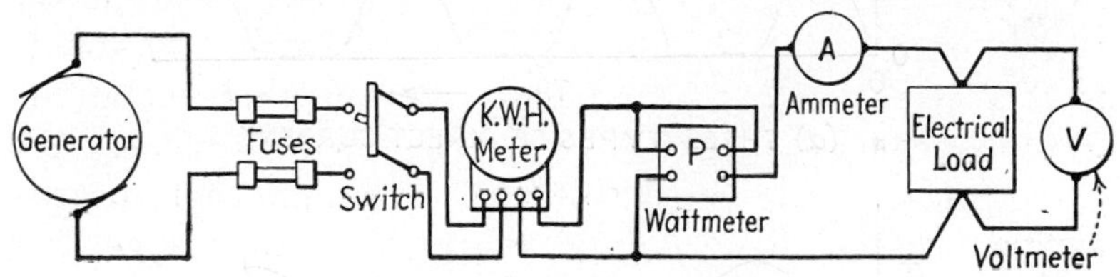

FIG. 2.—The electric circuit.

layer of copper. This whole subject of electrical conductors is so important that an entire chapter will be devoted to it. At that time the important properties of wires will be studied so that they may be used wisely and economically.

Figure 2 shows an electric circuit in which are included the essential parts discussed above. It should be studied carefully so that the arrangement of the various parts may be firmly fixed in mind.

Kinds of Electric Current.—There are several general kinds of electric current used in present-day practice, each one having its special field of application. They are (1) direct current, (2) alternating current, and (3) oscillating current.

A direct current is one in which the electrons move in the same direction, *always*—it is, in this respect, a *unidirectional* current. This implies that the source of supply is either a direct-current generator or a battery. When the direct current remains substantially constant, it is called a *continuous direct current.* A *pulsating direct current*, on the other hand, changes its magnitude from instant to instant but does so regularly; *i.e.*, the pulsations vary periodically. The current

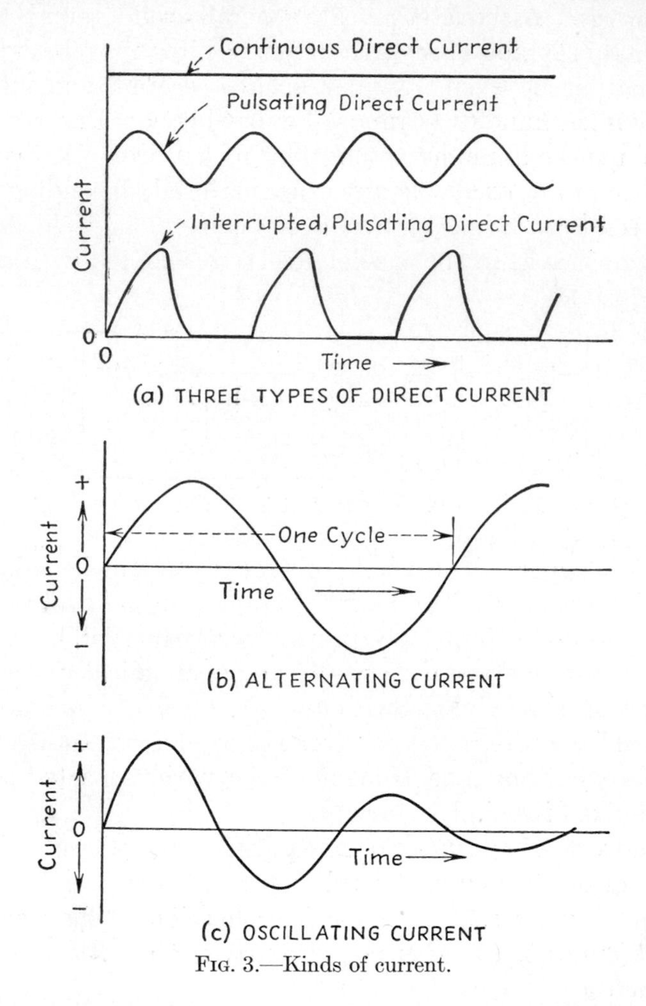

FIG. 3.—Kinds of current.

taken by the ignition coil in the electrical system of an automobile, for example, is both *interrupted* and pulsating.

An alternating current is one that varies in both magnitude *and* direction and does so with perfect regularity. All changes must take place similarly over given time periods and the *average value* over such periods is zero. Thus, a 60-cycle alternating current is one in which each positive and negative flow repeats itself faithfully every $\frac{1}{60}$ sec.; also, the changes that take place during the positive half of the cycle are repeated in the reverse direction during the negative half of the cycle. In alternating-current work the *frequency* is designated as *cycles per second*, or briefly cycles, and means merely the number of complete positive and negative pulses of the current flow for 1 sec. of time. If f represents the frequency in cycles per second, one cycle will occur in $1/f$ sec.

An oscillating current, obtained only in special circuits consisting of units of resistance, inductance, and capacitance (to be discussed later), is one in which successive cycles of alternating current vary regularly in magnitude, though the time and direction changes are unaffected. Such currents may infrequently be unidirectional in character and are generally present in communication circuits, and in power systems during sudden conditions of change.

SUMMARY

1. An electric current is a flow of negative particles called *electrons*. They always move toward the positive terminal of the source of supply.
2. For practical reasons the direction of current flow is generally assumed to be from the positive terminal of the source of supply (not *to* it).
3. A flow of electricity through circuits is useful only because it produces many electrical effects. Some of the more important of them are heating, magnetic, chemical, electromagnetic induction, physiological, thermo, piezo, photo.
4. The metals are generally good conductors of electricity because they contain enormous numbers of free electrons ready to move when an electric pressure is applied. Conversely, insulating materials are poor conductors because they have relatively few free electrons.

CHAPTER 2

WIRES AND CABLES AND THEIR ELECTRICAL PROPERTIES

Resistance.—All electric circuits oppose a current flow to some extent. This opposition makes itself felt by limiting the amount of current in the circuit, the extent of the limitation being determined by the magnitude of this opposition. For a given electric pressure, called the *voltage*, the current increases as the opposition is diminished, and vice versa. In electrical terms this opposition is called the *resistance* and *is* defined as *the property of a material that tends to oppose a flow of current.* Note that it is a *property of*, not something real. It is as much the property of the copper wire, for example, as is its hardness or its malleability, just as is the "wetness" of water or the "stiffness" of a spring. To distinguish the resistance property from the thing itself, the latter is called a *resistor*.

The unit of resistance is the *international ohm* and *is* defined as *the resistance of a column of mercury having standard dimensions of length and area, having a definite mass, and being at a definite temperature.* In accordance with an act of Congress passed in 1894, the specifications have been set as follows:

Mass = 14.4521 g.,
Length = 106.25 cm.,
Area = 1 sq. mm. uniform cross section,
Temperature = that of melting ice.

From the wording of the definition for an ohm it should be obvious that the resistance of a conductor of electricity of homogeneous and symmetrical construction depends upon four factors: (1) kind of material, (2) length, (3) area, and (4) temperature. As a general rule, the pure metals, *i.e.*, the elements, have the least resistance for the same dimensions of length and area; the alloys obstruct the flow of current to a greater extent than do the elements.

The Circular Mil-foot.—Since electric wires are usually circular in cross section, it has been found desirable to specify the area in terms of the circular unit instead of the customary square unit. In this way it is possible to dispense with the irrational number π in making calculations for the area. Thus, the area of a circular wire having a diameter of 1/1000 in., or 1 mil, is arbitrarily said to be 1 circular mil. (Actually such a wire has an area of 0.0000007854 sq. in.) And since the area varies directly with the diameter squared, *i.e.*, d^2, it should be clear that the area in circular mils can be determined by squaring the diameter d of the round wire expressed in mils, as shown in the accompanying table.

Mils Diameter	Circular Mils
1	1
2	4
3	9
10	100
50	2,500
250	62,500
etc.	etc.

It is convenient in practice to use the foot as the unit of length, for which reason the resistances of all conductors are specified and compared with each other on the basis of a wire having a diameter of 1 mil and a length of 1 ft. Such a unit is called a *circular mil-foot*, or briefly a *mil-foot*.

Resistivity.—For comparative reasons, as well as for calculating purposes, the resistances of all conductors are specified in terms of the mil-foot. This is known as the *resistivity* and is represented by the Greek symbol ρ. Table I lists the more common conducting materials found in electrical practice with their resistivities at 20°C.

TABLE I.—RESISTIVITIES OF COMMON ELEMENTS AND ALLOYS AT 20°C.

Element	ρ, ohms per mil-foot	Alloy	ρ, ohms per mil-foot
Silver	9.9	Brass	42
Copper (annealed)	10.37	German silver	199
Copper (hard drawn)	10.65	Manganin	265
Gold (pure)	14	Lucero	280
Aluminum	17	Advance	294
Magnesium	28	Constantan	302
Tungsten	33	Excello	550
Zinc	36	Nichrome	600–660
Nickel	47	Chromel	625–655
Iron (cast)	54		
Platinum	60		
Iron (commercial)	75		
Lead	132		
Mercury	577		

The elements copper and aluminum are generally used for transmission purposes in most indoor and outdoor installations. Copper is nearly always used for coils in electromagnets, and it is for this reason that it is generally referred to in the trade as *magnet wire*. The other elements are used only occasionally with the exception of tungsten, which is employed almost exclusively in the filaments of incandescent lamps. Note that silver has a slightly lower resistivity than copper, about 4.5 per cent less, which means that it would replace copper if it were as plentiful and as cheap. The alloys Lucero, Advance, Excello, Nichrome, and Chromel are commonly used in heating units because they resist oxidation at high temperatures, are mechanically strong and hard, and have comparatively high resistivities. The latter point is important in connection with the manufacture of domestic appliances because such heating elements must occupy little space for required values of resistance. The alloy Manganin is used where temperature changes must not affect the value of the resistance.

Calculation of Resistance.—As was pointed out above, the resistance of a conductor of uniform cross section depends upon four factors. If the resistivity, *i.e.*, the resistance per mil-foot, is specified at a given temperature, then it is proper to say that the resistance of a wire of length l ft. and area $C.M.$ circular mils is equal to

$$R = \rho \times \frac{l}{C.M.} \tag{1}$$

This equation merely states that the *resistance is directly proportional to the length and inversely proportional to the area*, where ρ is the factor of proportionality. Thus, 1,000 ft. of copper wire at 20°C. having a diameter of 0.0453 in. would have a resistance equal to

$$R = 10.37 \times \frac{1{,}000 \text{ ft.}}{45.3^2 \ C.M.} = 10.37 \times \frac{1{,}000}{2{,}052} = 5.05 \text{ ohms}$$

the number 10.37 being the resistivity of copper ρ.

It is easy to understand that as the length increases the resistance likewise increases, but some thought is necessary if it is to be seen that the reverse is true concerning the area. Large wires have less resistance than small wires because the number of free electrons per unit of length increases with the area. This is to say that more electrons will move upon the application of an electric pressure as the cross section is enlarged, for which reason it can be said that the opposition to the flow of current is reduced. Thus, *the resistance varies inversely as the area.*

The above equation is useful in many ways. When written

$$C.M. = \rho \times \frac{l}{R} \tag{1a}$$

it is possible to find the size of wire of a given material when the length and resistance are known. Or when written

$$l = \frac{R \times C.M.}{\rho} \tag{1b}$$

it is possible to determine how many feet of a given wire should be used to obtain a certain resistance. And, finally, it is possible to select the proper kind of wire from given values of R, $C.M.$, and l if the following equation is used:

$$\rho = \frac{R \times C.M.}{l} \tag{1c}$$

After the value of ρ is calculated, Table I should be consulted.

Wire Tables.—Wires used as electrical conductors are manufactured in accordance with standard specifications. For convenience it is found desirable to indicate wires of different cross-sectional areas by gauge numbers, successive numbers differing in diameter by a factor of about 1.26. This selection was made because a square mil has an area 26 per cent larger than a circular mil. The largest commercial-size round wire is No. 0000. Then comes No. 000, then No. 00, then No. 0, and next a series of numbers beginning with No. 1 and continuing to No. 40 and more. Note that the larger the number the smaller the area. In this country gauge numbers follow the original Brown and Sharpe (B & S) plan, now generally known as the American wire gauge (A. w. g.). Tables of various kinds are available for ready use and are consulted frequently by electrical men. Table II is one such compilation and contains a great deal of useful information. In addition to the various wire sizes from No. 0000 to No. 36 and their areas and diameters, it also indicates resistances per 1,000 ft., the number of feet in 1 lb., and facts pertaining to bare, plain enamel and Formex wires.

Table III is another useful compilation showing differences existing between round and square wires covered with two layers of cotton (d.c.c.). This table is interesting because it shows that a square wire has *about* 26 per cent more area than a round wire of the same gauge number. If it were not for the fact that in practice the corners are slightly rounded off to eliminate sharp edges, which would ordinarily cut through insulation, the above relationship would be exact. From what has been said, therefore, it should be true that a square wire of a certain gauge number should have the same area as a round wire of the next smaller gauge number. Thus, a No. 10 square wire is approximately equivalent in area to a No. 9 round wire.

In certain applications, particularly in connection with the winding of coils in large electrical machines, rectangular wires are very desirable. When placed carefully side by side, coils of rectangular wire take up much less space than those wound with round wires. Such wires are made commercially in a great variety of dimensions and may be purchased in much the same way as are round and square wires. Table IV is one such compilation, showing wires from 0.060 × 0.045 in. to 0.400 × 0.165 in. To obtain the area in circular mils, merely locate where the horizontal and vertical columns cross when the selected figures are extended across and down.

Other useful information in connection with these tables follows:

1. There are 1,273,000 *C.M.* in 1 sq. in.

2. For round wires, every change of three gauge numbers changes the area and resistance in the ratio of 2 : 1 or 1 : 2, depending upon the direction of the change.

3. For round wires, every change of 10 gauge numbers changes the area and resistance in the ratio of 10 : 1 or 1 : 10, depending upon the direction of the change.

4. As mentioned previously, every change of one gauge number changes the area and the resistance in the ratio of 1.26 : 1 or 1 : 1.26 (roughly $1\frac{1}{4}$: 1).

Cables.—As wires become larger in area, they become more difficult to handle because they lose flexibility. For some outdoor transmission lines and in factory wiring where conductors of relatively large cross-sectional area are necessary, it is found helpful to use *stranded* cables. These are bundles of small wires arranged in concentric layers and

TABLE II.—ROUND WIRES—STANDARD ANNEALED COPPER—AMERICAN WIRE GAUGE

A.w.g. No.	Circular mils	Bare			Plain enamel					Formvar or Formex				
		Diameter, mils	Resistance per 1,000 ft.		Diameter, mils	Turns per square inch	Feet per pound	Ohms per pound		Diameter, mils	Turns per square inch	Feet per pound	Ohms per pound	
			25°C.	75°C.				25°C.	75°C.				25°C.	75°C.
0000	211,600	460	0.050	0.060										
000	167,800	410	0.063	0.075										
00	133,100	365	0.079	0.094										
0	105,500	325	0.100	0.120										
1	83,690	289	0.126	0.150										
2	66,370	257	0.159	0.189										
3	52,640	229	0.202	0.240										
4	41,740	204	0.254	0.303										
5	33,100	182	0.319	0.381										
6	26,250	162	0.403	0.480	164		12.5	0.0050	0.0060	166		12.4	0.0049	0.0059
7	20,820	144	0.510	0.608	146		15.7	0.0079	0.0095	148		15.6	0.0078	0.0094
8	16,150	128	0.645	0.770	130		19.8	0.0125	0.0150	132		19.7	0.0124	0.0149
9	13,090	114	0.813	0.970	116		25.0	0.0198	0.0238	118		24.9	0.0197	0.0237
10	10,380	102	1.02	1.21	103		31.5	0.0315	0.0378	105		31.4	0.0314	0.0376
11	8,234	90.7	1.29	1.53	92.7		39.7	0.0501	0.0601	94.2		39.5	0.0498	0.0598
12	6,530	80.8	1.62	1.93	82.7		50.0	0.0796	0.0958	84.2		50.0	0.0794	0.0952
13	5,178	72.0	2.04	2.43	73.8		63.0	0.1265	0.1520	75.3		62.9	0.1260	0.1512
14	4,107	64.1	2.57	3.07	65.9		79.4	0.2012	0.2415	67.3		79.3	0.2005	0.2405
15	3,257	57.1	3.24	3.87	58.8		100	0.3197	0.3840	60.2		99.0	0.3152	0.378
16	2,583	50.8	4.10	4.89	52.4	358	126	0.5080	0.0610	53.8	340	125	0.5020	0.602
17	2,048	45.3	5.15	6.14	46.9	466	159	0.8086	0.970	48.2	425	158	0.8001	0.960
18	1,624	40.3	6.51	7.76	41.8	572	201	.285	1.54	43.1	530	199	1.271	1.525

19	1,288	35.9	8.21	9.79	37.4	718	253	2.040	2.45	38.6	660	250	2.061	2.475
20	1,022	32.0	10.3	12.3	33.4	875	319	3.245	3.89	34.6	800	315	3.197	3.84
21	810	28.5	13.0	15.5	29.9	1,080	402	5.153	6.18	31.0	990	398	5.094	6.11
22	642	25.3	16.5	19.7	26.7	1,332	507	8.198	9.75	27.7	1,200	503	8.188	9.80
23	509	22.6	20.7	24.7	23.8	1,650	639	13.02	15.6	24.9	1,500	633	12.89	15.48
24	404	20.1	26.2	31.2	21.3	2,045	805	20.65	24.8	22.3	1,820	794	20.38	24.4
25	320	17.9	33.0	39.4	19.0	2,500	1,010	32.84	39.4	20.0	2,200	1,000	32.37	38.8
26	254	15.9	41.8	49.9	17.0	3,090	1,280	52.14	62.5	17.9	2,700	1,260	51.42	61.7
27	201	14.2	52.4	62.5	15.2	3,806	1,610	83.11	99.5	16.1	3,300	1,580	81.32	97.5
28	160	12.6	66.6	79.4	13.6	4,670	2,030	131.6	157.5	14.4	4,000	2,000	129.8	156
29	127	11.3	82.8	98.7	12.2	5,640	2,550	209.2	251	13.0	4,700	2,520	206.2	247
30	100	10.0	106	126	10.8	6,860	3,220	332.4	399	11.6	5,500	3,160	326.1	391
31	79.7	8.9	134	159	9.7	8,320	4,050	528.2	633	10.4	6,500	3,990	519	623
32	63.2	8.0	165	197	8.8	10,060	5,120	839.3	1,010	9.4	7,700	5,050	829	995
33	50.1	7.1	210	250	7.8	11,956	6,430	1,335	1,600	8.4	9,000	6,330	1,310	1,570
34	39.8	6.3	266	318	6.9	14,250	8,160	2.124	2,550	7.5	10,500	7,940	2,071	2,485
35	31.5	5.6	337	402	6.1	16,940	10,200	3,364	4,140	6.7	12,500	10,050	3,306	3,970
36	25	5.0	423	504	5.5	20,000	12,850	5,347	6,410	6.0	14,900	12,650	5,247	6,300

TABLE III.—ROUND AND SQUARE DOUBLE-COTTON-COVERED ANNEALED COPPER WIRES

A.w.g. No.	Diameter, mils		Round d.c.c.							Square d.c.c.						
			Circular mils	Feet per pound	Turns per square inch	Resistance				Circular mils	Feet per pound	Turns per square inch	Resistance			
						1,000 ft.		Pound					1,000 ft.		Pound	
	Bare	Insul.				25°C.	75°C.	25°C.	75°C.				25°C.	75°C.	25°C.	75°C.
1	289	307	83,690	3.79	10.9	0.126	0.150	0.00048	0.00057	102,216	3.20	10.2	0.103	0.123	0.00033	0.00040
2	257	276	66,370	4.78	13.5	0.159	0.189	0.00076	0.00091	80,164	4.07	12.6	0.130	0.156	0.00053	0.00064
3	229	247	52,640	6.04	17.0	0.202	0.240	0.00122	0.00146	62,670	5.21	15.9	0.169	0.203	0.00088	0.00105
4	204	221	41,740	7.63	21.2	0.254	0.303	0.00193	0.00232	50,729	6.42	19.8	0.207	0.248	0.00133	0.00160
5	182	198	33,100	9.66	25.8	0.319	0.381	0.00308	0.00370	39,729	8.19	24.6	0.266	0.319	0.00218	0.00262
6	162	177	26,250	12.0	32.8	0.403	0.480	0.00485	0.00582	32,371	10.05	30.8	0.327	0.393	0.00328	0.00393
7	144	159	20,820	15.1	40.6	0.510	0.608	0.00770	0.00923	25,475	12.76	38.2	0.415	0.498	0.0053	0.00635
8	128	142	16,150	19.0	50.2	0.645	0.770	0.0123	0.0147	19,970	16.23	47.8	0.530	0.636	0.0086	0.01032
9	114	125	13,090	24.0	64.5	0.813	0.970	0.0195	0.0236	15,616	20.67	61.7	0.680	0.815	0.0140	0.0168
10	102	112	10,380	30.4	82.1	1.02	1.21	0.0310	0.0372	12,532	25.7	77.0	0.840	1.01	0.0216	0.0260
11	90.7	99.5	8,234	38.5	102	1.29	1.53	0.0485	0.0581	9,800	32.8	98.0	1.08	1.30	0.0354	0.0425
12	80.8	89.6	6,530	48.8	125	1.62	1.93	0.079	0.095	7,630	42.2	119	1.38	1.65	0.0583	0.0700
13	72.0	80.7	5,178	61.6	153	2.04	2.43	0.126	0.151	5,909	54.3	148	1.79	2.15	0.0970	0.1163
14	64.1	72.8	4,107	77.7	196	2.57	3.07	0.199	0.239	4,545	70.2	182	2.32	2.78	0.1630	0.1635
15	57.1	65.9	3,257	91.0	237	3.24	3.87	0.295	0.354							
16	50.8	59.6	2,583	122	278	4.10	4.89	0.500	0.600							
17	45.3	54.1	2,048	150	345	5.15	6.14	0.773	0.925							
18	40.3	49.1	1,624	189	440	6.51	7.76	1.23	1.47							
19	35.9	44.7	1,288	237	510	8.21	9.79	1.94	2.33							
20	32.0	40.8	1,022	298	601	10.3	12.3	3.07	3.68							
21	28.5	37.3	810	370	710	13.0	15.5	4.81	5.76							

22	25.3	33.6	642	461	845	16.5	19.7	7.62	9.13							
23	22.6	30.9	510	584	995	20.7	24.7	12.1	14.6							
24	20.1	28.4	404	745	1,175	26.2	31.2	19.5	23.4							
25	17.9	25.7	320	903	1,370	33.0	39.4	30.0	36.0							
26	15.9	23.8	254	1,118	1,590	41.8	49.9	46.6	45.9							
27	14.2	22.0	201	1,422	1,835	52.4	62.5	74.5	88.2							
28	12.6	20.5	160	1,758	2,130	66.6	79.4	111.7	134							
29	11.3	19.1	127	2,207	2,430	82.8	98.7	183	220							
30	10.0	17.8	100	2,534	2,730	106	126	268	321							
31	8.9	16.7	79.7	3,160	3,090	134	159	405	486							
32	8.0	15.8	63.2	3,910	3,390	165	197	631	756							
33	7.1	14.9	50.1	4,640	3,820	210	250	940	1,128							
34	6.3	14.1	39.7	5,470	4,180	266	318	1,405	1,685							
35	5.6	13.4	31.5	6,360	4,590	337	402	2,050	2,460							
36	5.0	12.4	25.0	7,310	4,950	423	504	3,000	3,600							

TABLE IV.—RECTANGULAR ANNEALED COPPER WIRES

Circular Mils (*within 3 per cent accuracy*)

Size	.045	.050	.055	.065	.075	.085	.095	.105	.115	.125	.135	.145	.155	.165
.060	2,890	3,210	3,460	4,290	5,000	5,750	6,430	7,170	7,920	8,700	9,470	10,200	10,900	11,700
.070	3,400	3,820	4,230	5,050	5,930	6,780	7,640	8,510	9,400	10,250	11,150	12,080	12,900	13,850
.080	3,920	4,400	4,880	5,820	6,820	7,800	8,800	9,800	10,860	11,800	12,850	13,900	15,000	16,000
.090	4,500	5,000	5,540	6,660	7,750	8,850	10,000	11,150	12,320	13,500	14,700	15,780	16,850	18,100
.100	5,000	5,600	6,210	7,400	8,700	9,930	11,200	12,500	13,800	15,100	16,320	17,700	18,900	20,150
.110	5,540	6,210	6,880	8,280	9,650	11,020	12,420	13,850	15,300	16,650	18,150	19,450	20,800	22,150
.120	6,100	6,820	7,580	9,030	10,530	12,120	13,700	15,200	16,850	18,300	19,800	21,250	22,700	24,200
.130	6,650	7,400	8,280	9,880	11,500	13,250	14,920	16,500	18,250	19,800	21,400	23,000	24,600	26,200
140	7,160	8,040	8,900	10,720	12,500	14,300	16,100	17,950	19,650	21,400	23,100	24,800	26,500	28,300
.150	7,750	8,700	9,650	11,500	13,500	15,400	17,380	19,250	21,000	22,900	24,800	26,600	28,400	30,300
.160	8,350	9,250	10,300	12,400	14,400	16,450	18,550	20,500	22,450	24,400	26,500	28,400	30,300	32,400
.170	8,870	9,930	11,020	13,250	15,400	17,620	19,700	21,800	23,900	26,200	28,200	30,200	32,300	34,400
.180	9,460	10,530	11,680	14,030	16,330	18,650	20,900	23,100	25,400	27,600	29,900	32,000	34,200	36,500
.190	10,000	11,200	12,420	14,900	17,350	19,700	22,000	24,350	26,900	29,200	31,600	33,800	36,100	38,500
.200	10,530	11,800	13,100	15,720	18,300	20,750	23,200	25,800	28,300	30,700	33,300	35,600	38,000	40,600
.210	11,120	12,500	13,860	16,500	19,200	21,750	24,350	27,100	29,700	32,250	35,000	37,400	39,900	42,600
.220	11,680	13,100	14,630	17,450	20,100	22,800	25,700	28,400	31,100	33,800	36,700	39,200	41,900	44,600
.230	12,300	13,800	15,280	18,250	21,052	23,830	26,900	29,700	32,500	35,300	38,400	40,000	43,800	46,700
.240	12,850	14,400	16,000	19,050	22,000	25,150	28,000	31,000	34,000	37,000	40,000	42,900	45,800	48,700
.250	13,500	15,100	16,630	19,800	22,900	26,200	29,200	32,300	35,300	38,500	41,600	44,700	47,700	50,800
.260	14,030	15,720	17,450	20,600	23,800	27,200	30,400	33,600	36,700	40,000	43,300	46,500	49,600	52.800
.270	14,700	16,330	18,130	21,400	24,900	28,200	31,600	34,900	38,200	41,500	44,900	48,300	51,500	54,800
.280	15,220	16,940	18,800	22,500	25,810	29,300	32,700	36,200	39,600	43,000	46,600	50,100	53,400	56,900
.290	15,750	17,700	19,450	23,000	26,750	30,300	33,900	37,400	41,000	44,500	48,200	51,900	55,300	58,900

.300	16,330	18,300	20,100	23,800	27,650	31,400	35,000	38,700	42,400	46,100	49,900	53,700	57,200	61,100
.310	16,850	18,900	20,800	24,800	28,600	32,400	36,200	40,000	43,800	47,600	51,500	55,500	59,100	63,300
.320	17,580	19,500	21,450	25,600	29,500	33,400	37,300	41,300	45,200	49,200	53,200	57,300	61,000	65,500
.330	18,130	20,100	22,150	26,400	30,450	34,500	38,500	42,600	46,600	50,700	54,800	59,000	63,400	67,500
.340	18,700	20,700	22,800	27,200	31,400	35,500	39,600	43,900	48,000	52,200	56,500	60,700	65,200	69,500
.350	19,200	21,300	23,500	28,000	32,300	36,500	40,800	45,200	49,500	53,800	58,100	62,800	67,200	71,500
.360	19,750	21,900	24,150	28,800	33,200	37,600	41,900	46,500	50,900	55,300	59,700	64,700	69,000	73,600
.370	20,300	22,500	25,000	29,600	34,100	38,600	43,100	47,800	52,300	56,800	61,300	66,500	71,000	75,600
.380	20,800	23,100	25,700	30,400	35,000	39,700	44,200	49,100	53,700	58,300	62,900	68,300	73,000	77,700
.390	21,400	23,700	26,400	31,200	35,900	40,700	45,400	50,400	55,100	59,900	65,100	70,200	74,800	79,700
.400	22,000	24,200	27,100	32,100	36,750	41,800	46,600	51,600	56,500	61,500	67,000	71,900	76,800	81,800

twisted slightly lengthwise. The numbers of strands in the various sizes of cables have been carefully worked out to provide the maximum area in the minimum space. The first standard cable containing the fewest number of strands has seven conductors, a central core conductor with six similar conductors placed around it. If more wires are needed in the cable, 12 additional wires surround the first layer of 6, thus making a total of 19 strands. A larger cable would contain 18 additional strands, making 37 strands. Successive additions have 24, 30, 36, 42, etc., strands so that the respective cables contain totals of 61, 91, 127, and 169 strands. Note that successive layers have *six more* strands than the preceding layers.

Table V shows how concentric-lay cables are constructed.

TABLE V.—NUMBER OF STRANDS IN CONCENTRIC-LAY CABLES

Layer number	Number of strands in layer	Total number of strands in cable	Outside diameter of cable, mils
Core	1	1	d*
1	6	7	$3d$
2	12	19	$5d$
3	18	37	$7d$
4	24	61	$9d$
5	30	91	$11d$
6	36	127	$13d$
7	42	169	$15d$
8	48	217	$17d$
9	54	271	$19d$

*d = diameter of each strand in mils.

As indicated above, standard cables are manufactured in accordance with definite numbers of strands, the size of each of the latter being determined on the basis of the desired total area in circular mils. Table VI gives a partial list of some of the more commonly used stranded cables.

TABLE VI.—BARE CONCENTRIC-LAY CABLES—ANNEALED COPPER WIRE

A.w.g. No.	Circular mils	No. of strands	Diameter of strands	Outside diameter, mils	Resistance per 1,000 ft.	
					25°C.	75°C.
....	500,000	61	90.5	815	0.0216	0.0257
....	450,000	61	85.9	773	0.0240	0.0286
....	400,000	61	81.0	729	0.0270	0.0321
....	350,000	37	97.3	681	0.0308	0.0368
....	300,000	37	90.0	630	0.0360	0.0428
....	250,000	37	82.2	575	0.0431	0.0515
0000	212,000	19	105.5	528	0.0509	0.0607
000	168,000	19	94.0	470	0.0642	0.0765
00	133,000	19	83.7	418	0.0811	0.0966
0	106,000	19	74.5	373	0.102	0.121
1	83,700	19	66.4	332	0.129	0.154
2	66,400	7	97.4	292	0.162	0.193
3	52,600	7	86.7	260	0.205	0.245
4	41,700	7	77.2	232	0.259	0.309
5	23,100	7	68.8	206	0.326	0.388
6	26,300	7	61.2	184	0.410	0.488
7	20,800	7	54.5	164	0.519	0.618
8	16,500	7	48.6	146	0.654	0.780

Copper-clad Steel Wires.—Whenever it is necessary to use a wire having a combination of fairly good current-conducting ability and high mechanical strength, the so-called "copper-clad" wire is used. In one manufacturing process of such wires a steel wire is first coated by an electrochemical process with a layer of copper and is then inserted into a copper tube. Both ends are next closed, whereupon the rod is heated and rolled; the final step is to draw the rod through dies until the proper diameter is obtained.

Two standard commercial grades of copper-clad wires are manufactured, namely, 30 per cent conductivity and 40 per cent conductivity. These merely express the conductivity (*i.e.*, "goodness") compared with a solid copper wire of the same cross section. In the accompanying table are shown the relative diameters and areas of the two grades.

Per cent conductivity	Per cent diameter of steel	Per cent area	
		Steel	Copper
30	89.2	79.5	20.5
40	82.7	68.2	31.8

Table VII lists some of the more commonly used copper-clad wires with their corresponding resistances. As a matter of interest it would be well to check some of the values with those given for copper in Table II. Such comparisons should show that a wire of 30 per cent conductivity material has about $3\frac{1}{3}$ times as much resistance as a copper wire of the same size, and that a wire of 40 per cent conductivity material has about $2\frac{1}{2}$ times as much resistance as a copper wire of the same area.

Table VII.—Copper-clad High-strength Wire (Copperweld Steel Co.)

A.w.g. No.	Actual diameter, mils	Circular mils	Resistance per 1,000 ft.	
			30 per cent conductivity	40 per cent conductivity
0000	460	211,600	0.165	0.124
000	410	168,100	0.208	0.156
00	365	133,225	0.262	0.197
0	325	105,625	0.330	0.248
1	289	83,520	0.422	0.317
2	258	66,565	0.530	0.397
3	229	52,440	0.673	0.504
4	204	41,615	0.848	0.636
5	182	33,125	1.065	0.798
6	162	26,245	1.344	1.008
7	144	20,735	1.701	1.276
8	128	16,385	2.153	1.615
9	114	12,995	2.714	2.036
10	102	10,404	3.390	2.543
11	91	8,281	....	3.195
12	81	6,561	....	4.032

Temperature-resistance Effects.—The resistance of all wires generally used in practice in electric circuits increases as the temperature is increased, though the per cent change differs for different materials. Experiment has shown that within the usual operating ranges of temperatures the resistance changes uniformly. For example, in the case of copper wire the total per cent change in resistance for a 100°C. change is 42.7 per cent, this being true whether the change is from 0°C. to 100°C. or from −20°C. to +80°C. or from 120°C. down to 20°C. Therefore, if the results of experiment are plotted on a graph such as that of Fig. 4, it will

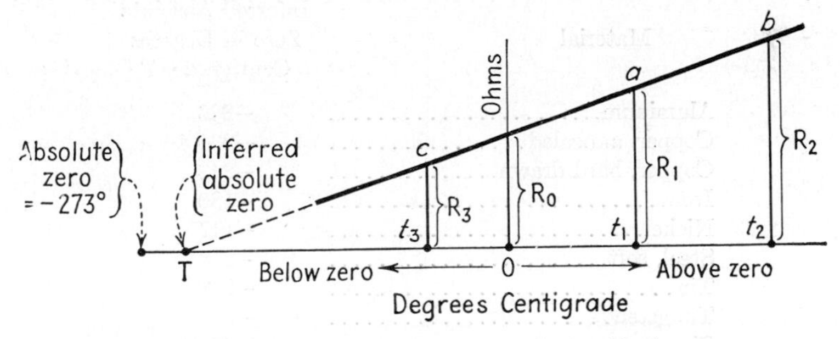

FIG. 4.—Resistance-versus-temperature relationship for copper.

be found that a perfect straight line can be drawn. This fortunate relationship between resistance and temperature, *i.e.*, a straight-line relationship, makes it possible to write an extremely simple equation based upon the rule of the similarity of right triangles. This equation may then be used to make calculations and predictions in electric circuits where the resistance has been altered by a change in temperature.

In Fig. 4 it should be noted that the results of the temperature-resistance test are shown by the heavy oblique straight line, and that the extended broken line is merely *inferred* for convenience to be a continuation of the experimental straight line. Understand that the region indicated by the broken line is below ordinary cold temperatures encountered in practice and is drawn only because it serves to locate the arbitrary but convenient *inferred absolute zero* for the metal concerned. This intersection of the extended experimental line with the X axis is generally above the real absolute zero of -273°C. For copper the *inferred absolute zero* is -234.5°C.[1] (an easy number to remember because it is a succession of numbers from 2 to 5); for aluminum it is -236°C.; for tungsten -202°C.; etc.

Table VIII gives the inferred absolute temperature values of the more commonly used materials.

TABLE VIII.—INFERRED ABSOLUTE TEMPERATURE VALUES FOR SEVERAL METALS

Material	Inferred Absolute Zero in Degrees Centigrade, T
Aluminum	−236
Copper, annealed	−234.5
Copper, hard drawn	−242
Iron	−180
Nickel	−147
Steel, soft	−218
Tin	−218
Tungsten	−202
Zinc	−251

Again, from Fig. 4 it is obvious that, by similar right triangles,

$$\frac{at_1}{bt_2} = \frac{OT + Ot_1}{OT + Ot_2} \quad \text{or} \quad \frac{R_1}{R_2} = \frac{T + t_1}{T + t_2}$$

Also

$$\frac{R_1}{R_3} = \frac{T + t_1}{T + (-t_3)} \quad \text{and} \quad \frac{R_2}{R_3} = \frac{T + t_2}{T - t_3}$$

Since $T = -234.5$ for copper, the above equation can be written in its general form

$$\frac{R_1}{R_2} = \frac{234.5 + t_1}{234.5 + t_2} \quad \text{(for copper only)} \qquad (2)$$

[1]Actually, the temperature-resistance curve bends toward a value slightly higher than −234.5°C. below a temperature of about −60°C.

If it is desired to calculate the resistance R_2 at some temperature t_2 when the resistance R_1 is known at temperature t_1, the above equation is changed to become

$$R_2 = R_1 \times \frac{234.5 + t_2}{234.5 + t_1} \quad \text{(for copper only)} \qquad (2a)$$

If it is desired to determine the temperature t_2 which changes a known resistance R_1 at temperature t_1 to a resistance of R_2, then the following equation should be used:

$$t_2 = \frac{R_2}{R_1} \times (234.5 + t_1) - 234.5 \quad \text{(for copper only)} \qquad (2b)$$

In order to illustrate the above equations, the following examples and their solutions will be given:

Example 1.—A coil of copper wire has a resistance of 84 ohms at a room temperature of 24°C. (*a*) What will be its resistance at 80°C.? (*b*) At −20°C.? (*c*) At what temperature will its resistance be 100 ohms?

Solution:

a. By Eq. (2*a*)

$$R_{(80)} = 84 \times \frac{234.5 + 80}{234.5 + 24} = 102.3 \text{ ohms}$$

b. By Eq. (2*a*)

$$R_{(-20)} = 84 \times \frac{234.5 - 20}{234.5 + 24} = 70.7 \text{ ohms}$$

c. By Eq. (2*b*)

$$t_2 = \frac{100}{84} \times (234.5 + 24) - 234.5 = 73°\text{C.}$$

Example 2.—A 100-watt, 120-volt tungsten filament lamp has a resistance of 144 ohms at normal operating (incandescent) temperature and a resistance of 10 ohms at a room temperature of 22°C. Calculate the temperature of the incandescent tungsten filament under normal operating conditions.

Solution. The inferred absolute zero temperature for tungsten is −202°C. from Table VIII. Therefore by Eq. (2*b*), modified for tungsten,

$$t_2 = \frac{R_2}{R_1} \times (202 + t_1) - 202$$

$$\therefore t_2 = \frac{144}{10} \times (202 + 22) - 202 = 2995°\text{C.}$$

Experiment 1. Determining the Number of Turns of Wire in a Coil

Objective: To determine the number of turns of wire in a coil of copper wire whose wire size and resistance are known.

Procedure: Obtain a cylindrical or rectangular coil of wire such as that used in any electromagnet or in one of the field coils in an electric motor. Determine its resistance (either by measurement, as explained in a subsequent chapter, or from the notation marked thereon) and the size of wire with which it is wound. Next, measure the *average length* of each *turn* (abbreviated A.L.T.). This may be done by carefully forming a short piece of copper wire over the coil in the direction of the winding so that it occupies a position halfway between the inside and outside edges. After clipping the wire where the measuring turn is completed, lay it out straight and scale its length in feet.

Calculations and Observations: Using the equation

$$R = \rho \times \frac{l}{C.M.} = \rho \times \frac{\text{A.L.T.} \times \text{turns}}{C.M.}$$

$$\text{Turns} = \frac{R \times C.M.}{\rho \times \text{A.L.T.}} \qquad (1d)$$

calculate the number of turns of wire in the coil.

If it is possible to unwind the taping without harm to the coil, try counting the number of turns to see how closely the calculations check with the actual number.

Experiment 2. Determining the Kind of Alloy Material Used in Constructing a Rheostat

Objective: To determine the kind of alloy used in a long solenoid type of rheostat.

Procedure: Obtain a long cylindrical type of rheostat in which a single layer of wire is wound over a porcelain, or other ceramic, tube. It has a movable slider and is commonly used in electrical laboratories for a great variety of purposes (see Fig. 5). Such a rheostat will usually have

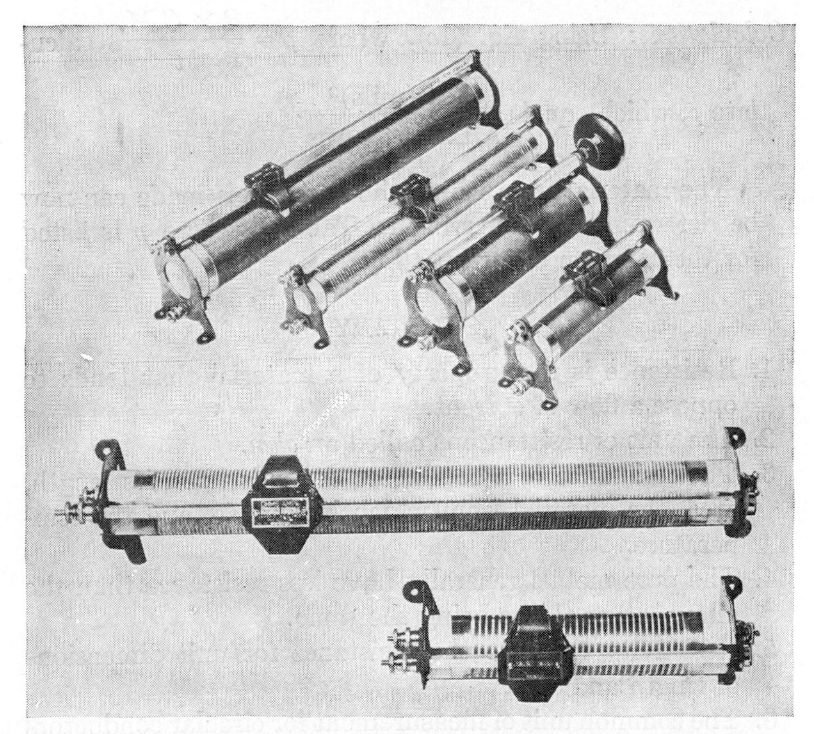

Fig. 5.— Various types and sizes of slide-wire rheostats. (*James G. Biddle Co.*)

its total resistance in ohms stamped on a metal plate attached to the unit. Record its value. Next, measure the diameter of the ceramic tube plus one thickness of the resistance wire, in feet. Then, gauge the wire accurately with a wire gauge or a micrometer and note its value in mils. Finally, count the number of turns of wire carefully from one end of the tube to the other. You should now have the following information:

a. Resistance of rheostat in ohms

b. Average length per turn (A.L.T.)
$= \pi \times$ diameter in feet

c. Diameter of the resistance wire in mils

d. Total number of turns of resistance wire

Calculations: Using Eq. (1*c*), where $\rho = \frac{R \times C.M.}{l}$, calculate ρ, which equals $\frac{R \times (\text{mils})^2}{\text{A.L.T.} \times \text{turns}}$.

The material from which the rheostat is made can now be determined by referring to Table I, where ρ is listed for the common electrical alloys.

SUMMARY

1. Resistance is the property of a material that tends to oppose a flow of current.
2. The unit of resistance is called an *ohm*.
3. The resistance of a conductor depends upon its length, area, the material from which it is made, and the temperature.
4. The pure metals generally have less resistance than the alloys, other things being the same.
5. Resistivity refers to the resistance for unit dimensions of length and area.
6. The common unit of measurement for circular conductors is the mil-foot.
7. Resistance may be calculated, if the dimensions and the kind of wire are known, by the equation $R = \rho \times l/C.M.$
8. All wires are standardized according to size, in circular-mil area, or gauge number. The standard gauge used in this country is the American wire gauge (A.w.g.).

9. Cables are made up of standard numbers of strands of wires. These are manufactured in various sizes on the basis of total circular-mil area, the number of strands and the size of each strand being selected in accordance with such desired areas.
10. Copper-clad wires are used where great strength and fair conductivity are essential. These are wires with a coating of copper over a steel core.
11. Two commercial types of copper-clad wire are made, namely, 30 per cent and 40 per cent conductivity. These designate their conductivity with respect to copper of the same cross-sectional area.
12. The resistance of all metals increases uniformly with increase in temperature. The resistance of copper increases 1 per cent for every increase of 2.34°C. (In practice this is usually taken as 1 per cent for every 2.5°C.)

QUESTIONS

1. Define electrical resistance. With what can it be compared in mechanical machines?
2. Distinguish between resistance and resistor.
3. Define the *international ohm* accurately.
4. Upon what four factors does the resistance of an electrical conductor depend?
5. What is meant by circular mil? circular mil-foot?
6. What is meant by the term "resistivity"? How does its value for different materials affect the current flow in an electric circuit, other things being the same?
7. Generally speaking, what kinds of material are best from the standpoint of low resistivity? high resistivity?
8. Why are such materials as Advance, Nichrome, and Chromel desirable as heating elements?
9. Why is copper wire often called *magnet wire*?
10. What material is used in the filaments of incandescent lamps? Why?

11. How does the resistance of a wire vary with its length? its area? Give reasons for your answer.
12. What change in the number of gauge numbers is necessary for an increase in resistance of 10 times?
13. If the area of one copper wire is twice that of another, how do their resistances compare per unit of length?
14. In the wire table, Table II, how do the areas of successive gauge numbers compare with each other? the diameters of successive gauge numbers?
15. What reasons can be given for *stranding* electrical conductors?
16. What rule applies to the number of strands used in concentric-lay cables?
17. What determines the size of each strand in a cable?
18. In Table VI, are the individual strands in the cables listed of standard size? Give reasons for your answer.
19. What is meant by a *copper-clad* wire? What advantages does it possess? Give practical uses for such wires.
20. Distinguish between copper-clad wires of 30 per cent and 40 per cent conductivity.
21. What effect does temperature have upon the resistance of an electrical conductor?
22. What kind of relationship exists between the temperature and the resistance of a conductor?
23. What is meant by the *inferred absolute zero*? How does its value differ from absolute zero?
24. What general rule can be used to determine the per cent variation in resistance of copper when the per cent variation in the temperature is known?
25. At what theoretical temperature will the resistance of an electrical conductor become zero?
26. Distinguish between the terms "resistivity" and "conductivity."

PROBLEMS

1. A coil of No. 21 copper wire has a resistance of 32.5 ohms at 25°C. (*a*) Referring to Table II, determine the num-

ber of feet of wire in the coil. (*b*) If each turn of wire is 24 in. long, calculate the number of turns in the coil.

2. The cylindrical coil of an electromagnet is wound with 450 turns of magnet wire whose diameter is 0.0159 in. If the inside and outside diameters of the coil are 1.5 and 2.5 in., respectively, determine its resistance (*a*) at 20°C., (*b*) at 75°C.
3. A heating unit for an electric ironer has a resistance of 12 ohms. If the cross section is rectangular, 0.0045 × 0.125 in., and its total length is 13 ft., determine (*a*) the resistivity of the material used, (*b*) the kind of wire.
4. A copper cable contains 37 strands of wire and has an area of 400,000 *C.M.* What is the diameter of each strand?
5. An incandescent lamp has a tungsten filament whose resistance is 240 ohms at its operating temperature of 2800°C. What will be the filament resistance at a room temperature of 20°C.?
6. Two copper wires *A* and *B* weigh exactly the same, *i.e.*, they have the same volume. If the resistance of wire *A* is 5 ohms and its diameter is four times as much as that of wire *B*, what is the resistance of wire *B*?
7. A wire whose diameter is 200 mils has a resistance of 2.5 ohms. After being drawn through special dies its diameter is reduced to 25 mils. Assuming no change in the resistivity of the material, calculate the resistance of the lengthened wire.
8. The distance between a source of supply and the location of a motor is 210 ft. What size wire (A.w.g. number) is used in the installation if the resistance is 0.17 ohm?
9. A copper wire having a resistance of 1.62 ohms per 1,000 ft. is to be replaced by a copper-clad wire having as nearly as possible the same resistivity. What gauge number should be selected for 30 per cent conductivity? for 40 per cent conductivity?
10. A cylindrical coil is wound with 1,405 turns of No. 17 gauge copper wire, each of which has an average length of

8 in. How many turns of No. 14 gauge aluminum wire should be used to give the same resistance as the copper coil if each turn has an average length of 9 in.?

11. The resistance of the armature winding of a motor is 0.15 ohm at a temperature of 21°C. (The motor was permitted to remain idle sufficiently long to assume a temperature equal to that of the surrounding air.) After a period of operation the motor is stopped and the armature resistance is measured again; it is then found to be 0.17 ohm. What was the average temperature rise of the armature-winding copper?

CHAPTER 3

DIRECT-CURRENT CIRCUITS—I
OHM'S LAW—POWER—ENERGY

Ohm's Law and the Electric Circuit.—The electric circuit is the basis of most energy transformations. As was pointed out in Chap. I, a circuit consists essentially of a source of supply, a consuming element, a control unit, a protecting device, meters and instruments, and connecting wires. Each one of these parts is constructed with electrical conductors, although they may or may not all be made of the same materials. All of them, however, oppose a current flow to some extent, and therefore they possess the property discussed in the previous chapter, *i.e.*, resistance. Generally speaking, it is true that, neglecting some parts of some measuring instruments, the element that has the greatest resistance in the circuit is the electrical device in which the useful energy conversion actually takes place. Thus, in the incandescent lamp the resistance may be 100 or more ohms; in the flatiron it may be about 30 ohms; in the electric motor it may be *equivalent* to approximately 5 ohms. The rest of the circuit, on the other hand, may have a total resistance of, perhaps, 0.1 ohm or less. It is well to bear these general facts in mind in studying the laws in this chapter that govern the flow of currents. The various resistances that go to make up the completed circuit must usually be combined for calculation purposes, and it is sometimes possible, though not always, to neglect all resistances except those representing the consuming devices. The latter will hereafter be called the *load,* for reasons that will become clear later.

When a resistance load is connected to a source of supply, a current flows. The value of the current in amperes (see definition of *ampere*, page 4) depends upon two factors: (1) the impressed electromotive force, hereafter designated as the voltage, and (2) the resistance. Although the rule that represents the relationship between these three factors, *i.e.*, amperes, volts, and resistance, is practically obvious now, it was not particularly so in 1826 when George Simon Ohm, the great German scientist, proved experimentally that *the current is directly proportional to the voltage and is inversely proportional to the resistance.* The statement that is embodied in one of the most important and fundamental laws in the whole field of electrical science merely means that

$$\text{1. For a fixed resistance, if the voltage is } \begin{cases} \text{increased the current rises} \\ \text{decreased the current diminishes} \end{cases}$$

$$\text{2. For a fixed voltage, if the resistance is } \begin{cases} \text{increased the current diminishes} \\ \text{decreased the current rises} \end{cases}$$

The above statements in equation form may be written

$$\text{Amperes} = \frac{\text{volts}}{\text{ohms}}$$

Substituting the symbols I for amperes, E for volts, and R for ohms,

$$I = \frac{E}{R} \text{ amp.} \tag{3}$$

If it is desired to find the voltage necessary to cause a current of I amp. to flow through a resistance of R ohms, then the equation should be written

$$E = I \times R \text{ volts} \tag{3a}$$

If it is required to find how many ohms of resistance a circuit should have in order that E volts should produce a current flow of I amp., then the following equation should be used:

$$R = \frac{E}{I} \text{ ohms} \tag{3b}$$

The following simple examples are given to illustrate Ohm's law:

Example 1.—A field coil of a generator has a resistance of 60 ohms. When connected to a 120-volt source the current will be

$$I = \frac{120}{60} = 2 \text{ amp.}$$

If the voltage is raised to 150 volts, the current will rise to 2.5 amp. If the voltage is lowered to 90 volts, the current will drop to 1.5 amp.

Example 2.—A telegraph relay having a resistance of 480 ohms requires a current of 50 milliamperes in order to operate. To do so the voltage must be

$$E = 0.05 \times 480 = 24 \text{ volts}$$

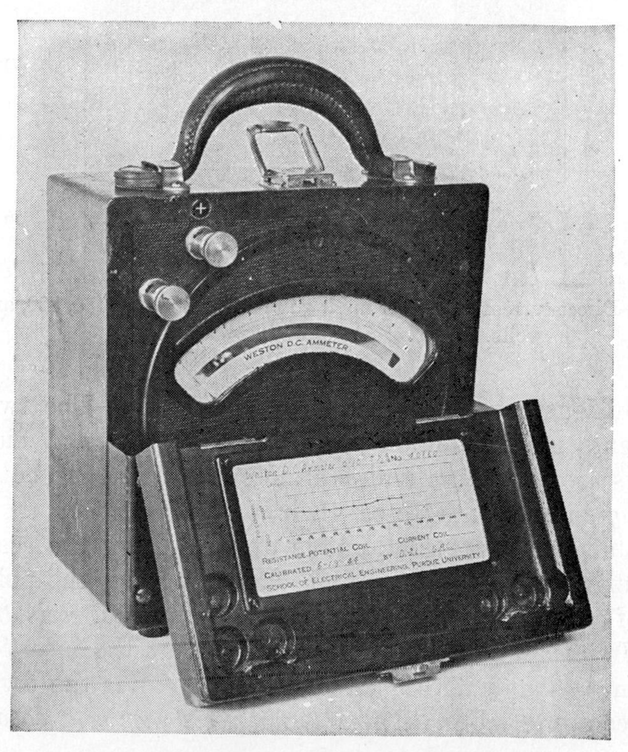

FIG. 6.—Direct-current ammeter. Note heavy metal terminals.

Example 3.—If the current in a 115-volt electric circuit must not exceed 15 amp. (if it does, the fuse will blow), the resistance must be *no less than*

$$R = \frac{115}{15} = 7.66 \text{ ohms}$$

Fig. 7.—Direct-current voltmeter having full-scale ranges of 150, 300, and 750 volts. (*Weston Electrical Instrument Corp.*)

The Measurement of Amperes and Volts.—The two instruments most commonly used in direct-current electric circuits are ammeters and voltmeters. These are both *indicating* instruments since their pointers deflect to their instantaneous values and move up and down the scale as their magnitudes change; if no change occurs, the pointers will, of course, remain stationary. *The internal resistance of a good ammeter is* exceedingly *low*, so that the insertion of such an instrument *in a circuit* does not alter the total resistance appreciably. *The internal resistance of a good volt-*

meter, on the other hand, *is very large*, so that its insertion *across a circuit* does not alter the total current appreciably.

Portable-type instruments are illustrated by the ammeter of Fig. 6 and the voltmeter of Fig. 7. Note particularly the heavy metal terminals on the ammeter and the small Bakelite-covered terminals on the voltmeter. In the former the current is comparatively large, hence the large metal connecting terminals; in the latter the current is usually a small fraction of an ampere, hence the light terminal connections.

Figure 8 shows (*a*) how an ammeter alone should be connected *in* a circuit, (*b*) how a voltmeter alone should be

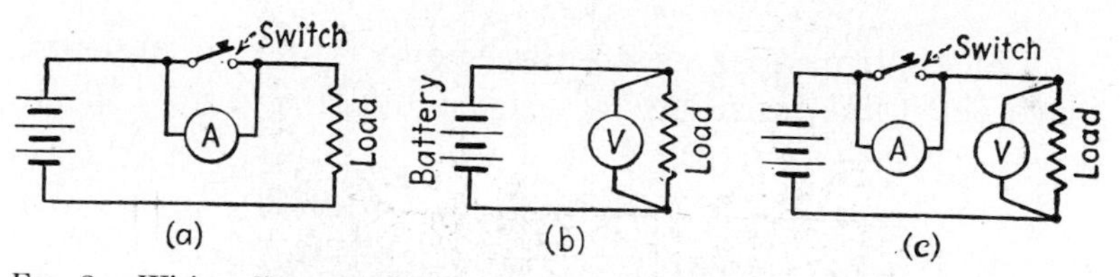

FIG. 8.—Wiring diagrams showing how to measure the current, voltage, and resistance of a load.

connected *across* a circuit, and (*c*) how both an ammeter and a voltmeter should be used.

Observe carefully that the ammeter in (*a*) and (*c*) is connected across a single-pole single-throw (s.p.s.t.) switch. This is an excellent precautionary measure for the protection of the low-resistance ammeter. The switch should be opened only if it is known that the deflection is within the range of the ammeter and when it is desired to read it; on other occasions the switch should be kept closed. If this practice is followed, ammeters will be less likely to be damaged. A voltmeter, however, may be kept permanently connected across a circuit because its high resistance is itself a sufficient limitation for its own low current.

Equal Resistors in Series.—Whenever resistors are connected in such a way that the current leaving one of them must enter directly the next succeeding one, so that the *same* current flows throughout its entire length, the resistors are said to be connected *in series*; the circuit is then known as a *series circuit.*

If the resistors all have exactly the same resistance, the total resistance of the circuit is then equal to the value of one of them multiplied by the number connected in series. Thus,

$$R_t = n \times R \tag{4}$$

where R_t = total resistance
R = resistance per unit
n = number of units in series

In Fig. 9, five equal resistors are shown connected in series. Since the total resistance of the circuit is $n \times R = 5R$, it

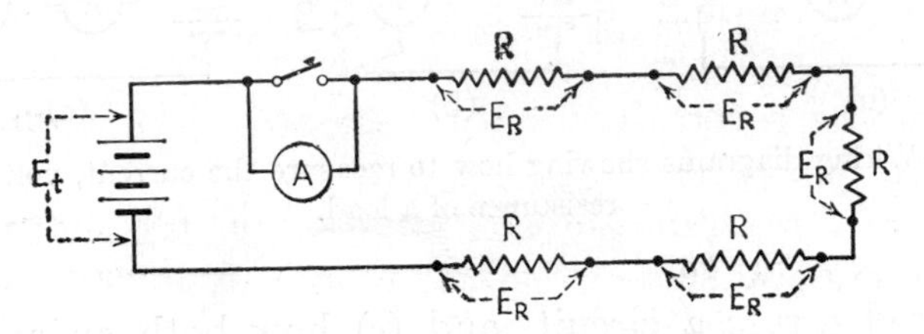

FIG. 9.—Five equal resistors in series.

follows that, by Ohm's law, the current I will be $E_t/5R$ [Eq. (3)]. Furthermore, since each one of the resistors requires $I \times R$ volts [Eq. (3*a*)], the total voltage required by all of the resistors will be

$$5 \times (I \times R) = 5 \times \frac{E_t}{5R} \times R = E_t$$

where E_t is the total impressed voltage.

It follows, therefore, that *in any series circuit in which all the resistors are alike, the voltages across the individual units* (called *voltage drops*) *are equal.*

A good practical example of such a circuit is one group of five 120-volt incandescent lamps connected in series in a streetcar where the trolley-to-track voltage is 600. Here, each lamp "receives" one-fifth of 600 volts, or 120 volts, which is its rated value. The lamps are thus properly operated, even though the line voltage is much too high for a single lamp. True, if one lamp should burn out, the whole "string" would be extinguished, just as they are in a "string" of Christmas-tree lights.

Unequal Resistors in Series.—A more general case than the one just considered is a series circuit in which the resist-

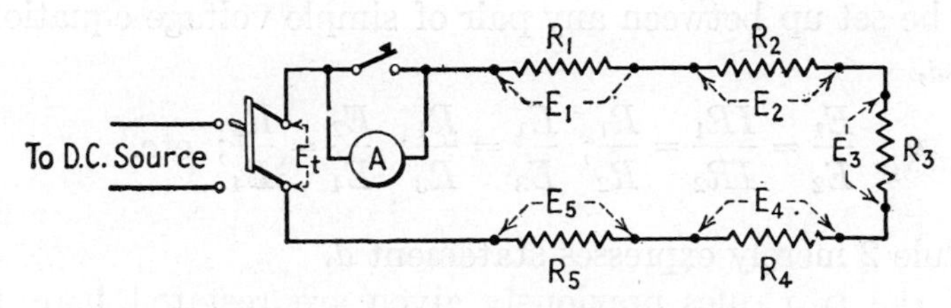

FIG. 10.—Five unequal resistors in series.

ances of the several units are unequal. Such a circuit is shown in Fig. 10.

The total resistance of such a group of resistors is equal to the numerical sum of the individual resistances; *i.e.*,

$$R_t = R_1 + R_2 + R_3 + R_4 + R_5 + \dots \tag{5}$$

Now

a. The current in the circuit will be, as before, $I = E_t/R_t$ amp.

b. Since this same current I flows in every part of the series circuit,

c. It follows that

$$E_1 = I \times R_1;\ E_2 = I \times R_2;\ E_3 = I \times R_3;$$
$$E_4 = I \times R_4;\ \text{and } E_5 = I \times R_5$$

d. Therefore,

$$(I \times R_1) + (I \times R_2) + (I \times R_3) + (I \times R_4) + (I \times R_5)$$
$$= I \times (R_1 + R_2 + R_3 + R_4 + R_5) = I \times R_t = E_t$$

If the four statements indicated above are carefully studied, the student should be able to understand the following two exceedingly important rules concerning *series circuits*:

1. *The voltage drops across the individual resistors in a series circuit are directly proportional to the magnitudes of the resistances.*

2. *The total impressed voltage across a group of series-connected resistors is equal to the sum of voltage drops across the individual units.*

Rule 1 is derived directly from statement *c* because ratios can be set up between any pair of simple voltage equations. Thus,

$$\frac{E_1}{E_2} = \frac{IR_1}{IR_2} = \frac{R_1}{R_2}; \quad \frac{E_1}{E_3} = \frac{R_1}{R_3}; \quad \frac{E_2}{E_4} = \frac{R_2}{E_4}; \quad \text{etc.}$$

Rule 2 merely expresses statement *d*.

If the two rules previously given are restated here for convenience, they become

3. *The current in every part of a series circuit is the same.*

4. *The total resistance of a series circuit is equal to the sum of the individual resistances.*

The following problem illustrates the practical value of the four rules listed above:

Example 4.—A series circuit consists of three resistors having resistances of 30, 40, and 50 ohms, respectively. The current is measured with an ammeter and is found to be 2 amp. Calculate (*a*) the voltage drops across the individual resistors and (*b*) the total impressed voltage.

Solution A: The same current flows in every part of the circuit. Therefore,

a. $E_{30} = 2 \times 30 = 60$ volts; $E_{40} = 2 \times 40 = 80$ volts;
$E_{50} = 2 \times 50 = 100$ volts

b. $E_t = 60 + 80 + 100 = 240$ volts

Solution B:

b. $R_t = 30 + 40 + 50 = 120$ ohms
$E_t = 2 \times 120 = 240$ volts

a. $E_1 = \frac{30}{120} \times 240 = 60$ volts; $E_2 = \frac{40}{30} \times 60 = 80$ volts;
$E_3 = \frac{50}{40} \times 80 = 100$ volts

Equal Resistors in Parallel.—When several resistors are connected in parallel, one end of each of the units is joined to one end of each of the others to form one junction, and the other ends are joined together to form another junction. Under this condition the *same* voltage is applied to all units simultaneously. If the resistors all have the same value of resistance, the currents through the individual units will be *equal*; each current will be a *different* one, but they will all have the same value.

Figure 11 shows a circuit of four equal resistances connected through an ammeter to a source of supply of E volts. Since

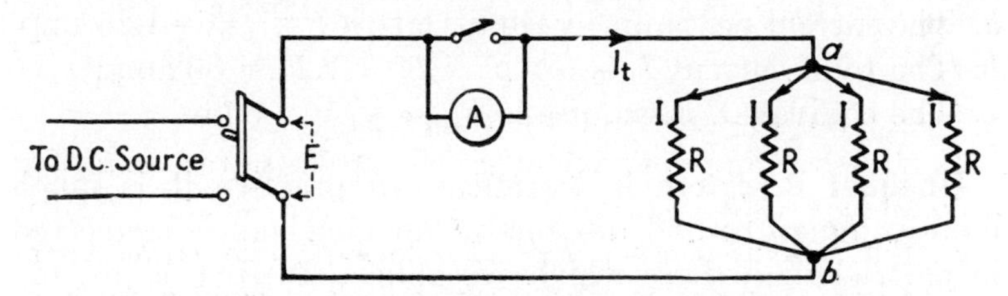

FIG. 11.—Four equal resistors in parallel.

the *same* voltage is impressed across all units at the same time, their currents, though independent of each other, will be equal and the total current entering junction a or leaving junction b will be

$$I_t = n \times I \text{ amp.} \qquad (6)$$

where n, in our example, is 4.

If it were desired to replace the four resistors by one that would be *equivalent* to their combination, it would have to "take" $4 \times I$ amp. when connected to a source of E volts. Thus, the equivalent resistance would have to equal $E/(4 \times I)$ ohms. But $I = E/R$ amp.

Hence $$R_{\text{eq}} = \frac{E}{4 \times I} = \frac{E}{4 \times E/R} = \frac{R}{4} \text{ ohms}$$

This means that a single resistor whose resistance is *equivalent* to a group of four equal resistances is merely one-fourth of a single resistance. Or, to make a general statement, *the equivalent resistance of a number of equal resistances in parallel is R/n ohms*, where R and n are as defined above.

In order to illustrate this principle, the following problem is given:

Example 5.—A large room has 24 150-watt, 120-volt incandescent lamps, all connected in parallel. If each lamp has a resistance of 96 ohms, calculate (*a*) the current through each lamp, (*b*) the total current taken by all lamps, (*c*) the equivalent resistance of the entire group.

Solution:

a. The current per lamp, by Ohm's law, is $I = \frac{120}{96} = 1.25$ amp.
b. The total current I_t is $n \times I = 24 \times 1.25 = 30$ amp.[1]
c. The equivalent resistance is $R_{eq} = \frac{96}{24} = 4$ ohms.

Unequal Resistors in Parallel.—In practice it is much more common to find resistors of unequal values connected in parallel than those which are alike. In such cases, the currents through the individual units will be different, the value of each one depending only upon the common impressed voltage and its own resistance. By Ohm's law, it should be obvious that the individual currents will be numerically related to each other because the *same* e.m.f. (*e*lectro*m*otive *f*orce or voltage) is applied to all of them simultaneously. Thus, if resistances A, B, C, and D are 10, 20, 30, and 40 ohms, respectively, and the applied voltage is 120, the currents will be 12, 6, 4, and 3, respectively. Note particularly that the resistance B is twice A, but that the current in B is one-half that in A; the resistance C is three times A, but the current in C is one-third that in A; also, the resistance D is four times A but the current in D is one-fourth that in A.

Stating the above in general terms, *the individual currents in a group of resistors connected in parallel are inversely proportional to their resistance magnitudes.*

[1]Check for (*b*)—$I_t = \frac{120}{4} = 30$ amp.

Figure 12 shows a parallel circuit of four unequal resistors connected to a source E. Here

$$I_1 = \frac{E}{R_1};\ I_2 = \frac{E}{R_2};\ I_3 = \frac{E}{R_3};\ \text{and}\ I_4 = \frac{E}{R_4}$$

Since the total current leaving the source, passing through the ammeter, and entering the junction a, or leaving junction b, must equal $I_1 + I_2 + I_3 + I_4$, it follows that

$$R_{eq} = \frac{E}{I_t} = \frac{E}{\dfrac{E}{R_1} + \dfrac{E}{R_2} + \dfrac{E}{R_3} + \dfrac{E}{R_4}} = \frac{1}{\dfrac{1}{R_1} + \dfrac{1}{R_2} + \dfrac{1}{R_3} + \dfrac{1}{R_4}} \qquad (7)$$

That is, *the equivalent resistance of a group of parallel-connected resistors is equal to the reciprocal* (one divided by

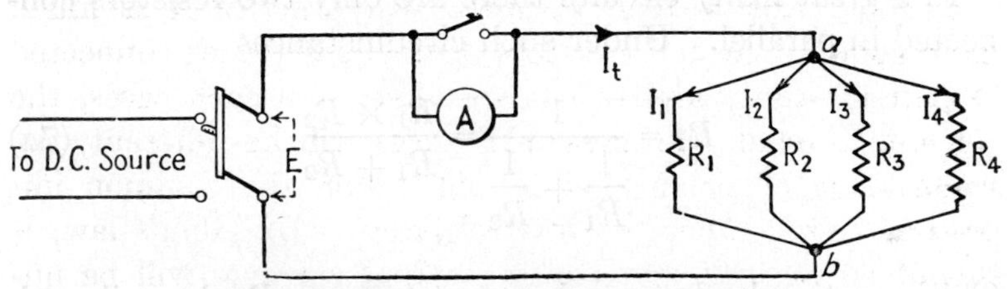

Fig. 12.—Four unequal resistors in parallel.

the number) *of the sum of the reciprocals of the individual units.* Understand that, when we speak of an equivalent resistance, we are dealing only with a numerical quantity, a fictitious number, not a real, physical unit having this number of ohms. It is merely *some* resistor that might be used to replace the parallel group, *i.e.*, replace it only if it would take exactly the same current when connected to exactly the same voltage source.

In making calculations for the equivalent resistance of a parallel circuit it should be remembered that *its value is always less than the magnitude of the smallest unit.* (This, of course, is the reverse of the situation in series circuits where the equivalent resistance is always greater than the largest unit.) Again using the numerical values of 10, 20, 30, and 40 ohms, respectively, the equivalent resistance is calculated to be

$$R_{eq} = \frac{1}{0.1 + 0.05 + 0.033 + 0.025} = \frac{1}{0.208} = 4.80 \text{ ohms}$$

Note that this value of 4.80 ohms is smaller than the smallest value of 10 ohms. Also, observe that

$$I_t = I_1 + I_2 + I_3 + I_4 = 12 + 6 + 4 + 3 = 25 \text{ amp.}$$

and

$$I_t = \tfrac{120}{4.80} = 25 \text{ amp.}$$

Thus we see that the equivalent resistance takes 25 amp., which is exactly the same current as for the four combined resistors.

In a great many circuits there are only two resistors connected in parallel. Under such circumstances

$$R_t = \frac{1}{\dfrac{1}{R_1} + \dfrac{1}{R_2}} = \frac{R_1 \times R_2}{R_1 + R_2} \tag{7a}$$

This equation leads to a short cut because R_{eq} is easily calculated *by dividing the product of the two numbers by their sum.*

In order to bring together all the points made under this heading, it will be desirable to summarize them. *For a parallel circuit*

1. The same voltage is impressed across all resistors simultaneously.

2. The total current flowing to the entire group is equal to the sum of the individual currents.

3. The individual currents are inversely proportional to the magnitudes of the individual resistances.

4. The equivalent resistance is equal to the reciprocal of the sum of the reciprocals of the individual resistances.

4*a*. The equivalent resistance of two resistances is equal to their product divided by their sum.

Power and Energy.—Power is the *rate* at which work is done. Energy is a measure of the work actually done. The reason we say a horse is more *powerful* than a man is that the former can do more physical work in a unit of time than can the latter. But, given sufficient time, a man can accomplish as much *work* as a horse; the same reasoning applies, of course, to other animals as well.

The unit of mechanical power is the horsepower, abbreviated hp., and it is equivalent to the rate of 33,000 ft.-lb. of work per minute. This unit of power was originated by James Watt in 1782 because he found it necessary to specify how much power his new steam engines would develop in terms of the horses they were intended to replace. In those days horses usually pushed a crank having a 12-ft. radius as they walked in a circle, the result being that pumps were operated to raise the water to elevated tanks. Since the average horse was *assumed* to exert a force of about 175 lb. and made $2\frac{1}{2}$ complete revolutions per minute, it followed that 1 hp. was equal to $(2\pi \times 12) \times (2\frac{1}{2}) \times 175$, or 33,000 ft.-lb. per minute. Little did Watt, the inventor of the steam engine, foresee that he was setting up a unit that would come into use throughout the world. And although he had absolutely nothing to do with the field of electricity, his name has been strangely honored by establishing *the unit of electrical power* as the *watt*. In terms of volts and amperes,

$$P \text{ (watts)} = E \text{ (volts)} \times I \text{ (amperes)} \tag{8}$$

If E/R is substituted for I in Eq. (8), it becomes

$$P = \frac{E^2}{R} \tag{8a}$$

and if $(I \times R)$ is substituted for E in Eq. (8), it becomes

$$P = I^2 \times R \tag{8b}$$

In each of the equations indicated above, the power in watts may be obtained if any two of the three units E, I, and R are known. Sometimes it is necessary to determine the value in ohms when watts and *either* E or I are known. In such cases the following equations are helpful:

$$R = \frac{E^2}{P} \text{ ohms} \tag{9}$$

$$R = \frac{P}{I^2} \text{ ohms} \tag{9a}$$

In order to determine precisely the relationship between the unit of mechanical power, the horsepower, and the unit of electrical power, the watt, very careful experiments were performed in which electrical energy was converted into mechanical energy. Accurate measurements taken in such tests have shown that 1 hp. applied for 1 hr., or 1 hp.-hr. of mechanical energy, is equivalent to 746 watts of electrical power applied for 1 hr., or 746 watt-hr. It follows, therefore, that

$$1 \text{ hp.} = 746 \text{ watts}$$

As indicated above, energy is the product of power and time, the selected units of either of these being quite immaterial. Thus, energy can be specified in such terms as foot-pounds, horsepower-hours, calories, and British thermal units (B.t.u.), or, for electricity, in watt-seconds, watt-hours and kilowatt-hours. Since the latter term is commonly used in making calculations for energy costs it is usually abbreviated kwh. Its significance is 1,000 watts of power used continuously for 1 hr., or any combination of kilowatts and hours whose product is exactly one.

To illustrate how these various terms and conversion factors are applied in actual electric circuits, the following problems will be solved:

Example 6.—A small factory has an installation of electrical machines, aggregating on the average 150 hp. in motors and 75 kw. in lighting and heating equipment. Assuming that the motors operate at an average efficiency[1] of

[1]If the efficiency is 70 per cent, the input will be $\frac{1}{0.70} = 1.43$ times as great as the output, indicated in horsepower above.

70 per cent, determine the total number of kilowatt-hours of energy used in the factory on the basis of 8 hr. a day and 22 days a month.

Solution:

Input to the motors = 1.43 × 150 = 215 hp.
= 215 × 0.746 = 160 kw.

Total kilowatt input to factory = 160 + 75 = 235 kw.

Total hours power used per month = 8 × 22 = 176 hr.

Total energy consumption per month = 235 × 176
= 41,360 kwh.

Example 7.—A load of incandescent lights connected in parallel to a 115-volt source consists of twenty 75-watt bulbs, thirty 100-watt bulbs, fifty 150-watt bulbs, and ten 300-watt bulbs. Determine (*a*) the resistance of each type of lamp, (*b*) the equivalent resistance of each group of lamps of the same wattage rating, (*c*) the total equivalent resistance of all the lamps, (*d*) the total incandescent lamp load in kilowatts.

Solution:

a. Resistances per lamp

$$R_{75} = \frac{\overline{115}^2}{75} = 176.4; \quad R_{100} = \frac{\overline{115}^2}{100} = 131.2;$$

$$R_{150} = \frac{\overline{115}^2}{150} = 88.2; \quad R_{300} = \frac{\overline{115}^2}{300} = 44.1$$

b. Resistance per group of same wattage

$$R_{75} = \frac{176.4}{20} = 8.82; \quad R_{100} = \frac{131.2}{30} = 4.37;$$

$$R_{150} = \frac{88.2}{50} = 1.76; \quad R_{300} = \frac{44.1}{10} = 4.41$$

c. $$R_{eq} = \frac{1}{\frac{1}{8.82} + \frac{1}{4.37} + \frac{1}{1.76} + \frac{1}{4.41}}$$

$$= \frac{1}{0.1134 + 0.229 + 0.568 + 0.227} = \frac{1}{1.1374} = 0.88 \text{ ohm}$$

Also

$$R_{eq} = \frac{(115)^2}{(20 \times 75) + (30 \times 100) + (50 \times 150) + (10 \times 300)}$$

$$= \frac{(115)^2}{15{,}000} = 0.88 \text{ ohm}$$

d. Total kilowatts

$$= \frac{(20 \times 75) + (30 \times 100) + (50 \times 150) + (10 \times 300)}{1{,}000} = 15$$

Example 8.—An electric ironer takes 1,250 watts when connected to a 110-volt source. What current does it take and what is its resistance?

Solution:

$$I = \frac{1{,}250}{110} = 11.36 \text{ amp.} \quad R = \frac{1{,}250}{(11.36)^2} = 9.7 \text{ ohms}$$

Electrical and Heat Energy.—It was pointed out previously (Chap. I) that a flow of current through a resistor always generates heat in the resistor. What happens, of course, is that electrical energy is converted into heat energy. If this heat energy raises the temperature of the copper wires in transmission lines, or the windings in motors or electromagnets, or in other electrical devices whose function it is to do work not related to heating, then we think of it as an energy loss. On the other hand, if this heat energy is made useful in such conveniences as toasters, percolators, flatirons, electric furnaces, and the like, we think only of the energy that *escapes* as an energy loss. Thus, for example, when only 70 per cent of the electrical energy supplied to a percolator is transferred to the water, it is proper to say that 30 per cent has been lost.

Since energy is the product of power and time, electrical energy may be determined from the equation

$$W = P \times t = E \times I \times t = I^2 \times R \times t \qquad (10)$$

where W = energy, watt-seconds or joules

t = time, seconds

and E, I, and R are as defined before.

If this energy is lost and the power is constant during the time it is applied, then it is customary to speak of the latter as a *power loss*, the usual designation for this being the *I square R loss*, or briefly the I^2R. Thus, in a transmission line having a resistance of 0.15 ohm and carrying a current of 50 amp., the power loss will be $(50)^2 \times 0.15 = 375$ watts.

However, when the electrical energy is to be applied to some useful heating device such as a water heater, it is desirable to know how many gram-calories[1] or British thermal units[2] of heat energy are represented by 1 unit of electrical energy.

Experiments, very carefully performed, have shown that

$$1 \text{ gram-calorie} = 0.24 \text{ watt-sec.}$$

Therefore,

$$H \text{ (calories)} = \begin{cases} 0.24\, P \times t & (11) \\ 0.24\, E \times I \times t & (11a) \\ 0.24\, \dfrac{E^2}{R} \times t & (11b) \\ 0.24\, I^2 \times R \times t & (11c) \end{cases}$$

Since there are 453.6 g. in 1 lb., the heat energy imparted to water (specific heat = 1) may be written in terms of its electrical-energy equivalent as follows:

$$(\text{Lb. } H_2O) \times (453.6) \times (°\text{C. temp. rise}) = 0.24\, P \times t$$

$$= 0.24\, E \times I \times t = 0.24\, \frac{E^2}{R} \times t$$

$$= 0.24\, I^2 \times R \times t \qquad (12)$$

The above equations will now be illustrated by the solution of two problems.

Example 9.—It is desired to raise the temperature of 1 qt. of water (2.08 lb.) in a percolator from 18°C. to 100°C. in 12 min. If the supply voltage is 120 and the heat loss by

[1]One gram-calorie is the heat required to raise the temperature of 1 g. of water 1°C.

[2]One B.t.u. is the heat required to raise the temperature of 1 lb. of water 1°F.

radiation is assumed to be 25 per cent, calculate (*a*) the electrical power required, (*b*) the resistance of the heating unit, (*c*) the current taken by the percolator.

Solution:

The heat energy required by the water

$$= 2.08 \times 453.6 \times (100 - 18) = 77{,}300 \text{ gram-calories}$$

Since there is a loss of 25 per cent by radiation, the heating unit must supply $\frac{77{,}300}{0.75} = 103{,}200$ gram-calories. Therefore, $103{,}200 = 0.24\, P \times (12 \times 60)$, or

$$a.\ P = \frac{103{,}200}{0.24 \times 720} = 597 \text{ watts (roughly 600)}$$

$$b.\ R = \frac{E^2}{P} = \frac{(120)^2}{600} = 24 \text{ ohms}$$

$$c.\ I = \frac{E}{R} = \frac{120}{24} = 5 \text{ amp.}$$

Example 10.—A 5-hp., 220-volt motor having an efficiency of 84.7 per cent is installed 154 ft. from a 230-volt source. Calculate (*a*) the current taken by the motor, (*b*) the resistance of the two wires connecting the source and the motor, (*c*) the power loss (I^2R loss) in the wires, (*d*) the size of wire used in the installation.

Solution:

$$a.\ \text{Power input to motor} = \frac{5 \times 746}{0.847} = 4{,}400 \text{ watts}$$

$$\text{Amperes input to motor} = \frac{4{,}400}{220} = 20$$

$$b.\ \text{Voltage drop from source to motor} = 230 - 220 = 10$$

$$\text{Resistance of two wires} = \frac{\text{voltage drop}}{I} = \frac{10}{20} = 0.5 \text{ ohm}$$

$$c.\ \text{Power loss} = I^2R = (20)^2 \times 0.5 = 200 \text{ watts}$$

$$d.\ \text{Resistance for 308 ft.} = 0.5 \text{ ohm}$$

$$\text{Therefore } \frac{R}{1{,}000 \text{ ft.}} = \frac{0.5}{0.308} = 1.63 \text{ ohms}$$

From Table II (page 26), No. 12 wire is used.

Efficiency of Transmission.—From what has been said above, it should be clear that power losses always occur in the wires of all electric circuits, whether these wires are the means of transmitting the electrical energy from one place to another or constitute the actual windings in the coils of motors, generators, transformers, electromagnets, and the like. The only useful energy is that converted into the form in which it may be utilized. It is obvious, therefore, that not all the energy is actually made available to the consumer. This merely means that the efficiency of utilization is always less than 100 per cent. In electrical-distribution and -transmission systems the I^2R losses occur in the connecting wires; in mechanical systems the losses may be in belts and pulleys where they constitute friction losses, or in steam lines where heat is lost by radiation. When the distance between source and consumer is short, the loss is small; when it is considerable, the loss may be great. Since the loss varies as the *square of the current* and the first power of the resistance, it is more economical and efficient to transmit electrical energy at high voltage than at low voltage. The reason for this is twofold: (1) the wire size may be reduced and, therefore, its cost, and (2) the power loss is less. If the power actually delivered to the load is divided by the total power put into the line at the source, the ratio is known as the *efficiency of transmission.* Thus,

$$\text{Per cent transmission efficiency} = \frac{\text{useful kilowatts}}{\text{total kilowatts}} \times 100 \qquad (13)$$

or, written another way,

$$\text{Per cent transmission efficiency} = \left(1 - \frac{I^2R \text{ losses}}{\text{total kilowatts}}\right) \times 100 \qquad (13a)$$

Equation (13*a*) is preferable because it usually yields more accurate results, especially when a slide rule is used for the calculation.

To illustrate how the transmission efficiency may be raised by increasing the transmission voltage the following problem will be solved:

Example 11.—(*a*) A load of 80 amp. is to be delivered by a 125-volt generator through wires having a total resistance of 0.02 ohm. Calculate the transmission efficiency. (*b*) If another generator having a voltage of 250 is used and the wire size is halved because the load current will now be only 40 amp. (the power output of the generator is assumed to remain unchanged), calculate the transmission efficiency.

Solution:

a. $\text{Power loss} = (80)^2 \times 0.02 = 128 \text{ watts}$

$$\text{Per cent transmission efficiency} = \left(1 - \frac{128}{125 \times 80}\right) \times 100$$
$$= 98.72 \text{ per cent}$$

b. $\text{Power loss} = (40)^2 \times 0.04 = 64 \text{ watts}$

$$\text{Per cent transmission efficiency} = \left(1 - \frac{64}{250 \times 40}\right) \times 100$$
$$= 99.36 \text{ per cent}$$

Cost of Electrical Service.—Residential consumers are generally charged monthly by electrical public-service companies on the basis of a sliding rate scale, the rate per kilowatt-hour decreasing in steps as the amount of energy used is increased. In most cases where the energy consumption is very low, or where special electrical installations are made for the convenience of those who are not in the direct load center, fixed minimum charges are made. For large consumers, on the other hand, it is customary to have a sliding scale of rates lower than residential rates for *energy* and, in addition, a charge for the maximum demand for *power*. In shops and factories where the power demands generally swing between very wide limits, the public-service companies must install extra overhead transmission equipment capable of taking care of the maximum requirements. And since this adds to the fixed charges for electrical service without increasing the energy income in proportion to the cost of such equipment, it has been generally agreed that a demand charge should be made in such instances on the basis of the maximum *power demand* when it exists for specified periods of time.

It must be understood, of course, that the primary basis for the cost of all electrical service is *energy*, measured in

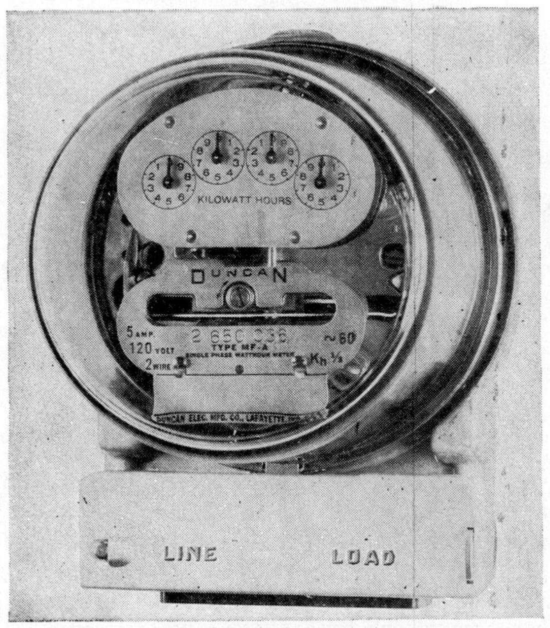

FIG. 13.—Five-ampere, 120-volt, 60-cycle, 2-wire watt-hour meter used principally in residential installations. Note: $k_h = \frac{1}{3}$. (*Duncan Electric Mfg. Co.*)

kilowatt-hours. For the measurement of such energy all installations are equipped with *watt-hour meters*, usually at a point in the line where the wires enter the building to be served. Figure 13 shows such a meter (for alternating-current systems) as it generally appears on the outside of a residence where service enters the building. Figure 14 illustrates a similar type of meter with the glass cover removed and with identifying notations indicating the various parts and adjusting elements.

Watt-hour meters are, in reality, small electric motors in which the speed of rotation of a flat aluminum disk is proportional to the power taken by the circuit. As this disk revolves, it operates upon a registering mechanism, through a system of accurately made gears, on which the *energy* consumption is indicated. The dials of these meters are read

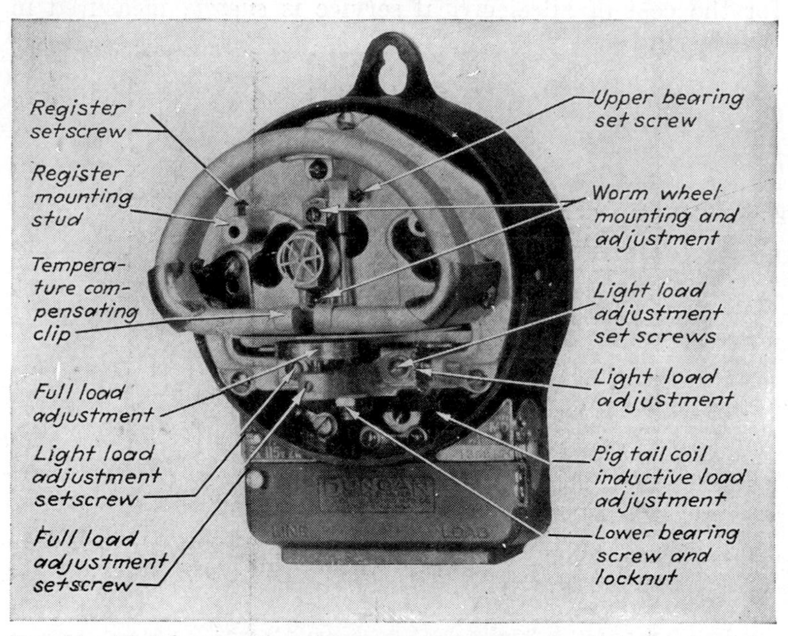

FIG. 14.—Watt-hour meter with glass cover removed. Note large number of adjustments to assure high degree of accuracy. (*Duncan Electric Mfg. Co.*)

monthly by properly trained men, and the energy cost is calculated from these meter readings taken on successive months.

A typical residential rate schedule might be the following: 5 cents per kilowatt-hour for the first 35 kwh.; 4 cents per kilowatt-hour for the next 35 kwh.; $2\frac{1}{2}$ cents for the next 130 kwh.; and 2 cents per kilowatt-hour for any additional energy consumption. For example, a customer who used 264 kwh. of energy for a month would pay

1st step:	35 × 0.05	=	$1.75
2d step:	35 × 0.04	=	1.40
3d step:	130 × 0.025	=	3.25
4th step:	64 × 0.02	=	1.28
	Total cost	=	$7.68

Where high-capacity, good load-factor units—such as electric water heaters—are installed, public service companies frequently give attractively low rates for energy consumptions in the upper brackets. In one such case, a charge of 1.3 cents per kilowatt-hour is made for energy in excess of 200 kwh.

Rate schedules for industrial power and light service, generally three-phase alternating current, vary somewhat on the basis of connected load, maximum demand and energy consumption. In addition to the basic charge for energy (kilowatt-hours) there are at least three other items of cost, representing property investment and operating expense, that must be included in the bill for service. The latter come under the headings of (1) maximum load and load factor, (2) adjustment for power factor,[1] and (3) adjustment for the cost of powerhouse fuel.

One such schedule for power and light service, available to customers having a Billing Maximum Load of 25 kilowatts or more, is the following:

Maximum Load Charge

$1.50 per month per kilowatt of Billing Maximum Load[2] in the month, where the maximum load is adjusted, for billing purposes, to a basic power factor of 0.80 lagging. For power factors *less* than 0.80 lagging, as determined from installed reactive kilovolt-ampere-hour meters, the maxi-

[1] See pp. 150–156.

[2] "The maximum load shall be measured by suitable indicating or recording instruments, and, in any month the maximum load shall be the average number of kilowatts in the thirty-minute interval during which the energy metered is greater than in any other thirty-minute interval in such month."

mum load is *increased proportionately*, whereas for power factors *greater* than 0.80 lagging the maximum load is *decreased proportionately*.

Energy Charge

2.25 cents per kilowatt-hour for the first 3,000 kwh. used in any month
1.8 cents per kilowatt-hour for the next 7,000 kwh. used in the same month
1.2 cents per kilowatt-hour for the next 10,000 kwh. used in the same month
1.0 cent per kilowatt-hour for the next 80,000 kwh. used in the same month
0.8 cent per kilowatt-hour for the next 100,000 kwh. used in the same month
0.7 cent per kilowatt-hour for all over 200,000 kwh. used in the same month

An actual bill taken from the files of the Public Service Company of Indiana, Inc., for electric service rendered a Lafayette, Indiana, manufacturer is given to illustrate how the monthly bill is calculated on the above schedule.

Example 12.—The following information, taken from meter readings and preliminary calculations, is given in connection with one month's electric service: total energy = 138,000 kwh.; maximum load = 475 kw.; average power factor = 0.672 lagging; fuel clause adjustment = 0.1141 cent per kwh. based on applicable average fuel cost of $0.1973 per million B.t.u. Determine cost of service to the customer.

Solution:

Maximum Load Charge

Billing Maximum Load (adjusted to power factor)

$$= 475 \times \frac{0.80}{0.672} = 565.5 \text{ kw.}$$

Maximum Load charge = 565.5 × $1.50 = $848.25

Fuel-clause Charge

138,000 × $0.001141 = $157.46

Energy Charge

3,000 kwh.	@ 0.0225	=	$ 67.50
7,000 kwh.	@ 0.018	=	126.00
10,000 kwh.	@ 0.012	=	120.00
80,000 kwh.	@ 0.010	=	800.00
38,000 kwh.	@ 0.080	=	304.00
138,000 kwh.	total	=	$1,417.50

Total monthly bill = 848.25 + 157.46 + 1,417.50
= $2,423.21

Dry Cells and Connections.—One of the common sources of electricity where portability and convenience are important is the *dry cell.* Such a cell is a *primary* source of power because it can be used immediately after the various parts are properly assembled and only so long as chemical energy can be converted into electrical energy. After the chemical components have been changed through this energy-conversion process, the cell is no longer serviceable and must be discarded.

A dry cell is not actually *dry* but contains within its cylindrical zinc container a moist compound of carbon granules and manganese peroxide together with a porous material of pulp saturated with sal ammoniac. A central carbon rod, nowhere touching the zinc container, is in active contact with the "pasty" mass, the so-called "electrolyte." The carbon rod always acts as the positive terminal (from which the current enters the external circuit), the zinc container always acts as the negative electrode (to which the current flows from the external circuit), and the electrolyte carries the current inside the cell from the negative electrode to the positive electrode. After the *active* materials, indicated above, have been assembled, the cell is sealed off by pouring hot pitch or sealing wax over the top, the purpose being to keep the electrolyte as moist as possible during its life. If the electrolyte of a dry cell dries out, the cell is ruined.

If a voltmeter of comparatively high resistance is connected across a dry cell, it will register about 1.5 volts. This is known as the *open-circuit voltage* since the voltmeter current is extremely low. All cells, regardless of size, have the same open-circuit voltage. However, the ability of a cell to deliver current is measured by its physical size, the reason being, of course, that the amount of chemical action and therefore the current depend upon the size of the zinc and carbon electrodes and the mass of the electrolyte. In order to determine the condition of a dry cell, *i.e.*, its usefulness as a source of electricity, a "short-circuit" test (not a voltmeter test) should be performed. This should be done by connecting one terminal of an ammeter of the proper range to one of the cell electrodes (say, the positive ammeter terminal to the carbon electrode) and then touching the wire, connected to the other ammeter terminal, to the zinc electrode *for an instant*. Be sure the ammeter, whose resistance is very low, is kept connected to the cell *only long enough to obtain the reading;* the longer the ammeter short circuit is maintained, the more the cell will be discharged. For example, the No. 6 dry cell, sometimes called a *hot-shot* cell, should give a deflection of about 25 amp. when in good condition; smaller cells like those used in flashlights will deliver about 5 amp. when new.

A more accurate indication of the condition of a cell is its *internal* resistance, *i.e.*, the resistance of the electrolyte between the central carbon rod and the inside of the zinc container. When first mixed and put into the cell, this material has a relatively low resistance, but with use the chemicals weaken and dry out, thereby causing the internal resistance to increase. From the standpoint of utility it is easy to understand that the lower the internal resistance the lower will be the internal voltage drop for a given current output, and, therefore, the greater will be the power delivered by the cell. And, vice versa, the larger the internal resistance the lower will be the power output. In fact, since the maximum power output of a dry cell occurs when its internal resistance equals the load resistance, the best operative condition will exist when the internal resistance is a minimum.

Thus
$$P_{\max} = \frac{E_{o.c.}}{R_i + R_L} = \frac{E_{o.c.}}{2\,R_i} \tag{14}$$

where $P_{\max}$ = maximum power output
$E_{o.c.}$ = open-circuit voltage of cell
R_i = internal resistance of cell
R_L = resistance of load

To determine the actual value of the internal resistance it is merely necessary to divide the open-circuit voltage (measured with a good high-resistance voltmeter) by the short-circuit current (measured with a good extremely low-resistance ammeter). If the ammeter resistance is neglected, it should be clear that the open-circuit voltage $E_{o.c.}$ is used only in overcoming the internal resistance R_i because of short-circuit current $I_{s.c.}$. Thus,

$$R_i = \frac{E_{o.c.}}{I_{s.c.}} \tag{15}$$

Dry cells may be connected in series or parallel. In making the series connection the condition of the cells is not especially important although it is desirable that the cells be similar as to size and condition of discharge. For the parallel connection, however, it is highly important that all cells be exactly alike in size, open-circuit voltage, and internal resistance. If this precaution is not observed, the good cell or cells will discharge through the poorer ones until they all reach the same condition. Obviously, this discharge process is unnecessarily wasteful.

Figure 15*a* shows a group of six cells connected in series, and Fig. 15*b* shows a group of six cells connected in parallel.

Note that the short, thick line represents the negative terminal and the long, thin line is the positive terminal; this is standard practice. Whenever cells are connected in combination, the result is a *battery; i.e.*, a battery is a group of cells no matter how they are connected. When all cells are similar,

1. In a series group the current is that of a single cell; the total voltage is n times the voltage per cell.

2. In a parallel group the voltage is that of a single cell; the total current is n times the current per cell.

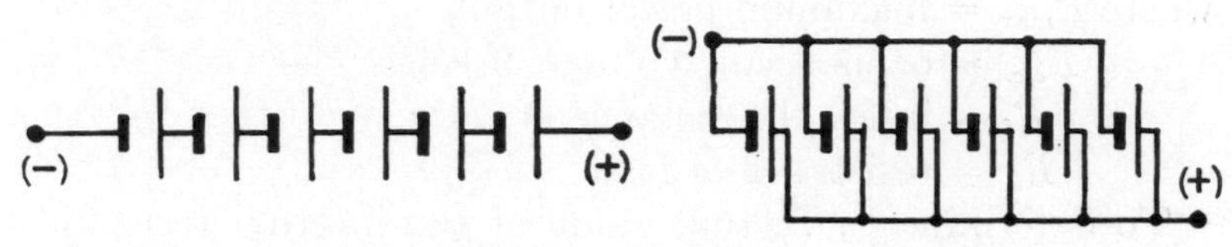

Fig. 15.—Series and parallel connections of dry cells.

Parallel-series and Series-parallel Connections.—When two or more series-connected sections (they may be resistors or dry cells) are connected in parallel, the combination is known as a *parallel-series* connection. Figure 16 shows three groups of series sections, $(a + b)$, $(c + d + e)$, and $(f + g + h + j)$, connected in parallel. Each of the series sections is a part (a minor) of the whole (the major). Note that the name "parallel series" uses the major grouping as

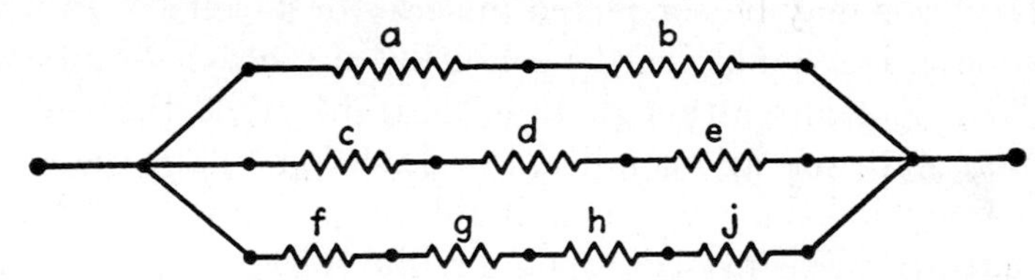

Fig. 16.—The parallel-series circuit.

the first term and the minor grouping as the second term. To solve such a circuit as the above, it is simply necessary to calculate the resistance of each series group (add the resistances) and then determine the equivalent resistance of the three resulting values in parallel.

Example 13.—In Fig. 16, $a = 4$ and $b = 5$; $c = 3$, $d = 9$, and $e = 6$; $f = 17$, $g = 12$, $h = 10$, and $j = 15$. Calculate (*a*) the equivalent resistance of the complete circuit, (*b*) the current through each path, and (*c*) the total current delivered to the circuit, if the impressed voltage is 216.

Solution:

$$a.\ R_{eq} = \frac{1}{\left(\frac{1}{4+5}\right) + \left(\frac{1}{3+9+6}\right) + \left(\frac{1}{17+12+10+15}\right)}$$

$$= \frac{1}{\left(\frac{1}{9}\right) + \left(\frac{1}{18}\right) + \left(\frac{1}{54}\right)} = \frac{1}{0.1111 + 0.0556 + 0.0185}$$

$$= \frac{1}{0.1852} = 5.4 \text{ ohms}$$

b. $I_1 = \frac{216}{9} = 24;\ I_2 = \frac{216}{18} = 12;\ I_3 = \frac{216}{54} = 4$

c. $I_T = 24 + 12 + 4 = 40$ amp.

Also $I_T = \frac{216}{5.4} = 40$ amp. (*Check*)

Example 14.— Referring to Fig. 17, calculate (*a*) the open-circuit voltage, (*b*) the total current delivered to a load of 0.65 ohm, and (*c*) the current per cell. (Assume that each cell has an open-circuit voltage of 1.5 volts and an internal resistance of 0.06 ohm.)

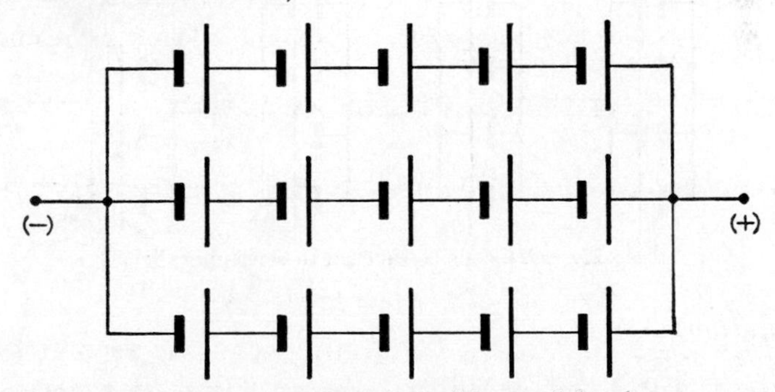

FIG. 17.—Dry cells connected in parallel series.

Solution:

a. $E_{o.c.} = 1.5 \times 5 = 7.5$ volts

b. The internal resistance of 5 cells in *series* $= 5 \times 0.06$
$= 0.3$ ohm

The internal resistance of 3 *parallel groups* of cells

$$= 0.3/3 = 0.1 \text{ ohm}$$

The total load and cell resistance $= 0.65 + 0.1$

$$= 0.75 \text{ ohm}$$

$$I_t = \frac{7.5}{0.75} = 10 \text{ amp.}$$

c. I (per cell) $= \frac{10}{3} = 3.33$ amp.

If two or more parallel-connected sections are connected in series, the combination is known as a *series-parallel* connection. Figure 18 shows four groups of parallel sections connected in series. In this connection the *major* grouping is the *series* and the *minor* grouping is the *parallel*. Note that the designation "series parallel" lists the major first and the minor second.

Example 15.—Referring to Fig. 18, calculate (*a*) the open-circuit voltage, (*b*) the total current delivered to a load of 0.25 ohm, and (*c*) the current per cell. (Assume that each cell has an open-circuit e.m.f. of 1.5 volts and an internal resistance of 0.05 ohm.)

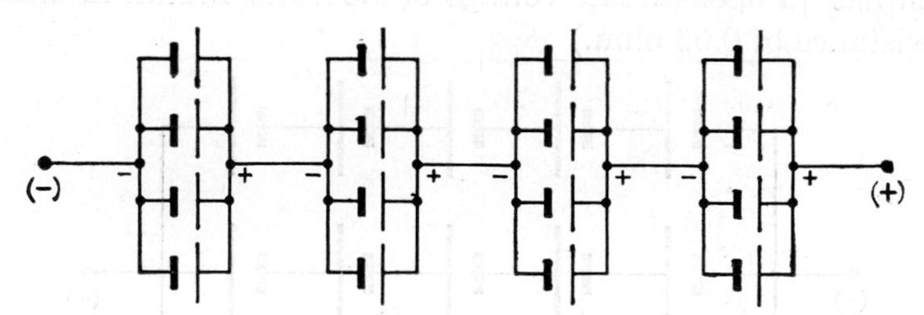

FIG. 18.—Dry cells connected in series parallel.

Solution:

a. $E_{o.c.} = 1.5 \times 4 = 6$ volts

$$b.\ I_t = \frac{6}{0.25 + \left(\frac{0.05}{4} \times 4\right)} = 20 \text{ amp.}$$

c. I (per cell) $= \frac{20}{4} = 5$ amp.

Example 16.—The network of resistors shown in Fig. 19 is a sort of parallel-series-parallel-series circuit. Using the values of resistance indicated thereon, determine (*a*) the equivalent resistance of the circuit, and (*b*) the current through each unit.

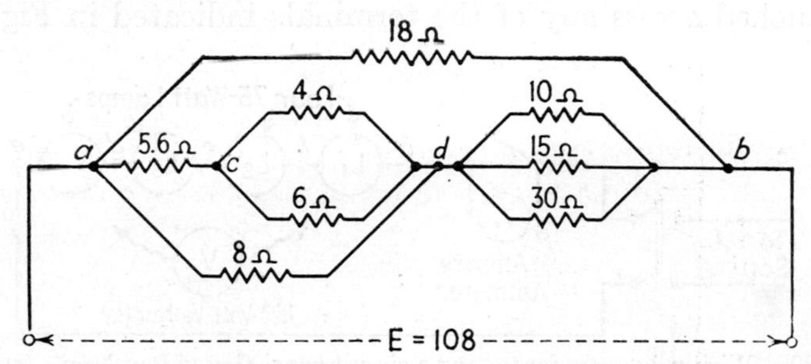

FIG. 19.—Network of resistors in parallel-series combinations.

Solution:

$$a.\ R_{cd} = \frac{4 \times 6}{4 + 6} = 2.4;\ R_{db} = \frac{1}{\left(\frac{1}{10}\right) + \left(\frac{1}{15}\right) + \left(\frac{1}{30}\right)} = 5;$$

$$R_{ad} = \frac{1}{\left(\frac{1}{5.6 + 2.4}\right) + \left(\frac{1}{8}\right)} = 4$$

$$R_{eq} = \frac{1}{\left(\frac{1}{18}\right) + \left(\frac{1}{4 + 5}\right)} = 6 \text{ ohms}$$

$b.\ I_{total} = \frac{108}{6} = 18$ amp.

$I_{18} = 6; I_8 = 6; I_{5.6} = 6; I_4 = 3.6$

$I_6 = 2.4; I_{10} = 6; I_{15} = 4; I_{30} = 2$

EXPERIMENT 3. EQUAL RESISTORS IN SERIES

Objectives: For *four* equal resistors connected in series, (*a*) to determine the total resistance, (*b*) to prove that the total resistance is equal to $4 \times R$ [Eq. 4], (*c*) to prove that the individual voltage drops are equal and are one-fourth of the total impressed voltage.

Procedure: Connect four 75-watt incandescent lamps in series and then, through a s.p.s.t. switch, to a 110/120-volt direct-current source. Across the switch connect a 1-amp direct-current ammeter. The leads of the 150-volt voltmeter should hang loosely and should be ready to be touched *across* any of the terminals indicated in Fig. 20.

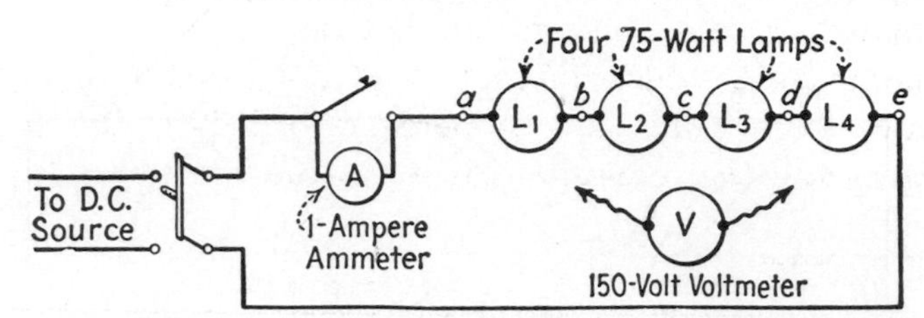

FIG. 20.—Wiring diagram for testing a circuit consisting of four lamps (or other resistors) in series.

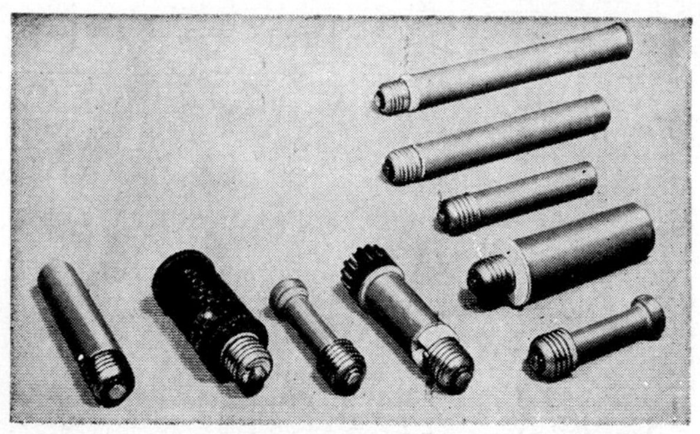

FIG. 21.—Edison screw-base type of resistor. (*Ward Leonard Electric Co.*)

[NOTE: Any other combination of equal resistors may be used in place of the incandescent lamps specified above. The Edison screw-base type of vitreous enameled units, such as those illustrated by Fig. 21, is excellent for these experiments. When using such resistors be sure the proper ranges of ammeter and voltmeter are selected.]

After closing the main switch, measure and record the following quantities: I amp.; E_1, E_2, E_3, and E_4 volts across lamps 1, 2, 3, and 4, respectively; $E_{(1+2)}$, $E_{(2+3)}$, and $E_{(3+4)}$ volts across lamps (1 + 2), (2 + 3), and (3 + 4), respectively; $E_{(1+2+3)}$ and $E_{(2+3+4)}$ volts across lamps (1 + 2 + 3) and (2 + 3 + 4), respectively; and, finally, the total impressed voltage across all four lamps in series (1 + 2 + 3 + 4). All of these voltages may be measured quickly by merely touching the proper terminals *a*, *b*, *c*, *d*, and *e* for an instant.

Calculations: A table similar to that given below should be made, with volts and amperes recorded in the proper spaces and the resistance calculated in each case.

	Lamps or resistors									
	1	2	3	4	1+2	2+3	3+4	1+2+3	2+3+4	1+2+3+4
Volts										
Amperes	←				(		)			→
Ohms										

The results of the test should prove that

a. $E_1 = E_2 = E_3 = E_4$

b. $E_1 + E_2 + E_3 + E_4 = E_{(1+2+3+4)} = E_{\text{total}}$

c. $4R_1 = 4R_2 = 4R_3 = 4R_4 = R_{(1+2+3+4)}$

d. $E_1 + E_2 = E_{(1+2)}$; $E_1 + E_2 + E_3 = E_{(1+2+3)}$; etc.

e. $2R_1 = 2R_2 = 2R_3 = 2R_4 = R_{(1+2)} = R_{(2+3)} = R_{(3+4)}$

f. $3R_1 = 3R_2 = 3R_3 = 3R_4 = R_{(1+2+3)} = R_{(2+3+4)}$

Experiment 4. Unequal Resistors in Series

Objectives: To show experimentally that when three unequal resistors are connected in series, (*a*) the total resistance is equal to the sum of the individual resistors, (*b*) the total impressed voltage is equal to the sum of the individual voltage drops, (*c*) the ratio of any two voltage drops is equal to the ratio of the corresponding resistances.

Procedure:

Part 1. Referring to Fig. 22*a*, connect three incandescent lamps of 60-, 75-, and 100-watt ratings in series. Insert a 1-amp. ammeter in the circuit as in the previous experiment. After closing the switch, carefully measure the following: I amp.; E_{60}, E_{75}, and E_{100}; $E_{(60+75)}$ and $E_{(75+100)}$; $E_{(60+75+100)}$. Record these values in a table similar to that given herein. The voltages may be measured as before by merely touching the voltmeter leads to the proper lamp terminals *a*, *b*, *c*, and *d* indicated in the figure. (NOTE: Any combination of three unequal resistances may be used in the place of the lamps specified above. If this is done, be sure the ammeter and voltmeter have the proper ranges.)

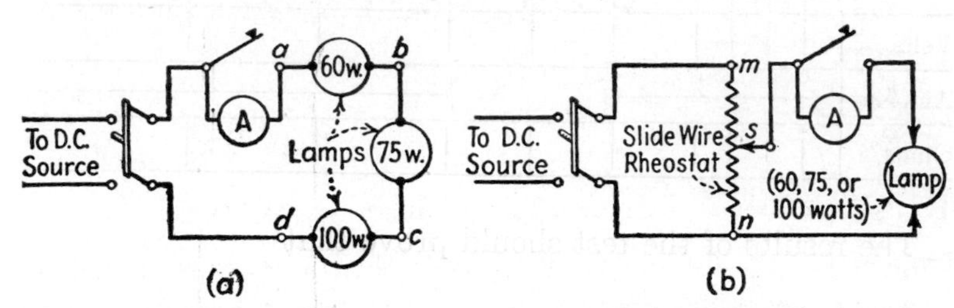

FIG. 22.—Circuit diagrams to verify resistance and voltage principles in a series circuit.

Part 2. Now connect a circuit as shown in Fig. 22*b*. Note that this consists of a slide-wire rheostat (see Fig. 5), an ammeter, and one lamp, the latter being successively a 60-watt, a 75-watt, and a 100-watt lamp. The purpose of this arrangement is to provide a simple means of adjusting the *current* accurately so that the temperatures at which the resistances are measured in Parts 1 and 2 are the same. For each lamp in turn start with the slider *s* at the lower end *n* of the rheostat, moving it up slowly toward *m* until the current is exactly the same as that in Part 1.

Calculations: A table should be made, as indicated on p. 81, in which all the data and calculations may be recorded.

	Lamps in series test (Part 1)						Single lamp test (Part 2)		
	60	75	100	60 + 75	75 + 100	60 + 75 + 100	60	75	100
Volts									
Amperes	←			(	)				→
Ohms									

The results of the test should prove that

a. $R_{60} + R_{75} + R_{100}$ (from Part 2) $= R_{(60+75+100)}$ (from Part 1)

b. $E_{60} + E_{75} + E_{100}$ (from Part 2) $= E_{(60+75+100)}$ (from Part 1)

c. $E_{60} + E_{75} = E_{(60+75)}$ and $E_{75} + E_{100} = E_{(75+100)}$ (from Part 1)

d. The individual lamp resistances of Parts 1 and 2 are the same.

e. $\frac{E_{60}}{E_{75}}$ (Part 1) $= \frac{R_{60}}{R_{75}}$ (Part 2); $\frac{E_{60}}{E_{100}} = \frac{R_{60}}{R_{100}}$; $\frac{E_{75}}{E_{100}} = \frac{R_{75}}{R_{100}}$

Experiment 5. Equal Resistors in Parallel

Objectives: To show experimentally that when four equal resistors are connected in parallel, (*a*) the equivalent (total) resistance is equal to one-fourth of the value of a single unit, and (*b*) the total current is equal to four times the value through a single unit.

Procedure: Connect four 75-watt incandescent lamps (or vitreous enameled type of resistors if these are available) in parallel as shown in Fig. 23. Note that a switch is included in each of the lamp circuits, in addition to a "line" switch across which a 3- or 5-amp. ammeter may be connected. A 150-volt voltmeter should be joined to terminals m and n as indicated. The purpose of the switches S_1, S_2, S_3, and S_4 is to permit the measurement of the individual currents by the use of a *single* ammeter. When S_1 is closed, with S_2, S_3, and S_4 open, the current I_1 is measured. Similar switching is used for the measurement of I_2, I_3, and I_4. When S_1, S_2, S_3, and S_4 are all closed, the total current is measured. The current measurements in this way will be accurate only if the voltage supply is maintained constant, or reasonably so.

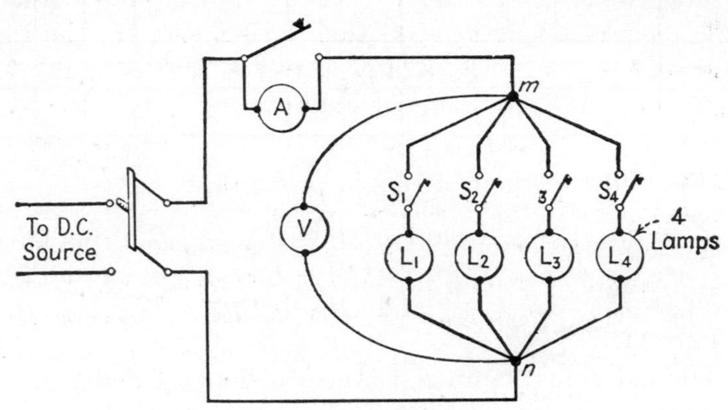

FIG. 23.—Wiring diagram for testing lamps connected in parallel.

Calculations: Data and calculations should be recorded in a table similar to that shown below.

	Lamps				
	1	2	3	4	(1 + 2 + 3 + 4)
Volts	←——(			)——→	
Amperes					
Ohms					

The results of the test should prove that

a. $I_1 = I_2 = I_3 = I_4$ and $R_1 = R_2 = R_3 = R_4$ (for similar lamps)

b. $I_{\text{total}} = I_1 + I_2 + I_3 + I_4 = 4\ I_{(\text{per lamp})}$

c. $R_{\text{total}} = \dfrac{R_{(\text{per lamp})}}{4}$

Measurements can also be made of any combination of two or three lamps in parallel.

Experiment 6. Unequal Resistors in Parallel

Objectives: To show experimentally that when three unequal resistors are connected in parallel, (*a*) the equivalent (total) resistance is equal to the reciprocal of the sum of the reciprocals of the individual resistances, (*b*) the total current is the sum of the currents in the individual branches, and (*c*) the currents through the individual resistors are *inversely* proportional to their resistance magnitudes.

Procedure: With the omission of lamp L_4 and its switch, Fig. 23 of the previous experiment will serve in this one. L_1, L_2, and L_3 should be 60-watt, 75-watt, and 100-watt lamps, respectively. In all other respects the performance of the experiment and the taking of data are exactly the same as for Experiment 5.

Calculations: Data and calculations should be recorded in a table similar to that given below.

	Lamps			
	60-watt	75-watt	100-watt	60-, 75-, and 100-watt
Volts	←—————(		)—————→	
Amperes				
Ohms				

The test results should verify that

a. $I_{60} + I_{75} + I_{100} = I_{(60+75+100)} = I_{\text{total}}$

b. $R_{(60+75+75)} = \dfrac{1}{(1/R_{60}) + (1/R_{75}) + (1/R_{100})} = R_{\text{eq}}$

c. $\dfrac{R_{60}}{R_{75}} = \dfrac{I_{75}}{I_{60}}; \dfrac{R_{60}}{R_{100}} = \dfrac{I_{100}}{I_{60}};$ and $\dfrac{R_{75}}{R_{100}} = \dfrac{I_{100}}{I_{75}}$

Experiment 7. Series-parallel Circuits

Objectives: (*a*) to determine the equivalent resistance of a series-parallel circuit consisting of one resistor (100-watt lamp) in series with a parallel group of two resistors (60- and 75-watt lamps). (*b*) To verify the result in (*a*) by calculating the equivalent resistance from the resistance values of the individual units.

Procedure: Set up a circuit like that shown in Fig. 24. Note that three switches S_1, S_2, and S_3 are included, the

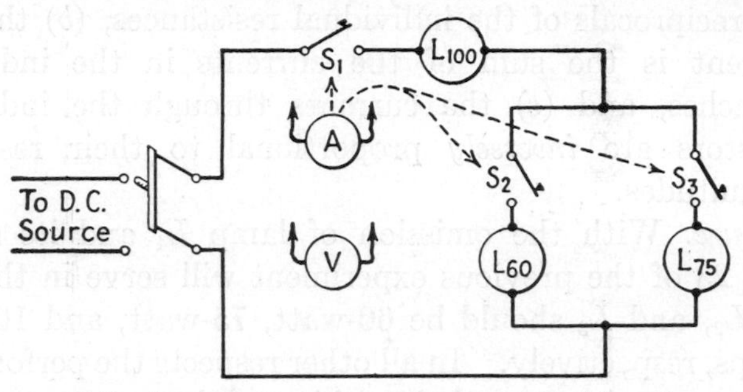

FIG. 24.—Wiring diagram for testing lamps connected in series parallel.

purpose being to provide a method for measuring the currents in every part of the circuit with the use of a *single* ammeter. To do this merely connect the ammeter (5-amp. range) across each of the switches in turn, *opening only that switch to which the ammeter is connected.* Voltmeter measurements (150-volt range) should be made in the usual way.

Calculations: A table similar to that given below should be prepared for the data and the calculations.

	Lamps			Total
	100-watt	60-watt	75-watt	
Volts		←——( )——→		
Amperes				
Ohms				

The results of the test should prove that

a. $I_{100} = I_{60} + I_{75}$

b. $E_{100} + E_{60} = E_{\text{total}}$

c. $R_{\text{total}} = R_{100} + \left(\dfrac{R_{60} \times R_{75}}{R_{60} + R_{75}}\right)$

EXPERIMENT 8. THE MEASUREMENT OF POWER

Objectives: To determine the power taken by a group of lamps by (*a*) the volt-ammeter method, (*b*) the watt-hour-meter method.

Procedure: If a direct-current watt-hour meter is not available (alternating-current watt-hour meters are much more common), it will be entirely satisfactory to use an alternating-current watt-hour meter and an alternating-current voltmeter and ammeter in this experiment. In that case the source of supply should, of course, be alternating current. The measured results with direct or alternating current are identical *if a lamp load is used.*

A circuit should be set up as shown in Fig. 25 for the measurement of the total power, the current, and the

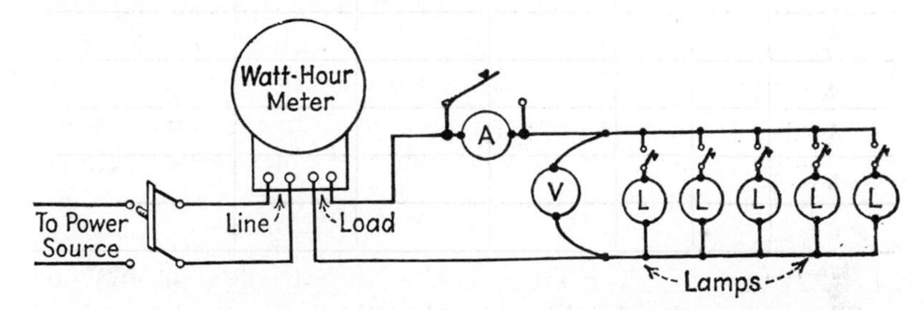

FIG. 25.—Measuring the power by the volt-ammeter and watt-hour-meter methods.

voltage delivered to a lamp load. The latter should consist of a group of five or more 75-watt lamps that can be operated "on" or "off" by switches or some other convenient method. The ammeter should have a 5-amp. range, and the voltmeter a 150-volt range. The disk constant of the wattmeter, k_h, which represents the number of watt-hours per revolution of the disk, is stamped on the meter and should be noted and recorded.

Starting with a single lamp *on*, measure the current and voltage, and determine the number of revolutions made by the disk in 1 hr. With a stop watch the latter can be done by counting the number of times a black mark on the disk appears in view over a period of exactly 6 min.; this number should then be multiplied by 10 to obtain the number of revolutions per hour. Then if the number of revolutions per hour is multiplied by k_h, the result will be the power in watts. Thus

$$P = \text{r.p.h.} \times k_h$$

The above should then be repeated for two, three, four, five, and six lamps.

Calculations: Data and calculations should be recorded in a table similar to the following:

No. of lamps	E	I	Disk revolutions		Power, watts	
			6 min.	1 hr.	$E \times I$	R.p.h. $\times k_h$*
1						
2						
3						
4						
5						
6						

*k_h = ...

The test results should prove that the power as determined by the volt-ammeter is equal to the value obtained by the watt-hour-meter method.

Experiment 9. Internal Resistance of Dry Cells

Objective: To determine the internal resistance of a number of dry cells.

Procedure: Following the method outlined under Dry Cells and Connections on pages 71–74, measure the open-circuit voltages and the short-circuit currents for a number of dry cells. It will be preferable to do this using cells whose conditions are somewhat variable, with some "fresh" ones mixed in with some rather old ones. Equation (15) should be used to calculate the values of the internal resistance of the various cells.

Calculations: A table similar to that indicated below should be used for recording the data and making the internal-resistance calculations.

Cell No.	$E_{o.c.}$	$I_{s.c.}$	R_i	Comparative condition of cell
1				
2				
3				

EXPERIMENT 10. DRY-CELL CONNECTIONS

Objectives: To connect a group of 12 *similar* dry cells in every possible symmetrical combination. For each connection, to measure the terminal open-circuit voltage and to estimate the current capacity of the battery.

Procedure: Using 12 similar dry cells (their condition should be as nearly the same as possible), connect them together in every possible symmetrical combination. These will include the following:

1. Series (see Fig. 15*a*)
2. Parallel (see Fig. 15*b*)
3. Parallel-series (see Fig. 17)
   a. 2 parallel group—6 cells in series per group
   b. 3 parallel groups—4 cells in series per group
   c. 4 parallel groups—3 cells in series per group
   d. 6 parallel groups—2 cells in series per group
4. Series-parallel (see Fig. 18)
   a. 2 series groups—6 cells in parallel per group
   b. 3 series groups—4 cells in parallel per group
   c. 4 series groups—3 cells in parallel per group
   d. 6 series groups—2 cells in parallel per group

In wiring up each of the combinations it will simplify matters and eliminate the possibility of error if the cells are first arranged neatly on the workbench in symmetrical groups, with the carbon and zinc terminals lined up to correspond with a wiring diagram made in advance. Circuit diagrams like those of Figs. 15, 17, and 18 should be used.

For each of the combinations measure the open-circuit voltage and calculate the total current that can reasonably be delivered on the basis of an assumed current of, say, 5 amp. per cell. In each case calculate the load resistance necessary for the measured voltage and the assumed current determined above, making sure that the total internal resistance of the battery, using an average value per cell, is included in the calculation.

Calculations: Prepare a table similar to that indicated below and record all data and calculations.

Connections*		$E_{o.c.}$	I_T†	Load resistance R_L
Series				
Parallel				
PARALLEL–SERIES	2-parallel 6-series			
	3-parallel 4-series			
	4-parallel 3-series			
	6-parallel 2-series			
SERIES–PARALLEL	2-series 6-parallel			
	3-series 4-parallel			
	4-series 3-parallel			
	6-series 2-parallel			

*For each connection make a complete neat wiring diagram, indicating thereon polarities, voltages, currents, and load resistance.

†Assume 5 amp. per cell as a reasonable current.

SUMMARY

1. Ohm's law states that "the current flowing in an electric circuit is directly proportional to the impressed voltage and inversely proportional to the resistance."
2. In equation form, Ohm's law states that

$$I = \frac{E}{R} \qquad E = I \times R \qquad R = \frac{E}{I}$$

3. A voltmeter is used to measure the e.m.f. *across* a circuit; it usually has a relatively high internal resistance and therefore takes a very low current for operation.
4. An ammeter is used to measure the current *in* a circuit; it must be connected in *series* in the circuit in which the current is to be measured. To protect an ammeter from accidental excess currents a short-circuiting switch should be used across its terminals; the switch should be opened only when the instrument is to be read.
5. The total resistance of a number of equal resistances in series is equal to the resistance per unit *multiplied* by the number of units in series.
6. The total resistance of a number of equal resistances in *parallel* is equal to the resistance per unit *divided* by the number of units in parallel.
7. The total resistance of a number of unequal resistances in series is equal to the numerical sum of the individual units.
8. The total resistance of a number of unequal resistances in parallel is equal to the reciprocal of the sum of the reciprocals of the individual units.
9. When a number of unequal resistors are connected in series, the voltage drops across the individual units are directly proportional to their respective resistance magnitudes.
10. When a number of unequal resistors are connected in parallel, the currents through the individual units are inversely proportional to their resistance magnitudes.

11. Power is the *rate* at which work is done; energy is a measure of the accomplished work.
12. Electrical power, in watts, is equal to volts times amperes in direct-current circuits.
13. The customary unit of electrical energy is the kilowatt-hour, abbreviated kwh. It represents the amount of energy taken by a circuit in which the product of watts and hours is equal to 1,000.
14. Energy rates for residential consumers of electricity are usually based upon a sliding scale; the cost per kilowatt-hour diminishes in steps as the energy consumption increases.
15. The energy rates to consumers of large amounts of electricity, such as factories, are somewhat lower, although they, too, are based on a sliding scale. To such electricity users charges are also made for maximum load and load factor, low power factor, and adjusted cost of powerhouse fuel.
16. The heat energy of 1 watt-sec. is equivalent to 0.24 of a gram-calorie.
17. The efficiency of transmission of an electrical-distribution system depends upon the copper losses in the wires from source to load. For a given amount of transmitted power, the transmission efficiency increases (*a*) as the voltage is raised, (*b*) as the size of the conductors is increased, and (*c*) as the distance between source and load is reduced.
18. The voltage of the common dry cell is about 1.5.
19. As more cells are connected in series-aiding, the total voltage increases, the value being the sum of the voltages of the individual cells.
20. Cells should not be connected in parallel unless they are similar and have the same internal resistance. The voltage of a parallel group is the voltage per cell. The total current delivered by a parallel group is equal to the current per cell multiplied by the number of cells connected in parallel.

TABLE IX.—BASIC-CURRENT FORMULAS FOR CALCULATING VALUES OF E, I, R, AND P

To determine	Formula—when given					
	I & R	E & I	E & R	P & E	P & I	P & R
E (volts).........	$I \times R$	....	....	....	P/I	$\sqrt{P \times R}$
I (amperes).......	...	....	E/R	P/E	....	$\sqrt{P/R}$
R (ohms).........	....	E/I	....	E^2/P	P/I^2	
P (watts).........	$I^2 \times R$	$E \times I$	E^2/R			

QUESTIONS

1. State Ohm's law in words; as a formula.
2. Distinguish between a voltmeter and an ammeter (*a*) as to the method of connecting them into a circuit, (*b*) as to their relative resistances.
3. What is the total resistance of a number of equal resistances connected (*a*) in series? (*b*) in parallel?
4. What is the total resistance of a number of unequal resistances connected (*a*) in series? (*b*) in parallel?
5. How can the total resistance of two unequal resistances connected in parallel be calculated quickly?
6. What relation do the voltage drops bear to each other in a series circuit?
7. What relation do the currents bear to each other in a parallel circuit?
8. Distinguish between power and energy.
9. What is a "horsepower"? What is its derivation?
10. In what three ways can the electrical power be determined in a circuit?
11. How many gram-calories are there in 1 watt-sec.? How many watt-seconds are there in a gram-calorie?
12. What is meant by the term "*I* square *R* loss"?
13. Define "efficiency of transmission."
14. What factors are responsible for the power loss in a transmission line?

15. What happens to the power loss in a transmission line?
16. How is it possible to reduce the power loss in a transmission system?
17. Upon what basis is the cost of electrical energy calculated for residential consumers? for factory consumers?
18. What unit is used in determining the energy charge? the maximum load charge?
19. Name the active constituent parts of a "dry cell."
20. What is the significance of the internal resistance of a dry cell? How can its value be determined?
21. Distinguish between series-parallel and parallel-series connections of dry cells.
22. Why should dissimilar cells *not* be connected in parallel?
23. Under what operating conditions should cells be connected in series? in parallel?

PROBLEMS

1. Calculate the resistances of (*a*) a 100-watt, 120-volt incandescent lamp, (*b*) a 600-watt, 115-volt electric toaster, (*c*) a 1,300-watt, 110-volt portable ironer.
2. A classroom has eight 150-watt, 115-volt lamps (connected in parallel). Calculate the equivalent resistance of the lamps and the total current delivered to them.
3. A streetcar has twenty 60-watt, 120-volt incandescent lamps arranged in four parallel groups of five lamps in series per group. The supply voltage is 600. (*a*) Make a wiring diagram showing the arrangement. (*b*) Calculate the equivalent resistance of all the lamps as connected. (*c*) Determine the current per lamp and the total current.
4. Referring to Fig. 26, determine the total resistance, the total current, and the power delivered to the coil under the following conditions: (*a*) with only switch S_1 closed, (*b*) with switches S_1 and S_2 closed, (*c*) with switches S_1, S_2, and S_3 closed, (*d*) with switches S_1, S_2, S_3, and S_4 closed.

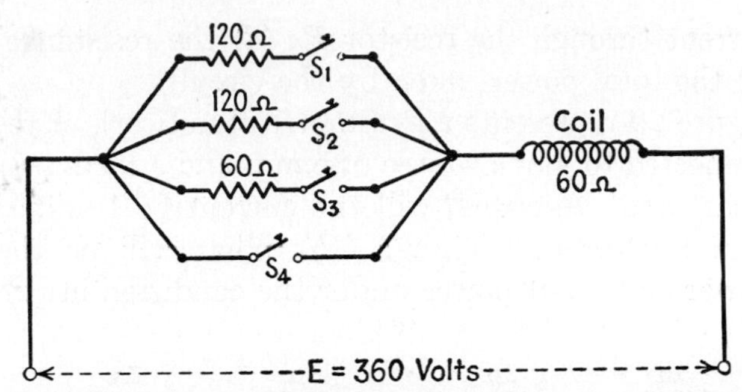

FIG. 26.—Circuit for Prob. 4 to vary the current in a coil.

5. Figure 27 shows a parallel-series circuit. If the voltage drop across the 8-ohm resistor is 48 volts, calculate (*a*) the total current I; (*b*) the impressed voltage E; (*c*) the power taken by the 12-ohm resistor; (*d*) the total power.

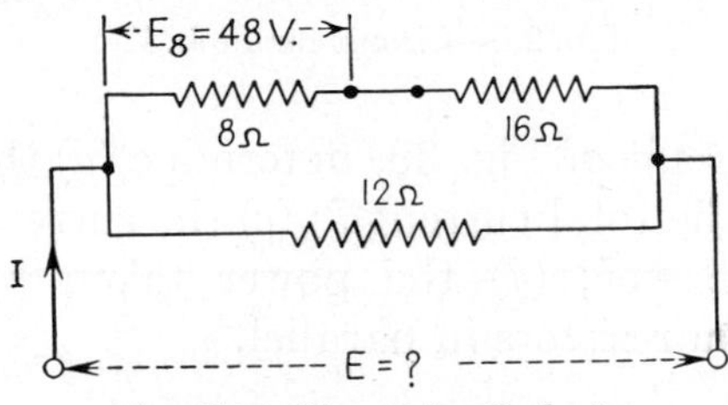

FIG. 27.—Circuit for Prob. 5.

6. Figure 28 shows a series-parallel circuit connected to a 120-volt source. If the voltage drop across the unknown resistor R is 40 volts, calculate (*a*) the voltage drop across the group of resistors in parallel; (*b*) the currents through the 10-ohm, 2-ohm, and 8-ohm resistors; (*c*) the

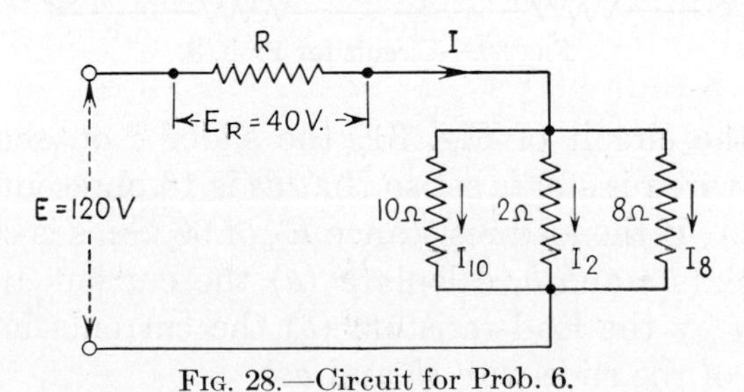

FIG. 28.—Circuit for Prob. 6.

current through the resistor R; (*d*) the resistance of R; (*e*) the total power taken by the circuit.

7. Figure 29 represents a symmetrical network of resistors connected to join a source of e.m.f. and a load. (*a*) For what input voltage E will the current be 1 amp. in the load resistor of 6 ohms? (*b*) What will be the load power and input power under the condition in (*a*)?

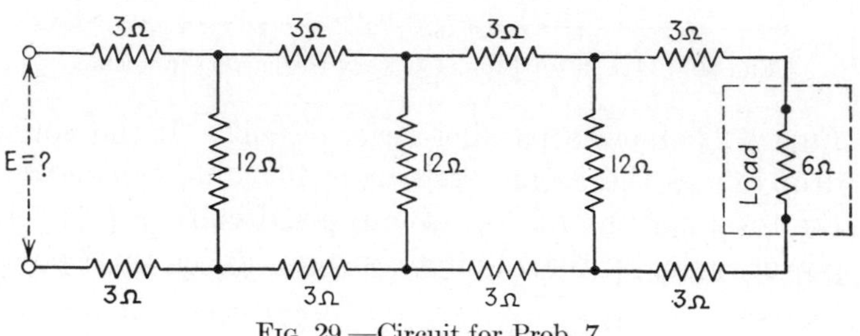

FIG. 29.—Circuit for Prob. 7.

8. For the circuit of Fig. 30, determine (*a*) the total resistance; (*b*) the total current I; (*c*) the current through the 10-ohm resistor; (*d*) the power taken by the 9-ohm and 18-ohm resistors in parallel.

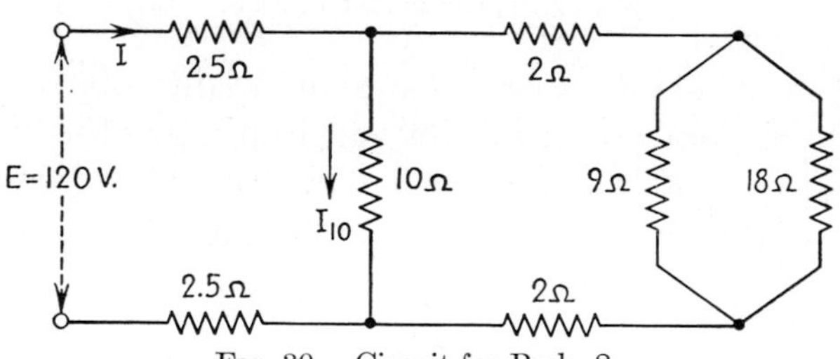

FIG. 30.—Circuit for Prob. 8.

9. For the circuit of Fig. 31, the slider *s* on the 64-ohm slide-wire resistor is set so that *as* is 16 ohms and *sb* is 48 ohms. If the load resistance R_L of 96 ohms is connected to points *s* and *b*, calculate (*a*) the current and power taken by the load resistor; (*b*) the currents in the sections of the slide-wire *sb* and *as*.

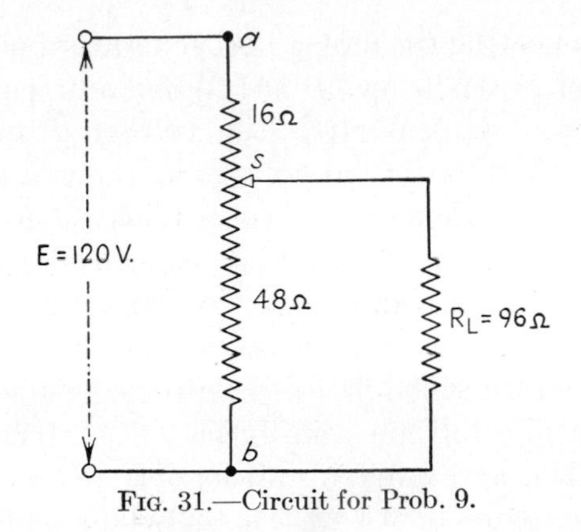

FIG. 31.—Circuit for Prob. 9.

10. A voltmeter having a resistance of 15,000 ohms is connected across a direct-current source and gives a 120-volt indication. When connected in series with a resistance R the voltmeter reads 48 volts. What is the value of the unknown resistor?
11. Two resistors, $A = 7{,}500$ ohms and $B = 15{,}000$ ohms, are connected in series across a 120-volt direct-current source. Two 15,000-ohm voltmeters are then simultaneously connected across the A and B resistors. What voltages, E_A and E_B, will be indicated?
12. A coil of copper wire takes 10 amp. from a 120-volt source when its temperature is 23°C. At what temperature does it operate when the current, with the same impressed voltage, drops to 9.23 amp.?
13. The voltage across a motor was measured and was found to be 230 volts. If it is connected by wires having a diameter of 0.204 in. to a 238.5-volt source, 140 ft. away, determine the current delivered to the motor.
14. How long will it take a 480-watt, 120-volt percolator to raise the temperature of 1 qt. of water from 15°C. to 100°C.? Assume a heat loss of 22 per cent. (Water weighs 8.33 lb. per gallon.) What is the resistance of the heating element?
15. A 50-hp., 230-volt motor operates at full load at an efficiency of 90 per cent. It is 560 ft. from a generator, the

wires connecting the motor and generator being No. 0000 (diameter = 0.460 in.). (*a*) What current does the motor take? (*b*) What is the voltage drop in the line wires? (*c*) What is the voltage at the generator?

16. In Prob. 15, calculate the copper loss (I_2R loss) in the line wires and the efficiency of transmission.
17. Using the rate schedule given on page 68, calculate the monthly bill for a residential consumption of 158 kwh.
18. Using the rate schedule for a power consumer, calculate the monthly bill on the basis of a consumption of 61,600 kwh. and a maximum load of 182 kw., a lagging power factor of 0.693, and a fuel-clause adjustment of 0.126 cent per kilowatt-hour.
19. Solve Prob. 18, assuming a lagging power factor of 0.921.
20. The open-circuit voltage of a dry cell is 1.5 volts. If an ammeter having a resistance of 0.015 ohm is connected momentarily across the cell and registers 20 amp., calculate the internal resistance of the cell.
21. Each one of a group of 16 dry cells develops an open-circuit voltage of 1.5 volts and can deliver a maximum of 5 amp. Show two symmetrical arrangements that will develop 6 volts, and calculate the total current and power for each combination.
22. Referring to Fig. 32, calculate (*a*) the total resistance of the circuit, (*b*) the total current delivered to the circuit, (*c*) the total power taken by the circuit.

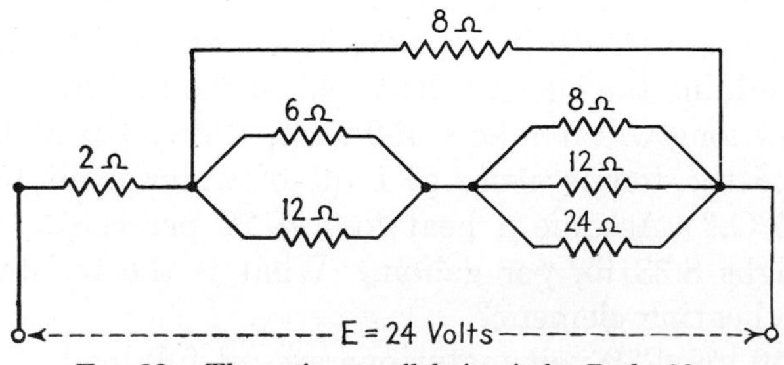

FIG. 32.—The series-parallel circuit for Prob. 22.

23. What is the distance in feet between a 240-volt source and a 228-volt load if No. 7 B & S gauge copper wires carry a current of 50 amp.?
24. The current through a copper winding was 2.5 amp. at a room temperature of 24°C. After a period of operation the current dropped to 2.1 amp. If the voltage remained constant, what was the temperature rise?
25. A storage battery has an open-circuit voltage of 6.6 volts. When 50 amp. is delivered, the battery voltage drops to 5.8 volts. (*a*) Calculate the internal resistance of the battery. (*b*) Determine the power in watts delivered by the battery to a load when the current is 100 amp.

CHAPTER 4

DIRECT-CURRENT CIRCUITS—II
KIRCHHOFF'S LAWS—BASIC THEOREMS

Kirchhoff's Laws.—Electric circuits that are more complex than those considered in Chap. 3, and particularly those that contain more than one source of e.m.f., are solved more readily by the application of laws and theorems that relate the several currents, e.m.f.'s, and resistance voltages in such circuits. Two simple but important laws that were first expressed by Gustav Kirchhoff, one for currents and the other for voltages, are known as *Kirchhoff's laws*. For direct-current circuits they may be stated as follows:

1. *The current law—the algebraic sum of the currents at any junction of an electric circuit is zero.*

2. *The voltage law—the algebraic sum of the e.m.f.'s and the resistance voltages in any continuous path of an electric circuit is zero.*

To understand the meaning and use of these laws it is important to recognize that the term "algebraic" refers to arbitrarily assumed *signs* (+ or −) given to indicate current directions, e.m.f.'s, and resistance voltages. Note particularly that there are three kinds of quantities, namely, currents represented by $+I$ or $-I$, voltages of sources of e.m.f. such as batteries or generators and represented by $+E$ or $-E$, and resistance voltages involving products of currents and resistances and represented by $+(I \times R)$ or $-(I \times R)$; a current or voltage is, therefore, correctly represented only when it is preceded by a plus (+) or minus (−) sign. Moreover, to be meaningful *all current directions and e.m.f. polarities must be properly identified on a circuit diagram* before current and voltage equations are written in accordance with the basic current and voltage laws. Assuming (1) that an *algebraic plus* is denoted by a current *to* a junction or a *potential rise* in passing through a source of e.m.f. or a resistor, and (2) that an *algebraic minus* is denoted by a current *away from* a junction or a *potential drop* in passing through a source of e.m.f. or a resistor, current and voltage equations may be correctly written; these may then be used simultaneously to determine unknown quantities.

To illustrate the application of the Kirchhoff law method in solving a complex circuit, Fig. 33 has been drawn. Care-

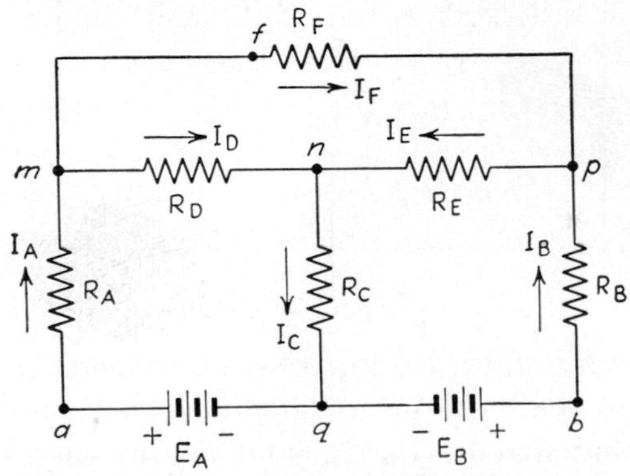

FIG. 33.—Network illustrating Kirchhoff's laws.

fully observe that the plus and minus polarities of the two batteries are properly shown and that arrows indicate arbitrary current directions through the six resistors. It should be pointed out, in this connection, that the choice of the current directions is immaterial and may or may not be correct; an incorrectly assumed current direction will merely yield a negative answer for that quantity although the numerical result will be correct. Referring to Fig. 33, the *current equations* may be written as follows:

At junction m: $+I_A - I_D - I_F = 0$
At junction n: $+I_D + I_E - I_C = 0$
At junction p: $+I_B + I_F - I_E = 0$
At junction q: $+I_C - I_A - I_B = 0$

Also, *voltage* equations may be written for the following loops:

Loop *amnqa*: $-I_AR_A - I_DR_D - I_CR_C + E_A = 0$
Loop *bpnqb*: $-I_BR_B - I_ER_E - I_CR_C + E_B = 0$
Loop *amfpbqa*: $-I_AR_A - I_FR_F + I_BR_B - E_B + E_A = 0$

Several numerical examples will now be given to illustrate the principles discussed.

Example 1.—Figure 34 shows a circuit in which two batteries A and B deliver current to a load resistor R_L through

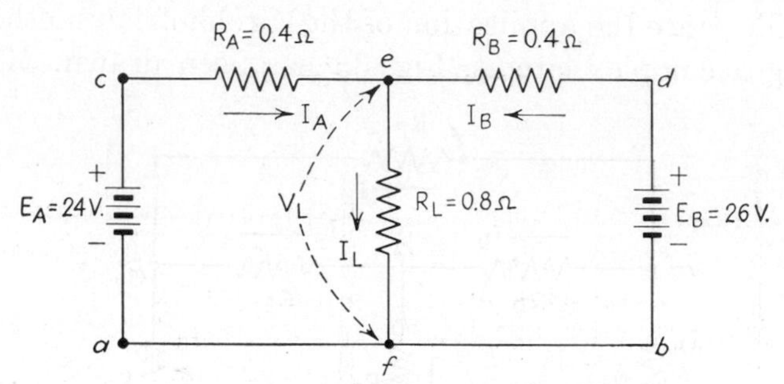

FIG. 34.—Circuit for Example 1.

line resistors R_A and R_B. For the values given (the internal resistances of the batteries are included in R_A and R_B), calculate (*a*) the currents I_A, I_B, and I_L; (*b*) the load voltage V_L; (*c*) the power P_L delivered to the load.

Solution:

a. At junction *e*:

$$+I_A + I_B - I_L = 0 \qquad \text{or} \qquad I_L = I_A + I_B$$

For loop *acedbfa*:

$$+24 - 0.4I_A + 0.4I_B - 26 = 0$$

from which
$$I_B = \frac{0.4I_A + 2}{0.4} = I_A + 5 \tag{1}$$

For loop *acefa*:

$$+24 - 0.4I_A - 0.8I_L = 0$$
$$+24 - 0.4I_A - 0.8(I_A + I_B) = 0$$

from which
$$+24 - 1.2I_A - 0.8I_B = 0 \tag{2}$$

Substituting (1) in (2),

$$+24 - 1.2I_A - 0.8I_A - 4 = 0$$

so that $I_A = \frac{20}{2} = 10$ amp.
Also $I_B = 10 + 5 = 15$ amp.
and $I_L = 10 + 15 = 25$ amp.

b. For loop *acefa*:

$$24 - 0.4I_A - V_L = 0$$

from which $V_L = 24 - (0.4 \times 10) = 20$ volts
Also $V_L = 26 - (0.4 \times 15) = 20$ volts
c. Finally, $P_L = 20 \times 25 = 500$ watts

Example 2.—Figure 35 represents a circuit in which a direct-current generator is connected to two storage batteries in parallel so that the latter may be charged. If the open-circuit battery voltages are $E_A = 108$ volts and $E_B = 110$ volts and the several resistances are as indicated on the diagram, calculate (*a*) I_A, I_B, and I; (*b*) the total power delivered by the generator; (*c*) the total power (I^2R) loss in the resistors; (*d*) the efficiency of the system.

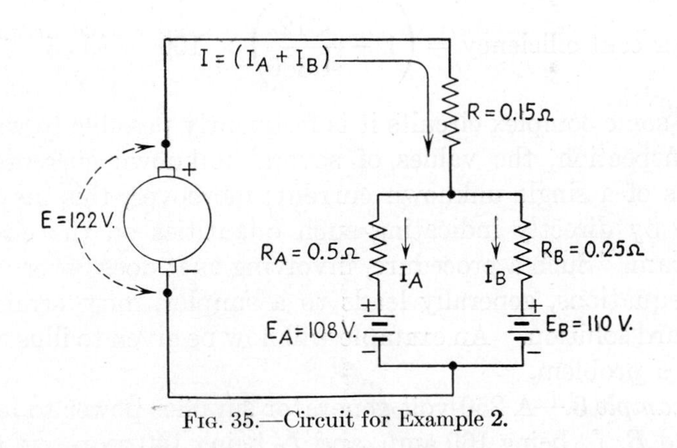

Fig. 35.—Circuit for Example 2.

Solution:

a. Writing two loop equations of voltage

$$+122 - 0.15(I_A + I_B) - 0.5I_A - 108 = 0$$
$$+122 - 0.15(I_A + I_B) - 0.25I_B - 110 = 0$$

By inspection, these equations indicate that

$$0.5I_A + 108 = 0.25I_B + 110$$

from which $$I_A = \frac{2 + 0.25I_B}{0.5} = 4 + 0.5I_B$$

Substituting this value of current in the second voltage equation,

$$122 - 0.15(4 + 0.5I_B) - 0.15I_B - 0.25I_B - 110 = 0$$
$$122 - 0.6 - 0.075I_B - 0.15I_B - 0.25I_B - 110 = 0$$

from which $$I_B = \frac{11.4}{0.475} = 24 \text{ amp.}$$

$$I_A = 4 + (0.5 \times 24) = 16 \text{ amp.}$$

and $$I = 24 + 16 = 40 \text{ amp.}$$

b. The generator power $= P_G = 122 \times 40 = 4{,}880$ watts

c. Total I^2R loss $= [(40)^2 \times 0.15] + [(16)^2 \times 0.5] + [(24)^2 \times 0.25] = 512$ watts

d. Per cent efficiency $= \left(1 - \frac{512}{4{,}880}\right) \times 100 = 89.55$

In some complex circuits it is frequently possible to write, by inspection, the values of several unknown currents in terms of a single unknown current; moreover, this may be done by directly indicating such quantities on the circuit diagram. Such a procedure, involving as it does fewer voltage equations, generally leads to a simpler, more straightforward solution. An example will now be given to illustrate such a problem.

Example 3.—A 250-volt generator supplies power to loads A and B, I_A being 160 amp. and I_B being 140 amp. A pair of wires, each 0.1 ohm, connects the generator terminals to those of load A; another pair of similar conductors, each 0.1 ohm, connects the A and B loads; finally, a third pair of wires, called feeders, each 0.05 ohm, joins the generator and load B terminals. Determine the voltages at loads A and B.

Solution: A wiring diagram representing the distribution system and showing all resistance values and voltages, is given in Fig. 36*a*; note particularly that there are *three* unknown currents, namely, I_1, I_2, and I_3. Since the system is completely symmetrical, top and bottom, it is quite

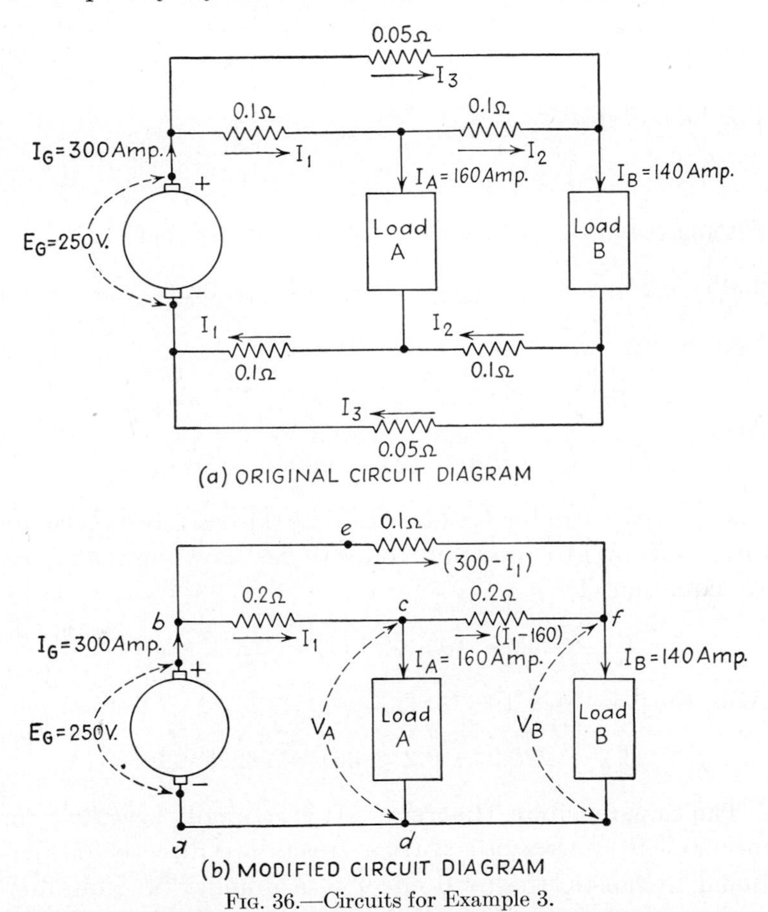

FIG. 36.—Circuits for Example 3.

proper to combine each pair of resistors that carry equal currents to yield a greatly simplified circuit diagram. Furthermore, since the generator must deliver a total of $(160 + 140) = 300$ amp., it should be clear that I_3 may be replaced by $(300 - I_1)$ amp.; also I_2 may be replaced by

$(I_1 - 160)$ amp. because, by Kirchhoff's first law,

$$(I_1 - 160 - I_2) = 0$$

With these simplifications Fig. 36*b* may be made to represent the problem.

For loop *abcda*:

$$+250 - 0.2I_1 - V_A = 0 \quad (1)$$

For loop *abefcda*:

$$+250 - 0.1(300 - I_1) + 0.2(I_1 - 160) - V_A = 0 \quad (2)$$

Setting equations (1) and (2) equal to each other,

$$250 - 0.2I_1 - V_A = 250 - 30 + 0.1I_1 + 0.2I_1 - 32 - V_A$$

from which

$$0.5I_1 = 62 \qquad \text{and} \qquad I_1 = 124 \text{ amp.}$$

Also

$$I_2 = I_1 - 160 = 124 - 160 = -36 \text{ amp.}$$

The negative sign for I_2 indicates that this current is actually directed from *f* to *c* and not from *c* to *f* as shown in the figure. By equation (1)

$$V_A = 250 - (0.2 \times 124) = 225.2 \text{ volts}$$

Also, since $V_B = V_A - 0.2I_2$,

$$V_B = 225.2 - 0.2(-36) = 232.4 \text{ volts}$$

The Superposition Theorem.—It is generally accepted, for mechanical systems, that when effects are directly proportional to causes, the total effect of a number of simultaneously applied causes is exactly the same as that of a composite cause that is equal to the sum of the component causes. This principle is just as valid when applied to electrical systems, where the individual components of currents, caused by the individual components of several e.m.f.'s, are directly proportional to one another. Since electrical circuits frequently have several properly distributed sources of voltage the principle is sometimes found to be very helpful in the solution of special types of problems. It has, in this regard, become an extremely worthwhile "electrical tool," and as such has been given the status of a *theorem.* Called the *superposition theorem,* it may be stated as follows: *In a network of resistors that is energized by two or more sources of e.m.f.* (a) *the current in any resistor or* (b) *the voltage across any resistor is equal to* (a) *the algebraic sum of the separate currents in the resistor or* (b) *the voltages across the resistor, assuming that each source of e.m.f., acting independently of the others, is applied separately in turn while the others are replaced by their respective internal values of resistance.*

This theorem is illustrated in the following numerical example.

Example 4.—A generator and a battery whose voltages are respectively $E_G = 129.6$ and $E_B = 126$ are connected in parallel, through line resistances R_1 and R_2, to deliver power to a common load R_L of 6 ohms. Using the method of superposition calculate (*a*) the currents supplied by the generator and the battery, and the current "taken" by the load; (*b*) the load voltage V_L; (*c*) the load power P_L. Figure 37*a* represents a wiring diagram of the circuit and shows the internal resistances of the generator and battery as well as those of the line wires.

Solution: The problem will be solved in three steps. In step 1 the battery will be replaced by its internal resistance of 1.2 ohms, and the circuit will be assumed to be energized by the 129.6-volt generator alone; this is shown in Fig. 37*b*. In step 2 the generator will be replaced by its internal resistance of 0.15 ohm, and the circuit will be assumed to be energized by the 126-volt battery alone; this is shown in Fig. 37*c*. In step 3 the separate currents in the various parts of the circuit will be combined algebraically to give the actual values in the composite circuit; this is done in Fig. 37*d*. The load voltage and power may then be readily determined.

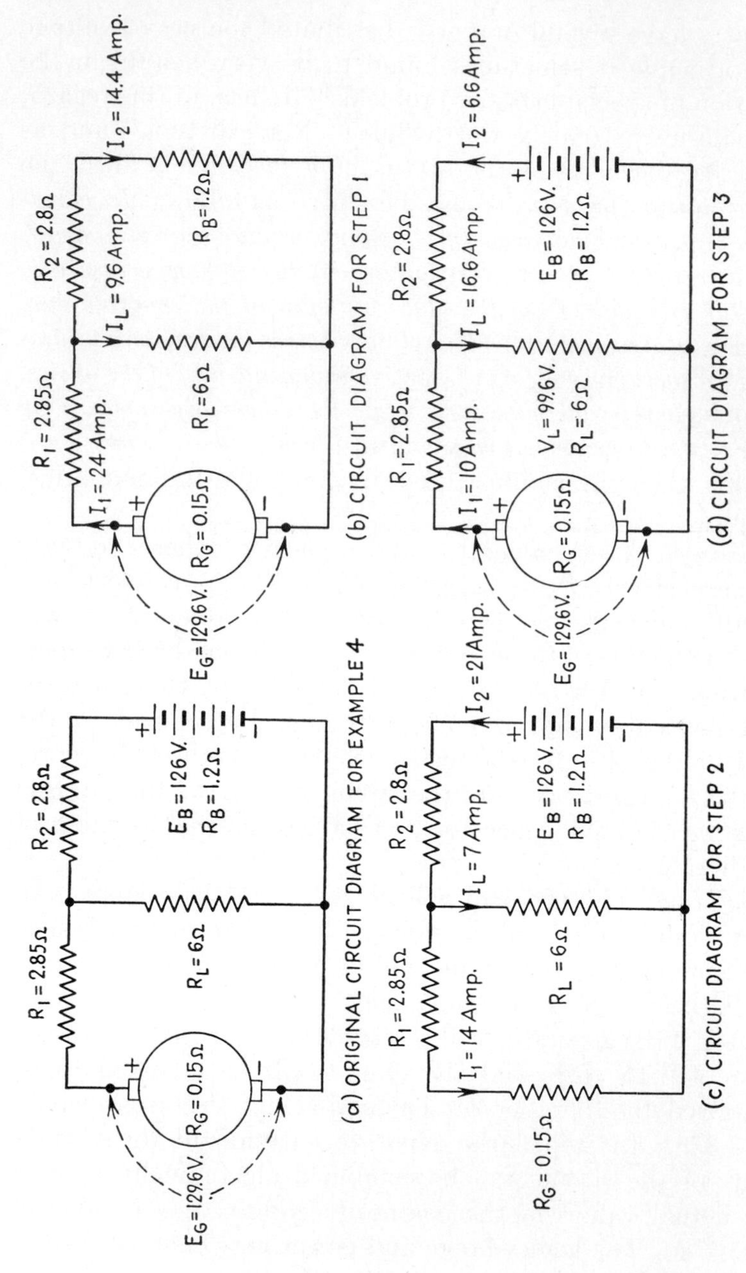

FIG. 37.—Circuit diagrams showing steps in the solution of Example 4.

a. Step 1:
Referring to Fig. 37*b*, the total resistance of the circuit is

$$R_t = (0.15 + 2.85) + \frac{6 \times (2.8 + 1.2)}{(6 + 4)} = 5.4 \text{ ohms}$$

and the total current $I_1 = \dfrac{129.6}{5.4} = 24$ amp.

The total current I_1 divides into two parts, so that

$$I_L = 24 \times \tfrac{4}{10} = 9.6 \text{ amp. and } I_2 = 24 \times \tfrac{6}{10} = 14.4 \text{ amp.}$$

Particularly note the *directions* of the first set of three currents.

Step 2:
Referring to Fig. 37*c*, the total resistance of the circuit is

$$R_t = (1.2 + 2.8) + \frac{6 \times (2.85 + 0.15)}{(6 + 3)} = 6 \text{ ohms}$$

and the total current is

$$I_2 = \tfrac{126}{6} = 21 \text{ amp.}$$

The total current I_2 divides into two parts, so that

$$I_L = 21 \times \tfrac{3}{9} = 7 \text{ amp.} \quad \text{and} \quad I_1 = 21 \times \tfrac{6}{9} = 14 \text{ amp.}$$

Observe the *directions* of the second set of three currents and compare them with the first set.

Step 3:
Referring to Fig. 37*d* the currents I_1, I_2, and I_L, from Figs. 37*b* and 37*c*, are *algebraically* combined. Thus

$$I_1 = (24 - 14) = 10 \text{ amp.}$$
$$I_2 = (21 - 14.4) = 6.6 \text{ amp.}$$
$$I_L = (9.6 + 7) = 16.6 \text{ amp.}$$

b. The load voltage is

$$V_L = 129.6 - 10(0.15 + 2.85) = 99.6 \text{ volts}$$

or

$$V_L = 126 - 6.6(1.2 + 2.8) = 99.6 \text{ volts}$$

c. The load power is

$$P_L = 99.6 \times 16.6 = 1{,}653.4 \text{ watts}$$

Thévenin's Theorem.—When a network of fixed resistances and constant sources of e.m.f., of any degree of complexity, is so disposed that only two terminals are accessible, the current through a load resistor that is connected to the

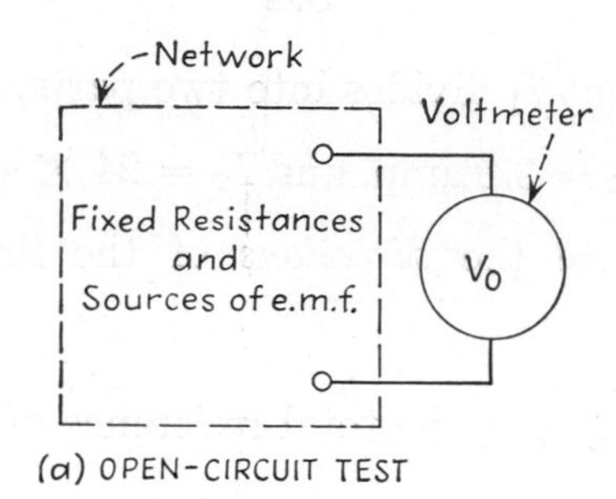

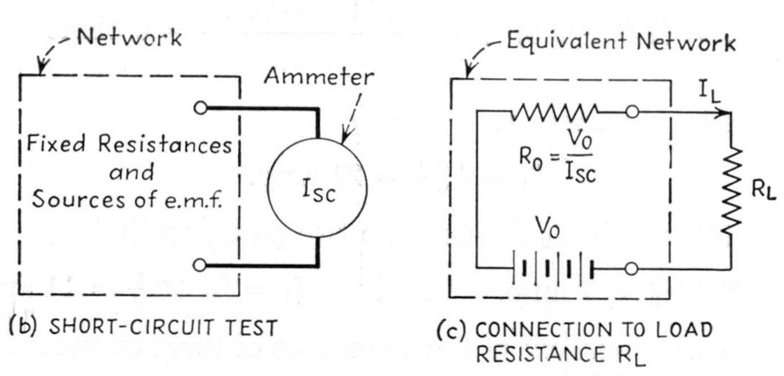

FIG. 38.—Circuits illustrating the method of determining the load current "delivered" by a two-terminal network.

two terminals may be readily determined if two simple tests are performed. These are (1) the open-circuit test and (2) the short-circuit test.

Consider Fig. 38*a*, which schematically represents a two-terminal network of constant e.m.f.'s and resistances; a high-resistance voltmeter, connected to the accessible terminals, will indicate the so-called *open-circuit voltage* V_o. If an extremely low-resistance ammeter is next connected to the same terminals, as in Fig. 38*b*, the so-called *short-circuit* *current* $I_{s.c.}$ will be measured. The two quantities thus determined may now be used to represent *an equivalent simple network* consisting of a single e.m.f. V_o in series with a single resistance R_o, in which the latter is equal to $V_o/I_{s.c.}$. Now then, if a resistor R_L is connected to the two terminals the load current will be

$$I_L = \frac{V_o}{R_o + R_L} \tag{16}$$

Example 5.—The open-circuit voltage at the two terminals of a two-terminal network was measured and found to be 96 volts. A short-circuit test was next performed and an ammeter reading of 6 amp. was indicated. Determine (*a*) the equivalent resistance R_o (looking back from the two terminals into the network); (*b*) the current and power "taken" by a load resistance of 176 ohms.

Solution:

a. $R_o = \frac{96}{6} = 16$ ohms

b. $I_L = \frac{96}{(16 + 176)} = 0.5$ amp.

$P_L = (0.5)^2 \times 176 = 44$ watts

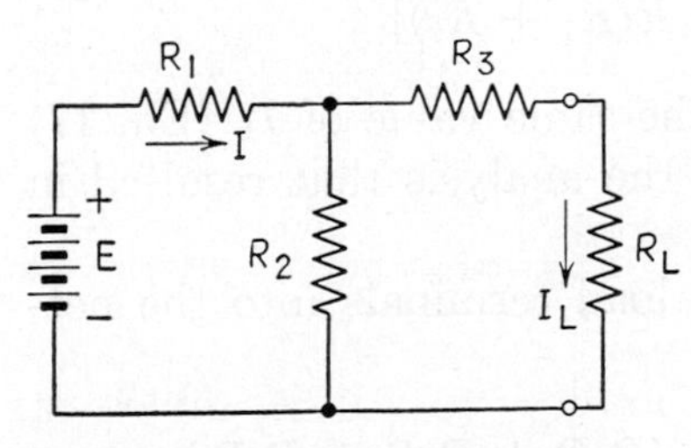

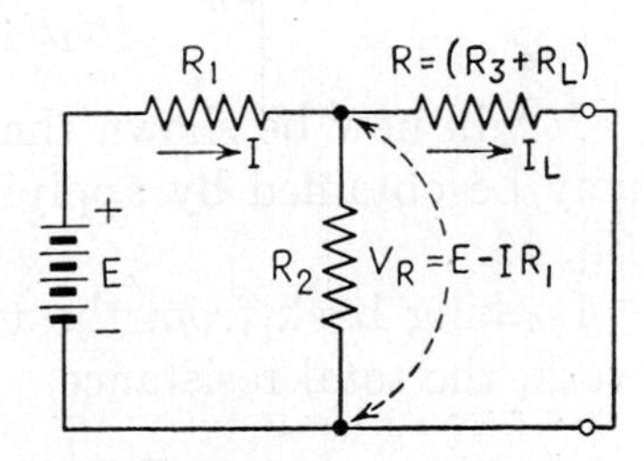

FIG. 39.—Circuits illustrating the method of determining the load current "delivered" by a T network.

The accuracy of the foregoing will now be demonstrated by considering the circuit illustrated in Fig. 39*a*. The network consists of a battery whose voltage is E, and three resistances R_1, R_2, and R_3 connected to form a so-called T. Since R_3 and R_L are in series it will be convenient, before proceeding, to replace $(R_3 + R_L)$ by R. Neglecting the internal resistance of the battery, the total resistance of the circuit will be

$$R_t = R_1 + \frac{R_2R}{(R_2 + R)} = \frac{(R_1R_2 + R_1R + R_2R)}{(R_2 + R)}$$

and the total current will be

$$I = \frac{E(R_2 + R)}{(R_1R_2 + R_1R + R_2R)}$$

But

$$V_R = E - IR_1$$

Therefore

$$I_L = \frac{E - ER_1\left(\dfrac{R_2 + R}{R_1R_2 + R_1R + R_2R}\right)}{R}$$

which, when simplified, becomes

$$I_L = \frac{ER_2}{[R_1R_2 + R(R_1 + R_2)]} \tag{17}$$

It will now be shown that the same value of I_L (Eq. 17) may be obtained by applying the analysis that resulted in Eq. 16.

Looking back from the two load terminals into the network, the total resistance

$$R_o = R + \frac{R_1R_2}{(R_1 + R_2)} = \frac{(R_1R + R_2R + R_1R_2)}{(R_1 + R_2)}$$

Also, with the output terminals *opened*, there will be no current through R; this means that the same voltage will be measured across R_2 as across the *open-circuited* network terminals (the resistance R would become merely an extension of the voltmeter leads when V_o is measured). It follows, therefore, that

$$V_o = E \times \frac{R_2}{(R_1 + R_2)}$$

By Eq. 16, the load current becomes

$$I_L = \frac{ER_2}{(R_1 + R_2)} \times \frac{(R_1 + R_2)}{(R_1R + R_2R + R_1R_2)}$$

which reduces to

$$I_L = \frac{ER_2}{[R_1R_2 + R(R_1 + R_2)]} \tag{17}$$

Note that this equation for the load current I_L is exactly the same as that previously determined by a straightforward solution of Fig. 39.

The analysis leading to Eq. 16 was first proposed by M. L. Thévenin in the latter part of the nineteenth century, and has since been recognized as being an important principle in electric-circuit theory. Properly called *Thévenin's theorem*, it may be stated as follows: *In any two-terminal network of fixed resistances and constant sources of e.m.f. the current flowing in a load resistor connected to the output terminals is equal to the current that would flow in the same resistor if it were connected in series with* (a) *a simple e.m.f. whose voltage is measured at the open-circuited network terminals, and* (b) *a simple resistance whose magnitude is that of the network looking back from the two terminals into the network with all of the sources of e.m.f. replaced by their internal resistances.*

In addition to its great usefulness in experimental laboratory procedures, Thévenin's theorem has been applied to the solution of many networks in which the values of V_o and R_o are readily computed. In such cases it is often possible to simplify the calculation considerably, as well as reduce the number of computations. The following example is given to illustrate the application of the theorem to a practical problem.

Example 6.—The two-terminal battery-resistor network shown in Fig. 40 is to be connected to a load resistance of 150 ohms. What load current and power will be delivered?

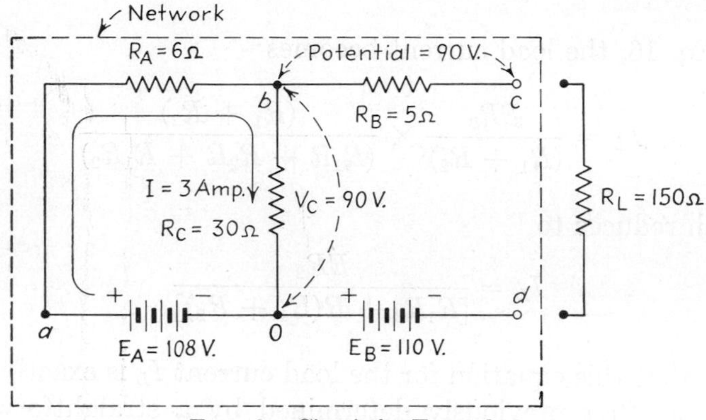

FIG. 40.—Circuit for Example 6.

Solution: With load terminals *c,d* open, the current in loop *OabO* will be

$$I = \frac{108}{(6 + 30)} = 3 \text{ amp.}$$

Under this condition, the voltage drop across resistor R_c will be

$$V_c = 30 \times 3 = 90 \text{ volts}$$

If point O is assumed to be at *zero* potential, point b will be at a +90-volt potential; furthermore, point c will have the same potential as point b, *i.e.*, +90 volts, because there is no current in R_B. But point d is at a potential that is 110 volts *below* point O, *i.e.*, at −110 volts. It follows, therefore, that the *potential difference* between points c and d is

$$V_o = +90 - (-110) = +200 \text{ volts}$$

Next, looking back into the network from points c and d, and neglecting the internal resistances of the batteries, the equivalent resistance

$$R_o = 5 + \frac{30 \times 6}{(30 + 6)} = 10 \text{ ohms}$$

Hence, by Eq. 16,

$$I_L = \frac{200}{(150 + 10)} = 1.25 \text{ amp.}$$

and

$$P_L = (1.25)^2 \times 150 = 234.4 \text{ watts}$$

Δ–Y and Y–Δ Transformations.—Resistors are sometimes interconnected to form rather complex networks; they may, in fact, be so complex that the common rules, applicable to simple series and parallel circuits, cannot be used for the calculation of equivalent resistances, branch currents, and voltage drops. Under such conditions it is generally

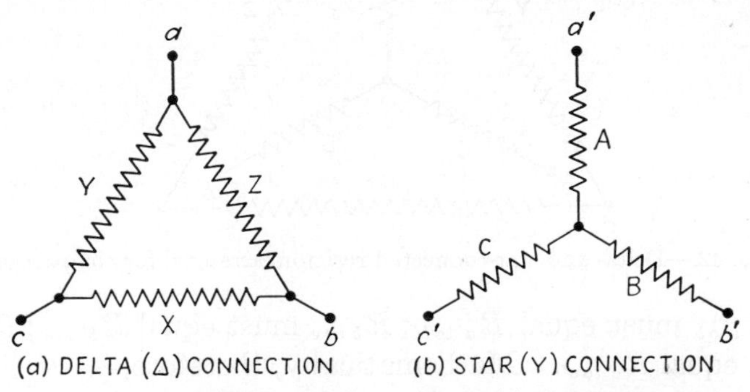

FIG. 41.—Three resistors connected in two ways.

necessary to transform all or parts of the complex circuits into *electrically equivalent* circuits that lend themselves to simple and straightforward solutions. Two elemental arrangements of resistors, within and parts of larger networks, that are frequently responsible for the difficulties indicated are *Δ-connected* resistors and *Y-connected* resistors; they are shown in Fig. 41. Significantly, the transformation of a delta (Δ) into an equivalent star (Y) or a star (Y) into an equivalent delta (Δ) may often convert a circuit that is difficult to handle into one that is comparatively simple. The following analysis will show how this may be done.

Consider Fig. 42 which, for convenience, shows a star within a delta. The star-connected resistors are labeled A, B, and C, and the delta-connected resistors are labeled X, Y, and Z. Note particularly the symmetrical placement of X opposite A, Y opposite B, and Z opposite C; this has been done for a special reason that will become clear later. Now then, if the delta is to be electrically equivalent to the star the resistance between any pair of terminals on the delta must be equal to *corresponding* terminals on the star. That

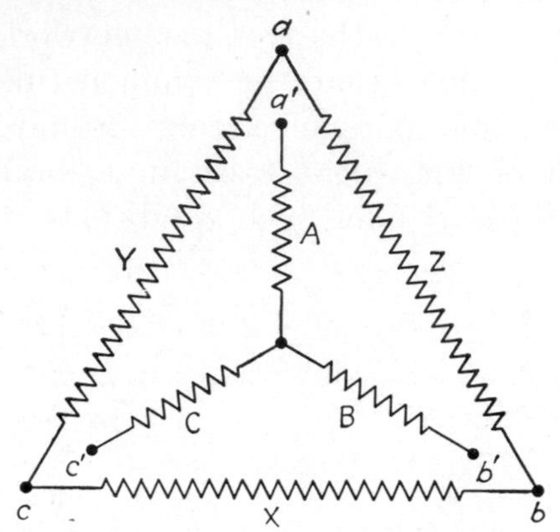

FIG. 42.—Delta- and star-connected resistors arranged for comparison.

is: $R_{a \text{ to } b}$ must equal $R_{a' \text{ to } b'}$; $R_{b \text{ to } c}$ must equal $R_{b' \text{ to } c'}$; $R_{c \text{ to } a}$ must equal $R_{c' \text{ to } a'}$. Mathematically, therefore,

$$A + B = \frac{Z(X + Y)}{X + Y + Z} = \frac{XZ + YZ}{X + Y + Z} \qquad (a)$$

$$B + C = \frac{X(Y + Z)}{X + Y + Z} = \frac{XY + XZ}{X + Y + Z} \qquad (b)$$

$$C + A = \frac{Y(X + Z)}{X + Y + Z} = \frac{XY + XZ}{X + Y + Z} \qquad (c)$$

Subtracting (a) from (b)

$$C - A = \frac{XY - YZ}{X + Y + Z} \qquad (d)$$

Adding (c) to (d)

$$2C = \frac{2XY}{X + Y + Z} \qquad (e)$$

from which

$$C = \frac{XY}{X + Y + Z} \tag{18}$$

By a similar procedure it will be found that

$$B = \frac{XZ}{X + Y + Z} \tag{19}$$

and

$$A = \frac{YZ}{X + Y + Z} \tag{20}$$

Equations (18), (19), and (20) represent transformations from delta to star. Observe that *each of the resistances in the star is equal to the product of the resistance of the adjacent arms of the delta divided by the sum of the three delta resistances.*

The following analysis will yield the three equations that transform a star into an equivalent delta. Dividing (18) by (19)

$$\frac{C}{B} = \frac{Y}{Z} \qquad \text{or} \qquad Z = \frac{B}{C}Y \tag{f}$$

and dividing (19) by (20)

$$\frac{B}{A} = \frac{X}{Y} \qquad \text{or} \qquad X = \frac{B}{A}Y \tag{g}$$

Substituting (f) and (g) in (20)

$$A = \frac{Y\left(\frac{B}{C}Y\right)}{\left(\frac{B}{A}Y\right) + Y + \left(\frac{B}{C}Y\right)} = \frac{\frac{B}{C}Y}{\frac{B}{A} + 1 + \frac{B}{C}}$$

$$= \frac{\frac{B}{C}Y}{\left(\frac{AB + BC + CA}{AC}\right)} = \frac{(AB)Y}{AB + BC + CA}$$

from which

$$Y = \frac{AB + BC + CA}{B} \tag{21}$$

By a similar procedure it will be found that

$$Z = \frac{AB + BC + CA}{C} \tag{22}$$

and

$$X = \frac{AB + BC + CA}{A} \tag{23}$$

Equations (21), (22), and (23) represent transformations from star to delta. Observe that *each of the resistances in the delta is equal to the sum of the products of the resistances in the star, taken two at a time, divided by the resistance in the opposite leg.*

Several examples will now be given to illustrate the practical application of the two sets of equations.

Example 7.—Referring to Fig. 42, the three resistances in a delta-connected group of resistors are: $X = 35$ ohms, $Y = 25$ ohms, and $Z = 40$ ohms. (*a*) Calculate the three resistances A, B and C of an equivalent star. (*b*) Using the three star resistances computed in (*a*) show that, when reconverted to a delta, they will yield the values originally given.

Solution:

(*a*) Since a transformation from a delta to a star involves a denominator $(X + Y + Z)$ that is common to the three equations (18), (19), and (20), this sum will first be determined; it is equal to $(35 + 25 + 40)$ or 100 ohms. Therefore,

$$A = \frac{YZ}{100} = \frac{25 \times 40}{100} = 10 \text{ ohms}$$

$$B = \frac{XZ}{100} = \frac{35 \times 40}{100} = 14 \text{ ohms}$$

$$C = \frac{XY}{100} = \frac{35 \times 25}{100} = 8.75 \text{ ohms}$$

(*b*) Since the transformation from star to delta involves a numerator $(AB + BC + CA)$ that is common to the three equations (21), (22), and (23), this quantity will first be determined; it is equal to $(10 \times 14) + (14 \times 8.75) + (8.75 \times 10)$ or 350 ohms. Therefore,

$$X = \frac{350}{A} = \frac{350}{10} = 35 \text{ ohms}$$

$$Y = \frac{350}{B} = \frac{350}{14} = 25 \text{ ohms}$$

$$Z = \frac{350}{C} = \frac{350}{8.75} = 40 \text{ ohms}$$

Example 8.—The wiring diagram shown in Fig. 43*a* is known as a Wheatstone-bridge circuit; when the potential

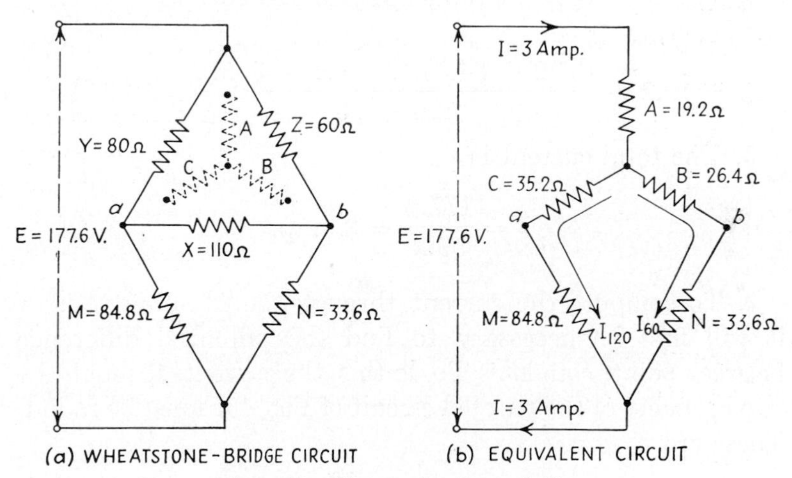

FIG. 43.—Circuits for Example 8.

difference between points *a* and *b* is zero the bridge is said to be balanced. For the resistance values given the bridge is *unbalanced*, and it is desired to find (*a*) the equivalent resistance of the circuit; (*b*) the total current *I*; (*c*) the current in the 110-ohm resistor between points *a* and *b*.

Solution:

a. The equivalent resistance of Fig. 43*a* will be found by first transforming the delta-connected resistances X, Y, and Z into an equivalent star; the latter is shown represented by A, B, and C, inside the delta. The individual values of resistance may be readily computed by Eqs. (18), (19), and (20), and are

$$A = \frac{60 \times 80}{250} = 19.2 \text{ ohms}$$

$$B = \frac{60 \times 110}{250} = 26.4 \text{ ohms}$$

$$C = \frac{80 \times 110}{250} = 35.2 \text{ ohms}$$

Joining the equivalent star to the remaining two arms M and N, the simplified circuit appears like Fig. 43*b*. Solving the latter,

$$R_{eq} = 19.2 + \frac{(35.2 + 84.8) \times (26.4 + 33.6)}{120 + 60} = 59.2 \text{ ohms}$$

b. The total current is

$$I = \frac{177.6}{59.2} = 3 \text{ amp.}$$

c. To compute the current through the 110-ohm resistor it will first be necessary to find the potential difference between points a and b. To do this, the currents through the two branches of the parallel circuit of Fig. 43*b* must be found. These are

$$I_{120} \text{ (the left branch)} = \frac{60}{120 + 60} \times 3 = 1 \text{ amp.}$$

$$\text{and} \quad I_{60} \text{ (the right branch)} = \frac{120}{120 + 60} \times 3 = 2 \text{ amp.}$$

The voltage drop across M is $84.8 \times 1 = 84.8$ volts, and the voltage drop across N is $33.6 \times 2 = 67.2$ volts. Therefore, the potential difference between a and b will be

$$E_{a-b} = 84.8 - 67.2 = 17.6 \text{ volts}$$

Hence, the current through the 110-ohm resistor is

$$I_{110} = \frac{17.6}{110} = 0.16 \text{ amp}$$

Example 9.—Figure 44a illustrates a rather complex network of six resistors, in which four units are interconnected

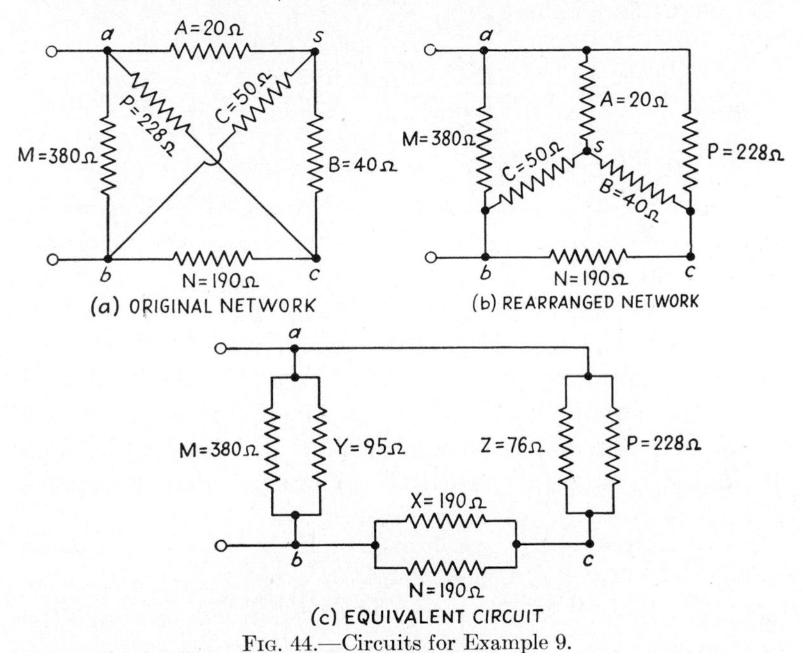

FIG. 44.—Circuits for Example 9.

to form a four-sided geometrical pattern while the other two units join diametrically opposite points. For the values given on the diagram it is desired to determine the equivalent resistance of the network between points a and b.

Solution: Before attempting to solve the circuit it will first be desirable to rearrange the resistors to show clearly that the three star-connected units, labeled A, B, and C, may be transformed into a delta to yield a comparatively simple network. Figure 44*b* indicates the rearrangement suggested. To recognize the electrical similarity of the two sketches, note particularly in Fig. 44*b* that point s has been moved to the center of the diagram; that M, N, and P are still connected, respectively, to points ab, bc, and ca; and that A, B, and C are still connected, respectively, to points as, cs, and bs. If the star-connected resistors A, B, and C are next transformed into an equivalent delta, the individual values of X, Y, and Z may readily be found by Eqs. (21), (22), and (23). These are

$$X = \frac{(20 \times 40) + (40 \times 50) + (50 \times 20)}{20} = 190 \text{ ohms}$$

$$Y = \frac{3{,}800}{40} = 95 \text{ ohms}$$

$$Z = \frac{3{,}800}{50} = 76 \text{ ohms}$$

Rearranging the original resistors M, N, and P with those of the newly computed resistors X, Y, and Z, the simplified equivalent circuit of Fig. 44*c* is obtained. It is interesting to observe that X is in parallel with N, Y is in parallel with M, and Z is in parallel with P. The equivalent resistance of each pair of resistors is, therefore,

$$R_{MY} = \frac{380 \times 95}{475} = 76 \text{ ohms}$$

$$R_{NX} = \frac{190 \times 190}{380} = 95 \text{ ohms}$$

$$R_{PZ} = \frac{228 \times 76}{304} = 57 \text{ ohms}$$

and the total equivalent resistance is

$$R_{eq} = \frac{76 \times (95 + 57)}{76 + (95 + 57)} = 50.7 \text{ ohms}$$

Maximum-power-transfer Theorem.—Direct-current generators are usually capable of delivering considerably more current and power than they are designed to deliver. Being electromagnetic machines their maximum outputs are, however, somewhat limited by internal magnetic reactions which, in part, are responsible for changes in terminal voltage; under conditions of excessive load, often as much as two or three times normal, such machines are incapable of maintaining voltages that are considered satisfactory from an operating point of view. Moreover, as currents exceed name-plate ratings, heat losses—I^2R losses—may be developed at rates that are greater than the heat-dissipating abilities of such machines; in such cases temperatures may reach values that are considered unsafe. Finally, since the power transferred from generator to load is usually large it is imperative that over-all efficiencies be kept as high as possible; this latter point is particularly important because, as will be pointed out presently, efficiencies drop off very rapidly as load currents approach maximum values.

What has been said about power-distribution systems involving generators does not usually apply to small battery circuits and communication networks. The latter generally involve comparatively small amounts of power so that *maximum power transfer* is often more important than other considerations. What follows will, therefore, be concerned with small battery-powered networks in which it is desired to determine the conditions that prevail when the *load power* is maximum.

Consider Fig. 45, which illustrates a simple series circuit, consists of a battery, a pair of line wires, and a variable load resistor. When the load resistance R_L is very large the current will be small and the load power P_L will be low. As the load resistance is reduced to a very low value the current approaches a maximum, the voltage drop in $R_B + 2R_l$ will be large, the load voltage E_L will be small, and the power P_L will again be low. For limiting values, if $R_L = \infty$ (an open circuit), $I_L = 0$ and $P_L = 0$; also, if $R_L = 0$ (a short circuit),

$E_L = 0$ and $P_L = 0$. It should be clear, therefore, that for some value of R_L, not ∞ or zero, the power P_L will be maximum; in fact, as the following illustrative example will show, the maximum power transferred to the load will occur when $R_L = R_B + 2R_l$.

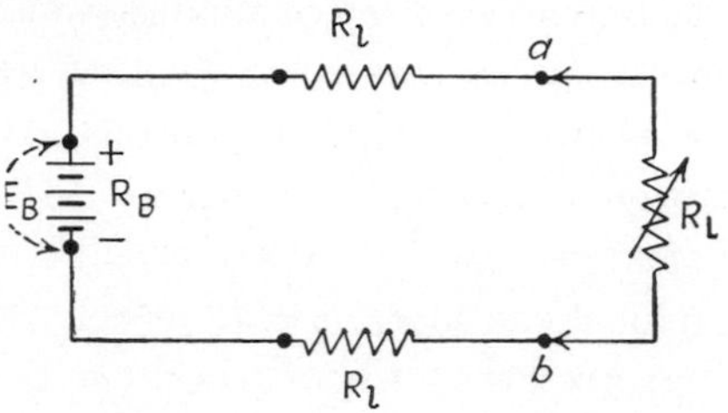

FIG. 45.—Simple circuit with variable load resistor.

Figure 46 duplicates Fig. 45, with the exception that numerical values are shown for the various elements of the circuit; note particularly that the load resistance R_L is variable. Assuming arbitrary values between 7.2 ohms and 0.2 ohm for R_L, a table has been prepared to indicate that (*a*) the maximum power transfer occurs when $R_L = R_B + 2R_l$ and (*b*) the efficiency at maximum load power is 50 per cent.

Load resistance R_L	Total resistance $R_t = R_L + 0.8$	Current $I_L = \frac{E}{R_t}$	Battery power $P_B = E_B I_L$	Load power $P_L = I_L^2 R_L$	Efficiency Eff. $\frac{P_L}{P_B} \times 100$
7.2	8.0	3.0	72	64.8	90.0
3.2	4.0	6.0	144	115.2	80.0
2.2	3.0	8.0	192	140.8	73.3
1.6	2.4	10.0	240	160.0	66.7
1.2	2.0	12.0	288	172.8	60.0
1.0	1.8	13.33	320	177.8	55.5
0.8	1.6	15.0	360	180.0	50.0
0.6	1.4	17.14	412	176.3	42.8
0.4	1.2	20.0	480	160.0	33.3
0.2	1.0	24.0	576	115.2	20.0

A careful study of the table shows clearly that, although the total power delivered by the battery increases with increasing values of load current, the *load power* rises to a maximum when $I_L = 15$ amp., after which it continues to drop; also, when the load power is a maximum, at 15 amp., the circuit efficiency is 50 per cent. This can only mean that above the 15-amp. load current the power losses increase at a faster rate than does the total battery power. It is also interesting to observe that the point of maximum load transfer occurs when the load resistance R_L is equal to the resistance looking back into the circuit from the load terminals; *i.e.*, $R_L = R_B + 2R_l = 0.8$ ohm.

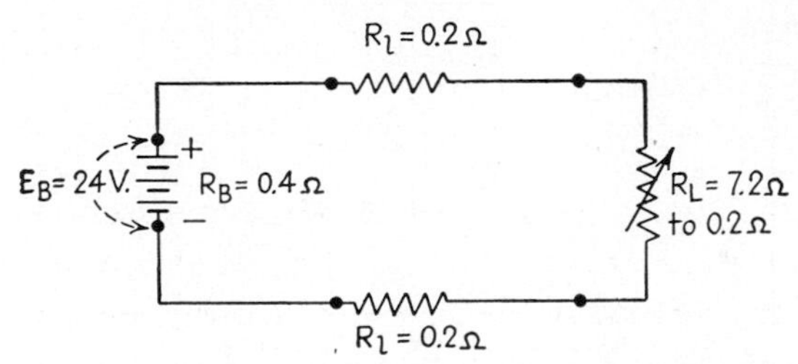

FIG. 46.—Circuit to illustrate maximum power transfer.

Although the foregoing numerical example is not a rigid mathematical proof that all direct-current circuits will behave similarly, it is nevertheless a fact, and it can be shown that *the maximum power transferred to a load resistor occurs when it has a value equal to the resistance of the network looking back from the load terminals with all the sources of voltage replaced by their internal resistances.* This is the *maximum-power-transfer theorem.*

Example 10.—A 120-volt battery, having an internal resistance of 0.5 ohm, is connected through line resistances of 9.5 ohms to a variable load resistor. For what load resistance will the latter consume maximum power, and what will be the maximum power?

Solution:

$$R_L = 0.5 + 9.5 = 10 \text{ ohms}; \; P_L = \left(\frac{120}{10 + 10}\right)^2 \times 10$$

$$= 360 \text{ watts}$$

Example 11.—Figure 47 represents a circuit in which two batteries supply power through line resistors to a variable load resistor. For the values given on the diagram calculate (*a*) the ohmic value of R_L when its power is a maximum; (*b*) the maximum load power P_L; (*c*) the total power delivered by both batteries; (*d*) the over-all efficiency under the above condition.

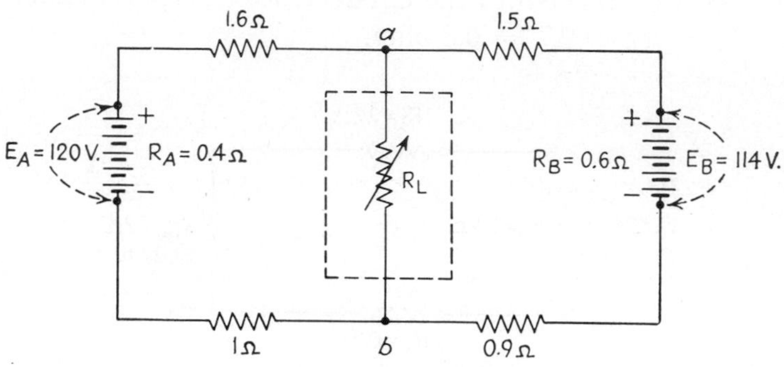

FIG. 47.—Circuit for Example 11.

Solution:

a. Looking back from the load terminals, with the two sources of e.m.f. replaced by their internal resistances, the circuit consists of two 3-ohm resistances in parallel; thus

$$R_L = \frac{3}{2} = 1.5 \text{ ohms}$$

b. With the load resistor disconnected, the circulating current

$$I = \frac{E_A - E_B}{R_{\text{circuit}}} = \frac{120 - 114}{0.4 + 1.6 + 1.5 + 0.6 + 0.9 + 1.0}$$
$$= \frac{6}{6} = 1 \text{ amp.}$$

and the open-circuit voltage across terminals *ab* is

$$E'_{ab} = 120(1 \times -3) = 114 + (1 \times 3) = 117 \text{ volts}$$

For maximum load power, the load voltage must be

$$E_L = \frac{E'_{ab}}{2} = \frac{117}{2} = 58.5 \text{ volts}$$

Therefore, the load current for maximum power is

$$I_L = \frac{E_L}{R_L} = \frac{58.5}{1.5} = 39 \text{ amp.}$$

and the maximum load power is

$$P_L = 58.5 \times 39 = 2{,}281.5 \text{ watts}$$

c. Since the voltage drop between battery A and terminals ab is $120 - 58.5 = 61.5$ volts, battery A must deliver

$$I_A = \frac{61.5}{3} = 20.5 \text{ amp.}$$

and $$P_A = 120 \times 20.5 = 2{,}460 \text{ watts}$$

Also, since the voltage drop between battery B and terminals ab is $114 - 58.5 = 55.5$ volts, battery B must deliver

$$I_B = \frac{55.5}{3} = 18.5 \text{ amp.}$$

and $$P_B = 114 \times 18.5 = 2{,}109 \text{ watts}$$

The total power delivered by both batteries will, therefore, be

$$P_{\text{total}} = 2{,}460 + 2{,}109 = 4{,}569 \text{ watts}$$

d. Using the values of power calculated above,

$$\text{Per cent efficiency} = \frac{P_L}{P_{\text{total}}} \times 100 = \frac{2{,}281.5}{4{,}569} \times 100 = 49.93$$

or slightly less than 50 per cent.

SUMMARY

1. Kirchhoff's *current law* states that the algebraic sum of the currents at any junction of an electric circuit is zero.

2. Kirchhoff's *voltage law* states that the algebraic sum of the e.m.f.'s and the resistance voltages in any continuous path of an electric circuit is zero.
3. In setting up Kirchhoff's laws in equation form it is important that proper signs (+ or −) be given to the various terms.
4. The signs used in setting up the equation form of Kirchhoff's laws are taken from sketches upon which arbitrary current directions are noted.
5. Wherever possible complex circuits may be simplified by representing one or more unknown currents and voltages in terms of other similar quantities. Such modifications often lead to a reduction of the number of equations required for a solution.
6. The superposition theorem (see p. 104) often makes it possible to solve a complex circuit more easily when the circuit contains several sources of e.m.f.; this is done by subdividing the computation into a number of elementary solutions.
7. Thévenin's theorem (see p. 108) has great usefulness when applied to the experimental solution of complex networks. Where the open-circuit voltage and the resistance looking back into the network are readily computed in a two-terminal network, the theorem is extremely helpful when applied to the solution of complicated circuits.
8. Some complex networks consist of deltas and stars that make straightforward solutions difficult. When either is transformed to the other in given circuits, the latter are often greatly simplified; they are then readily handled mathematically by ordinary methods.
9. A given delta is said to be transformed into a star when each unit of the star is equal to the product of the adjacent sides of the delta divided by the sum of the three sides of the delta.
10. A given star is said to be transformed into a delta when each unit of the delta is equal to the sum of the products of the star units taken two at a time divided by the opposite leg of the star.

11. Power equipment, *i.e.*, generators, are usually capable of delivering much more power than their normal ratings.
12. Limitations upon power equipment beyond their ratings are (*a*) internal magnetic reactions; (*b*) excessive voltage drop; (*c*) high temperature rise; (*d*) low efficiency.
13. Battery sources and sources of power in communication circuits are often operated to transfer maximum power, although this is generally accompanied by very low efficiency.
14. The maximum-power-transfer theorem states that a load resistor receives maximum power when its ohmic value is equal to the resistance of the network looking back from the load terminals, with all the sources of voltage replaced by their internal resistances.

QUESTIONS

1. State the Kirchhoff law that applies to the current at any junction in an electric circuit.
2. State the Kirchhoff law that applies to the e.m.f.'s and the resistance voltages in any continuous path of an electric circuit.
3. How are the plus and minus current signs determined?
4. How are the plus and minus voltage signs determined for batteries and for generators?
5. How are the plus and minus voltage signs determined for resistors?
6. What will be the effect upon the solution of a problem if a current direction is arbitrarily assumed incorrectly?
7. In a complex circuit containing several unknown currents and voltages how is it possible to reduce the number of simultaneous equations to effect a solution.
8. State the superposition theorem.
9. Under what circuit conditions may the superposition theorem be used to advantage?
10. State Thévenin's theorem.
11. Under what circuit conditions may Thévenin's theorem be used to advantage?

12. What is meant by the open-circuit voltage, in Thévenin's theorem?
13. What is meant by the resistance of the network looking back into the network in Thévenin's theorem?
14. State the rule that will make it possible to transform a delta into a star.
15. State the rule that will make it possible to transform a star into a delta.
16. Make a sketch of a simple Wheatstone bridge. (*a*) Show how one of the deltas may be transformed into a star to simplify the circuit. (*b*) Show how one of the stars may be transformed into a delta to simplify the circuit.
17. State the maximum-power-transfer theorem.
18. What is meant by the resistance of the network looking back from the load terminals with all sources of voltage replaced by their internal resistances?
19. Why is it not desirable to overload direct-current generators?
20. In a simple series circuit having a battery source of power what is the efficiency when maximum power is transferred to a load?
21. Why is the power transferred to a load very low when the load resistance is extremely high or extremely low?
22. Why is the efficiency of a system very low when the transferred power is high?
23. Assume two batteries having equal open-circuit voltages and delivering currents through equal line resistances. If the internal resistance of one battery is larger than the other, which will be capable of transferring more maximum power? Why?

PROBLEMS

1. Referring to Fig. 33, reverse the polarity of battery E_B and the current direction through resistor R_B. (*a*) Write Kirchhoff's current equation for junction *p*. (*b*) Write Kirchhoff's voltage equation for circuit *bqnmfpb*.

2. Referring to Fig. 34, change R_A to 0.2 ohm, R_B to 0.3 ohm, and R_L to 0.5 ohm. With the same battery polarities, and with $E_A = 24$ volts and $E_B = 26$ volts as shown, calculate (*a*) the currents I_L, I_A, and I_B; (*b*) the load voltage V_L; (*c*) the load and battery powers P_L, P_A, and P_B.
3. Referring to Fig. 34, what will be the current in the load resistor R_L if (*a*) battery *B* is replaced by a wire of negligible resistance? (*b*) if battery *A* is replaced by a wire of negligible resistance?
4. What will be the current in the circuit of Fig. 34 if the load resistor R_L is removed?
5. How much power would be delivered to a load resistance R_L of 0.2 in the circuit of Fig. 34?
6. Referring to Fig. 35 assume a 6-volt battery, having negligible resistance, to be connected in series between the positive terminal of the generator and the 0.15-ohm resistor. Calculate the battery currents I_A and I_B if the added line battery is connected (*a*) additively; (*b*) subtractively.
7. Figure 48 represents a circuit in which a load resistance is connected to a slide-wire rheostat. Calculate the

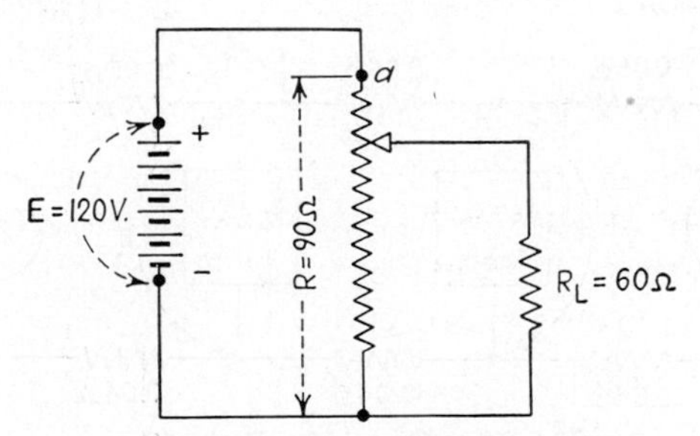

FIG. 48.—Circuit for Probs. 7 and 8.

power delivered to R_L when the slider (*a*) is at point *a*; (*b*) is moved down to a point one-third from *a*; (*c*) is moved down to a point two-thirds from *a*.
8. Referring to Fig. 48, determine the value of R_L for a load voltage of 48 volts, when the slider is halfway between the ends of the slide-wire rheostat. For this

condition calculate also the power taken by the load resistance.

9. Referring to Fig. 36, assume that the current in load A is 140 amp. and that the current in load B is 160 amp. With all other data similar to the values given in the diagram, calculate the load voltages V_A and V_B.
10. For the circuit of Fig. 49 determine (*a*) the potential difference between A and B; (*b*) between x and y.

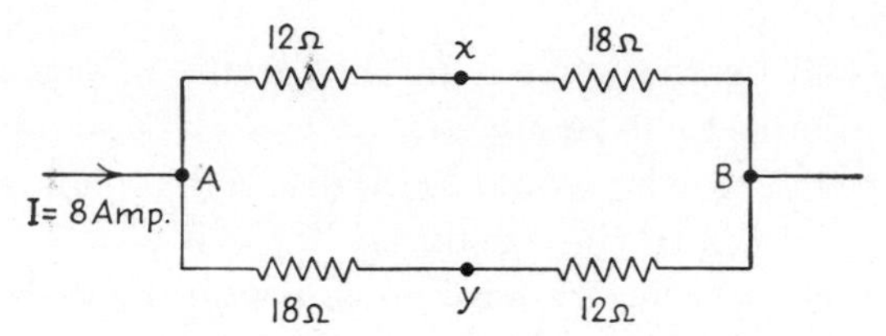

FIG. 49.—Circuit for Probs. 10 and 11.

11. Referring to Fig. 49, find the magnitude and direction of the current in a conductor of negligible resistance that connects points x and y.
12. For the circuit of Fig. 50 calculate (*a*) the currents delivered by generators 1 and 2; (*b*) the load voltages E_A and E_B.

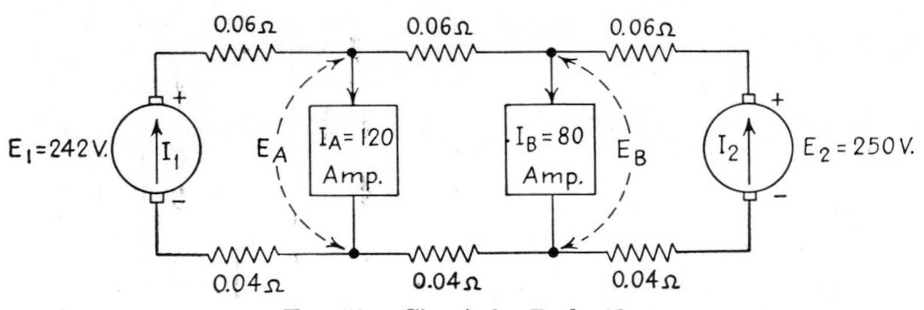

FIG. 50.—Circuit for Prob. 12.

13. In Fig. 51 the currents in loads A, B, and C are respectively 10, 50, and 20 amp. Determine (*a*) the load voltages E_A, E_B, and E_C; (*b*) the powers delivered to loads A, B, and C.
14. Referring to Fig. 40, what would be the current in a conductor of negligible resistance (a short circuit) that connects points c and d?

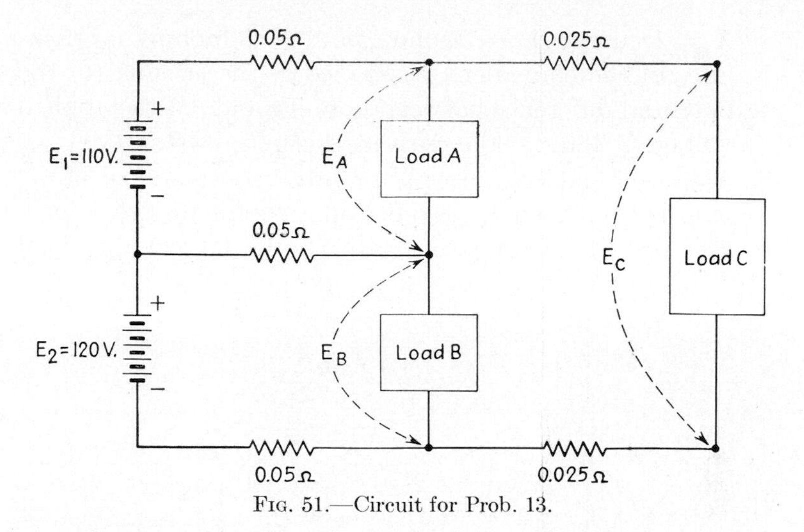

FIG. 51.—Circuit for Prob. 13.

15. Referring to Fig. 52, calculate the currents delivered by batteries A and B.

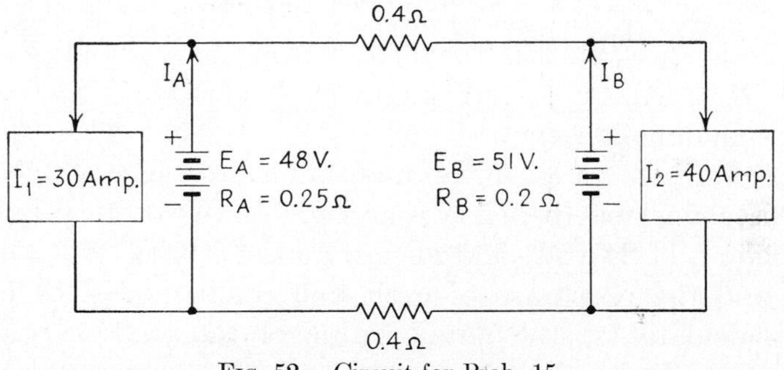

FIG. 52.—Circuit for Prob. 15.

16. For the circuit of Fig. 53 calculate (a) the total equivalent resistance of the network to which power is delivered by the battery; (b) the battery current. (*Hint:* Transform the star-connected resistors A, B, and C into an equivalent delta in which X is connected to points c and a, Y is connected to points a and b, and Z is connected to points b and c.)
17. The ohmic values of the resistances of the Wheatstone-bridge circuit of Fig. 43 are $M = 6$ ohms, $N = 21$ ohms,

$X = 18$ ohms, $Y = 12$ ohms, and $Z = 6$ ohms. Calculate (*a*) the equivalent resistance of the circuit; (*b*) the potential difference between points *a* and *b* if the applied voltage is 120; (*c*) the current through resistor *X*.

18. A 24-volt battery, having an internal resistance of 0.2 ohm is connected by two 0.3-ohm conductors to a variable resistor (see Fig. 45). (*a*) For what value of load

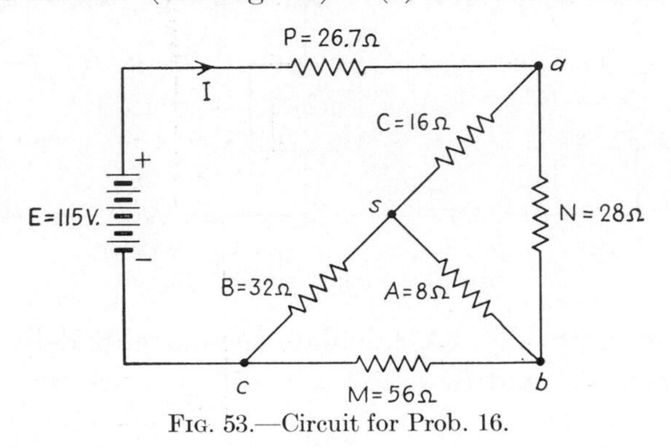

FIG. 53.—Circuit for Prob. 16.

resistance R_L will the load power be maximum? (*b*) What will be the maximum load power and the corresponding efficiency?

19. Referring to Fig. 45, assume that a resistance of 0.8 ohm is connected to points *a* and *b*. If the battery has an e.m.f. of 24 volts and an internal resistance of 0.2 ohm, and the resistance of each line conductor is 0.3 ohm, calculate (*a*) the ohmic value of the load resistance, connected between points *a* and *b*, for which its power will be maximum; (*b*) the maximum load power and the corresponding efficiency.

CHAPTER 5

ALTERNATING-CURRENT ELECTRIC CIRCUITS AND MEASUREMENTS

Closing and Opening Direct-current Circuits.—In a direct-current circuit the only *opposition* offered to the flow of a continuous (steady) current is the equivalent resistance of all the material parts used in the construction of the electric circuit. The rules governing such circuits were studied in the previous chapter where, it should be pointed out, the relation between amperes, volts, and ohms (Ohm's law, $I = E/R$) applies only to a steady-state condition, *i.e.*, a condition that exists after the current has reached a steady or fixed value. Ordinarily, we overlook entirely what takes place when a direct e.m.f. is *suddenly* impressed upon a circuit or is suddenly removed from the circuit. What happens in the exceedingly short period of time before the current is established at its steady value, or has died down to zero when the circuit is opened, may often be as important, or even more so, than the conditions that are finally established. If the electric circuit is so constructed that very little magnetism is created, practically no energy is stored in a magnetic field (to be discussed fully later). Under this condition the current rises abruptly, and almost instantaneously, to its steady-state value. In Fig. 54*a*, which applies to a nonmagnetic device of 10 ohms resistance, it is noticed that the current rises almost instantly to 10 amp. when an e.m.f. of 100 volts is suddenly applied by the closing of the switch. However, if the same 10-ohm resistor is coiled around a good grade of magnetic steel, the 10-amp. current value is reached in a little over 1 sec. (see Fig. 54*b*), for the reason that time is required to store the magnetic energy in the magnetic substance and the space around it. To expect an instantaneous rise in current as in Fig. 54*a*, where no magnetic energy is stored, would mean that infinite power would have to be used; this is obviously not possible when magnetic energy must be stored. It follows, therefore, that in a circuit such as Fig. 54*b* the current must *lag* behind the e.m.f. that produces it. The same reasoning applies to the opening of a circuit in which a magnetic field must dissipate its energy; here the current of 10 amp. dies to zero in a period of over 1 sec. (see Fig. 54*c*), during which time arcing occurs at the switch.

Again in Fig. 54*b*, it should be understood that magnetic energy is continually being stored in the magnetic substance

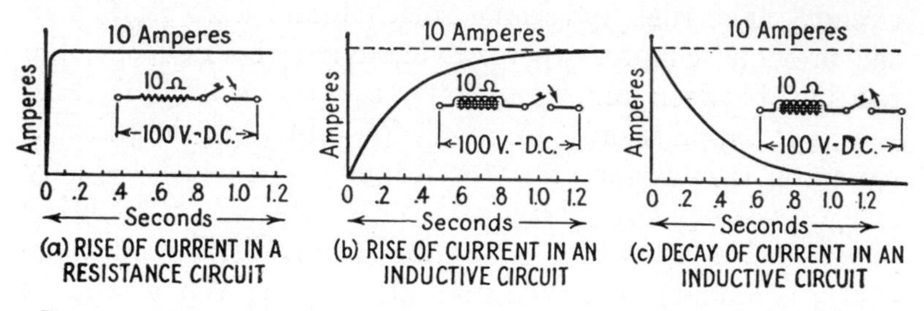

FIG. 54.—*Current*-versus-*time* relations in resistance and inductive circuits.

and field as the current increases. And since every increase in current represents a further increase in magnetic energy, it follows that the latter tends to prevent the current from increasing in value. The situation is similar to the condition that exists when a rubber tire is pumped up; as the energy stored up in the rubber increases, it tends to prevent an increase in air pressure in the tire although forced by considerable pressure from an air pump. In other words, it is only during the energy-storing period that opposition is developed to the increase in current; after that period is passed, the current is stabilized at $I = E/R$ amp. Suppose now that the e.m.f. is suddenly removed, as in Fig. 54*c*, or, in other words, the circuit is opened. Under this condition the current is prevented from dying out instantly because the stored magnetic energy cannot be released and restored to the circuit instantly; the current, therefore, decreases gradually to zero as shown.

If a direct-current circuit is repeatedly closed and opened with a simple interrupter, such as that used in the "break-and-make" arrangement of the ignition system of an automobile, the current curve would be made up of a succession of curves like that of Fig. 54*b* and *c*. If the interrupter operated every 2 sec., the current would rise to 10 amp. and drop to zero with successive "makes" and "breaks." However, if the interrupter had a shorter period of operation of, say, 0.2 sec., the current would never reach 10 amp. or drop to zero but would vary between two intermediate values.

Inductance.—The *property* of any electric circuit that opposes a *change* in the value of the current is known as *self-inductance,* or briefly *inductance.* This is the property that is responsible for the lag of the current behind the impressed voltage in the circuits represented by Fig. 54*b* and *c*, where the current does not rise to its ultimate E/R value instantly or fall to zero instantly. If the circuit conditions are such that it takes the current a long time to *change* from zero to its final value, or drop from some definite value to zero, the inductance is comparatively high. On the other hand, if the current makes its complete *change* in an exceedingly short time, the inductance is very low or practically zero. Note that the *circuit conditions* determine the value of the inductance and, therefore, the time lag; the time lag is affected by neither the magnitude of the current nor the voltage. This *inductance property* is analogous to inertia in a mechanical body; in the electric circuit the current (flow of electrons) lags behind the applied voltage, whereas in the mechanical body such as the automobile or the rotating flywheel the motion lags behind the applied force. In this connection it is interesting to note that it is the inertia of the moving automobile that keeps it moving for a long time after the clutch is disengaged or keeps the flywheel rotating for many minutes after the source of power is removed.

In electric circuits the inductance property manifests itself through the creation, or induction, of an opposing voltage whose value generally changes from instant to instant. At the moment a switch is closed in a highly inductive direct-current circuit, the opposing *induced* voltage is quite large; under this condition the current will be low because the *difference* between the constant impressed voltage and this countervoltage is low. As the current rises to its ultimate value, the countervoltage diminishes, and this in turn gives rise to a larger current. Finally, when the current has reached its E/R value, the countervoltage is zero so that opposition to change is no longer present. Understand that, when the current is changing, there is opposition to such change; when the current is not changing, no such opposition can be created.

Now, *if the current changes at the rate of 1 amp. per second and the induced voltage opposing such change is 1 volt, the circuit is said to possess unit inductance*, or *1 henry*. The factors responsible for the magnitude of the inductance in henrys are the following: (1) the number of turns of wire in the coil, (2) the cross-sectional area and the kind of magnetic core material placed inside of the coil, (3) the axial length of the coil, (4) the general constructional arrangement of the magnetic and electric circuits with respect to each other. To illustrate how the inductance in henrys is affected by such conditions as indicated, the following examples are given:

1. An incandescent lamp filament, or a Nichrome heater element like that used in a space heater, has practically zero inductance.

2. A coil of wire, wound over a wooden form $2 \times 1\frac{1}{2}$ in. in cross section and 2 in. in height, having 172 turns of No. 17 wire, was found to have an inductance of 0.0009 henry.

3. A coil of wire similar to that described in (2) but having 344 turns was found to have an inductance of 0.0035 henry, practically four times as great for twice as many turns.

4. The same coil described in (3) but placed over the central limb of a core of laminated steel in the shape of an E was found to have an inductance of 0.034 henry, practically 10 times as great.

5. Finally, the same arrangement as described in (4) was modified by having a straight bar section placed over the open ends of the E and was found to have an inductance of 0.32 henry, practically 10 times as much.

By studying the above values in henrys and conditions under which they were obtained, it is possible to make some general statements about the inductance properties of common electric devices:

1. A straight wire, or a coil of wire wound around a circular form of small diameter, like that in a tungsten filament lamp or a Nichrome heater unit, is practically noninductive. This is true of all electric heating units such as fireplace heaters, flatirons, toasters, and the like.

2. The inductance of a coil of wire varies as the *square* of the number of turns, other things remaining unchanged. Neither the size of the wire nor the kind or shape of the wire (assuming, of course, that the wire is of a nonmagnetic substance) has any effect upon the inductance.

3. The inductance of any coil of wire varies directly with the cross-sectional area of the form around which it is wound. A large coil will have a greater inductance than a small one, both with the same number of turns of wire, because the former can produce more magnetism per ampere of current than the latter. In this respect it may be interesting to note that a coil of wire wound with half its turns in one direction and the other half in the opposite direction will possess practically no inductance for the reason that very little (or no) magnetism can be produced by such a winding. (Magnetism is discussed in detail in a subsequent chapter.)

4. The grade of magnetic core material around which a coil of wire is wound has a very great effect upon the value of the inductance. This is true because the core material is

responsible to a very large extent for the amount of magnetism produced by each ampere per turn of wire.

5. Since, as was pointed out above, the amount of magnetism has a direct bearing upon the value of the inductance, the arrangement of the electric and magnetic materials with respect to each other (the design) will greatly affect the inductance.

In short, this extremely important property of inductance may be attributed to one solid fact, namely, the extent to which magnetism links with, or passes through, a coil of wire. It does not matter how or where this magnetism is originally created; the only thing that counts is whether magnetism links with the circuit. And it should, of course, be thoroughly understood that the *effect of inductance* is manifested only when the current changes; *i.e.*, the magnetism linking with the turns of wire must change before the inductance property can oppose the current change. If the student has a clear conception of inductive circuits and their properties, he will be in an excellent position to understand the operation of all sorts of alternating-current devices and machines.

The Advantages of Alternating-current Systems.—Direct-current electricity has many applications in industry, on the farm, in transportation (automobiles, airplanes, railroads, ships, etc.), in communication systems (telephones, telegraphs, radio, etc.), and in the home. But aside from the relatively few primary sources of direct-current power used for such purposes, electricity is generated as alternating current in more than 90 per cent of all the generating stations in this country. This alternating-current energy is then transmitted over wires where it may or may not be used in this form. In a large percentage of commercial applications the alternating-current energy is used in the operation of lighting circuits, motors, heating units, and the like, but there are many industrial and domestic uses that find direct current more desirable than alternating current. Electrolytic processes such as electroplating, electrorefining, electrotyping, and the production of aluminum and fertilizers must use direct-current electricity; also, many motor applications such as elevators, printing presses, and traction systems are generally superior when operated from direct-current systems. In such cases the originally generated alternating current is rectified by means of machines or electronic devices (vacuum or gas tubes and their accompanying electrical units) into direct current.

The reasons for the general superiority of alternating-current systems are the following:

1. The alternating-current generators can be constructed to develop rather high voltages (6,600 and 13,200 volts), which in turn can be raised to much higher values by means of transformers for long-distance transmission purposes. Since high-voltage transmission of electrical energy is more efficient and the equipment used in this connection more satisfactory and economical, it serves to extend the possibilities of such service. Transformers can, of course, be used to lower the high voltage at the receiver end just as they are used to raise the voltage at the sending end of a transmission system.

2. The so-called "alternating-current induction motor" is one of the most rugged and most trouble-free machines in general use in industry. It has such excellent operating characteristics for a great many commercial applications that much alternating current is generated to power it.

3. Alternating-current generators can be constructed in very much larger sizes than direct-current generators. Since the larger machines are more economical to build from the standpoint of cost per kilowatt, the generating stations are bigger and more efficient and may, therefore, serve much greater areas at comparatively low cost.

The Alternating-current Ampere.—An alternating current is one in which the motion of electrons is in one direction for a given period of time and then in the opposite direction for an equal period of time, this sequence being repeated many times per second. If a current flow in one direction is arbitrarily indicated as positive, then a flow in the reverse direction is called *negative.* One complete positive and negative period is represented by one cycle, the latter occurring in $1/f$ sec., where f is the frequency of the alternating current in cycles per second. Thus, one cycle of a 60-, 50-, or 25-cycle current occurs in $\frac{1}{60}$, $\frac{1}{50}$, or $\frac{1}{25}$ sec., respectively. Most alternating currents and voltages vary in accordance with a function known in trigonometry as a *sine,* since this variation is generally regarded as pure, or perfect, at least from the standpoint of the operation of alternating-current machinery and equipment. In order to visualize such positive and negative sine variations of current flow it is customary to represent them by waves such as the one indicated in Fig. 55. Note how smooth is the

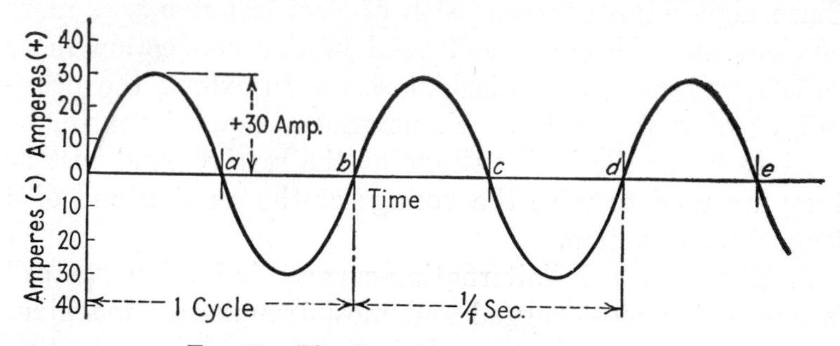

FIG. 55.—The sine wave—*current* versus *time.*

variation in current from zero to a positive maximum of 30 amp., then back to zero at a, then to a maximum of 30 amp. in the reverse direction, and finally back to zero at b, to complete one cycle. Another cycle is shown between b and d, this occurring in $1/f$ sec. Since the value of the current *at any instant of time* is proportional to the *sine* of the distance from O, it is convenient to designate the time axis in degrees instead of seconds. This is shown in Fig. 56, in which one cycle is represented by 360 deg., from a to e. At angle $b = 90°$, the current is a maximum passing through k and is equal to mn, which is $I_{max} \times \sin 90°$ or I_{max}. At angle $f = 30°$, the current is $I_{max} \times \sin 30°$, or $0.5\, I_{max}$. At angle $c = 180°$, $I = 0$; at angle $d = 270°$, the current is $-I_{max}$; at angle $e = 360°$, $I = 0$.

An alternating-current ampere *cannot* be defined in terms of an electrochemical deposit of a pure metal in an electrolytic cell, as was done for the direct-current ampere (see

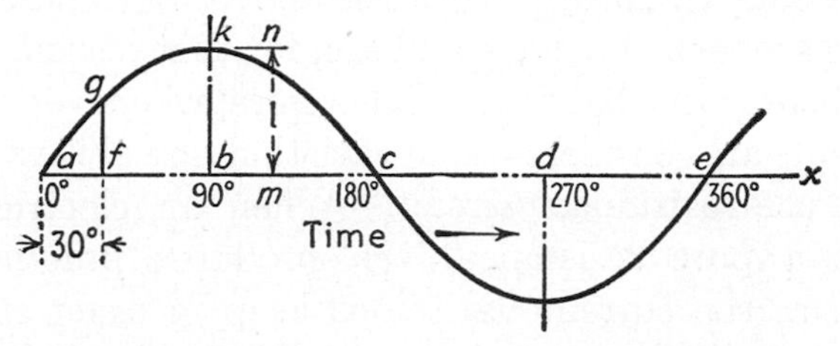

FIG. 56.—The sine wave—*current* versus *degrees*.

Chap. I, page 4), because the net amount of material carried from one plate to another during each cycle of an alternating current is zero. The alternating-current ampere can, however, be defined in terms of the amount of *heat* developed, for the reason that heat is produced in a resistor regardless of the direction in which the current flows. Thus, *an alternating-current ampere* is said to flow in a circuit if it *produces heat at the same rate as a direct-current ampere through the same resistance.*

Calculation for the sine variation of current shows that 70.7 per cent of the maximum value is equivalent to a steady direct current, since both will develop heat at exactly the same rate when passing through the same resistance. If this effective heating current is called I_{eff}, the effective current can be expressed in terms of the maximum value I_{max} in this way:

$$I_{eff} = 0.707\ I_{max} \tag{24}$$

All common alternating-current ammeters are calibrated to register effective amperes. If an ammeter indicates 30 amp., it is proper to assume that twice during each cycle the instantaneous maximum value is 30/0.707, or 42.4 amp., once positive and once negative. And since the impressed voltage that causes the sine variation of current through the resistance circuit also varies in accordance with a sine function, the same rule may be applied to it. Thus,

$$E_{\text{eff}} = 0.707\, E_{\text{max}} \text{ volts} \tag{25}$$

It is true, of course, that some circuit conditions may alter the sine variations discussed above, but these are beyond the scope of this book and are, for that reason, not considered here. In what follows, therefore, whenever alternating currents are considered, sine variations are always implied.

The Pure-resistance Circuit.—When an electric circuit contains a pure resistance, *i.e.*, produces practically no magnetism, the current variations keep in exact step with the impressed-voltage variations. Since the voltage and current both follow sine functions, the current is zero when the voltage is zero, a positive maximum when the voltage is a positive maximum, and a negative maximum when the voltage is a negative maximum. Under this condition *the current is* said to be *in phase with the voltage. This is true only in pure-resistance circuits.* Figure 57 shows a current wave in phase with a voltage wave.

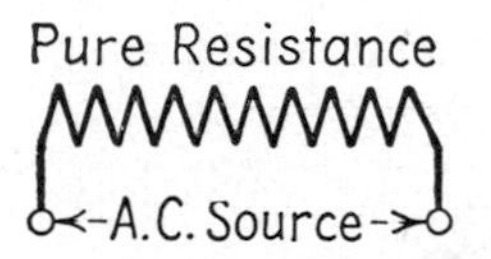

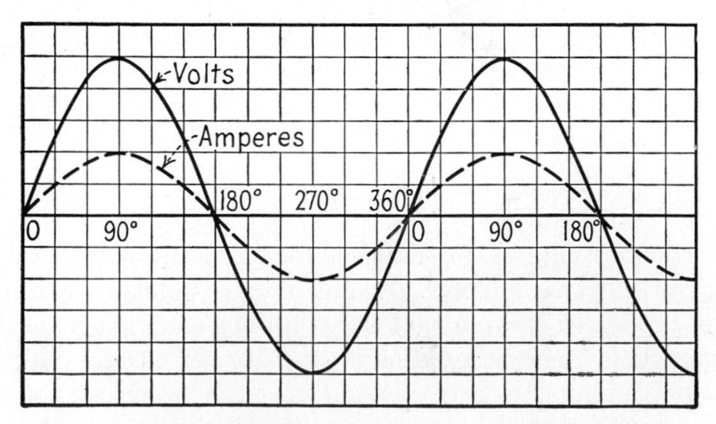

FIG. 57.—Current and voltage waves in a pure-resistance circuit.

Circuits such as this can be treated as though they were direct-current circuits because both act in exactly the same way. This applies not only to the rule that the effective current is equal to the effective voltage divided by the resistance ($I_{eff} = E_{eff}/R$), but also to the fact that the average power delivered to the resistance is equal to ($E_{eff} \times I_{eff}$) as well as ($I^2_{eff} \times R$) and (E^2_{eff}/R). All heating devices such as percolators, water heaters, curling irons, and the like, as well as incandescent lights, are pure-resistance circuits of a practical nature. To be sure, the power delivered to such circuits varies from instant to instant, being zero at 0 deg., 180 deg., 360 deg., etc., and a maximum at 90 deg., 270 deg., etc., but the average power is nevertheless the same as though the current and voltage were direct current and of the same magnitudes as the effective alternating current and voltage.

The Pure-reactance Circuit.—Imagine next a coil of wire wrapped around a good quality of magnetic steel so that a current flowing through the coil will produce a very strong magnetic effect. Assume further that the size of the wire used in constructing the coil is so large in cross section that its resistance is negligible, or zero. The latter is, of course, theoretically impossible, but it can be practically approached quite closely. Such an arrangement is known as a *pure-reactance* circuit because the magnetism produced by the current will react with the voltage variations. And, as was pointed out under Inductance (page 135), the current will lag behind the voltage. Actually the lag of the current behind the voltage will be exactly 90 deg., as is indicated in Fig. 58.

Note that, when the voltage is a maximum at 90 deg., the current is zero, and that not until the voltage drops to zero, at 180 deg., does the current rise to its maximum value. Further in the cycle, at 270 deg., the current drops to zero as the voltage passes through its negative maximum and at 360 deg. rises to a negative maximum when the voltage drops to zero.

In this circuit the opposition to the flow of current is

determined solely by the inductive reactance, which is equal to

$$X_L = 2\pi fL \text{ ohms} \tag{26}$$

where X_L is known as the inductive reactance in ohms, f is

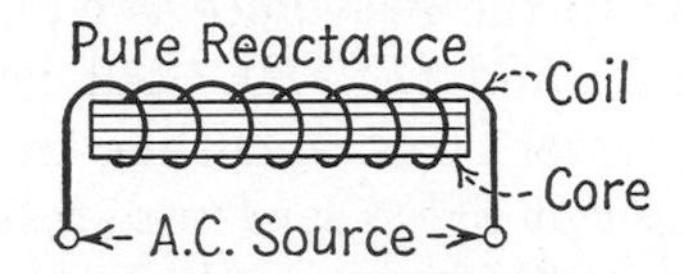

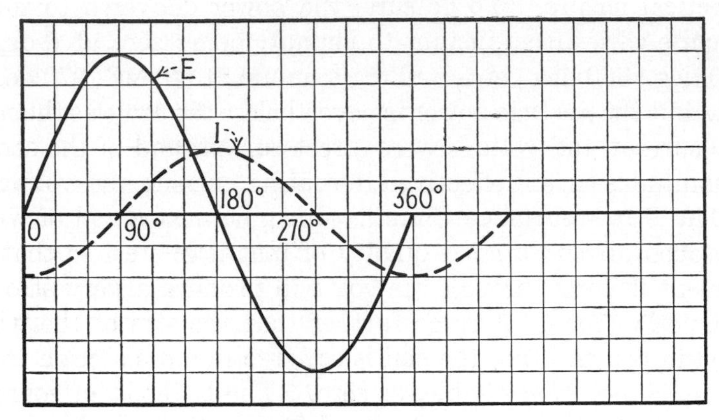

FIG. 58.—Current and voltage waves in a pure-inductance circuit.

the frequency in cycles per second, and L is the inductance of the circuit in henrys.

In order to determine the effective current, it is merely necessary to divide volts by ohms and this will equal $E_{\text{eff}}/2\pi fL$.

Whereas a pure resistance merely opposes a flow of current, while the latter remains in phase with the voltage, it should be clearly understood that *a pure reactance*, resulting from inductance, not only opposes a flow of current but also *causes the current to lag behind the voltage by exactly* 90 *deg.*

Another important fact concerning a pure-reactance circuit is that the average power delivered to it is zero. This comes about in this way: During the first quarter cycle the energy delivered to the reactance coil is used to store magnetic energy; during the next quarter cycle exactly this amount of magnetic energy is released and is returned to the power source. Thus, during one-half of the cycle the average positive power *from the source to the reactance* equals the average negative power *from the reactance to the source.* And since the same conditions exist during the next half cycle, it follows that the average power supplied by the source in one complete cycle is absolutely zero.

The Series Resistance-reactance (Impedance) Circuit.—The next circuit to be considered is one containing a combination of resistance and reactance. Such circuits are extremely common in practice since they are represented by all sorts of electromagnetic devices and machines. The latter are generally coils of wire having appreciable resistance wrapped around laminated steel cores of good magnetic quality. Obviously, such electric circuits fall between the classifications of pure-resistance and pure-reactance circuits. If, in a circuit containing resistance only (Fig. 57), the current is in phase with e.m.f., and in a circuit containing reactance only (Fig. 58), the current lags 90 deg. behind the e.m.f., it is logical to expect that in a circuit containing both resistance *and* reactance the current will lag behind the voltage by an angle greater than 0 deg. and less than 90 deg. This is shown in Fig. 59 where the current, for example, lags behind the voltage by 45 deg. Such a condition would exist if the resistance (in ohms) is equal to the inductive reactance $2\pi fL$ (in ohms). Note particularly that the current is zero at 45 deg. and rises to its maximum value 45 deg. *after* the voltage has reached its maximum value.

Actually, of course, the resistance and reactance properties are part of the single coil of wire wrapped around an iron core. For convenience, however, the resistance and reactance are generally represented diagrammatically as separate units, as in Fig. 59, because it is intended that the two properties should designate their separate effects, (1) pure resistance, which acts to limit a current flow but maintains the current and voltage in phase, and (2) pure reactance, which acts to limit a current flow and also causes the current to shift 90 deg. behind the voltage. Since it is desirable to distinguish between a pure resistance or a pure reactance and a combination of the two, the latter is known as an *impedance*.

When the resistance of an impedance coil is large compared with its reactance, the angle of lag is small. If, on the other

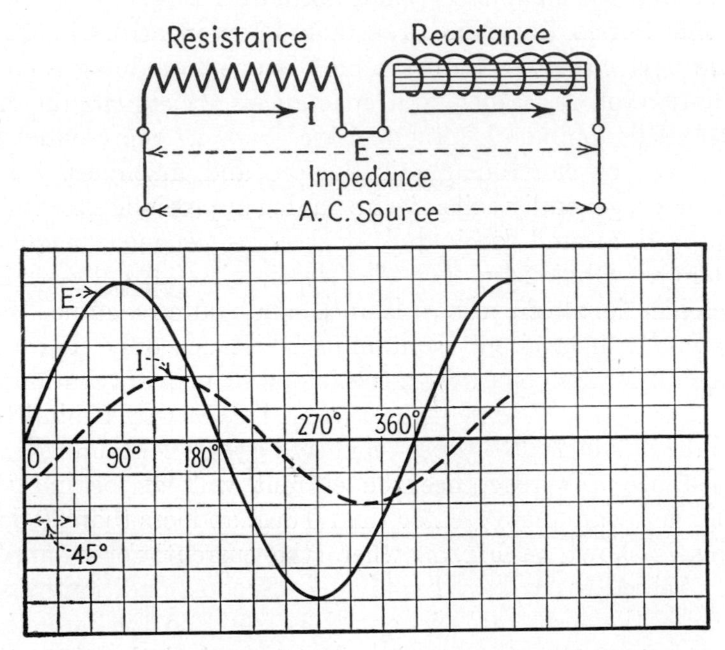

FIG. 59.—Current and voltage waves in a series *R-L* circuit.

hand, the reactance is large compared with its resistance, the angle of lag will be large. Actually, a pure resistance such as a heater element may be considered electrically as an impedance with negligible reactance. And by the same reasoning a reactance may be considered as an impedance with negligible resistance.

We now come to a rather important point concerning the calculation of the impedance of a coil, in ohms, from the known values of its resistance and reactance. One thing is certain and that is that it is *not* equal to the numerical sum of these two values. The reason is that the resistance causes the current to have its maximum value in phase with the voltage, while the reactance causes the current to have its maximum value 90 deg. behind the voltage. It may, therefore, be inferred that resistance and reactance have peculiarities that are shown 90 deg. apart, and it is because of this that the impedance in a circuit bears the same relation to resistance and reactance that the hypotenuse of a right-angle triangle bears to the two remaining sides. The relationship between these three factors is shown in Fig. 60. Thus, we see that the impedance, whose symbol is Z, is equal to the square root of the sum of the squares of the resistance R and the reactance X_L; *i.e.*,

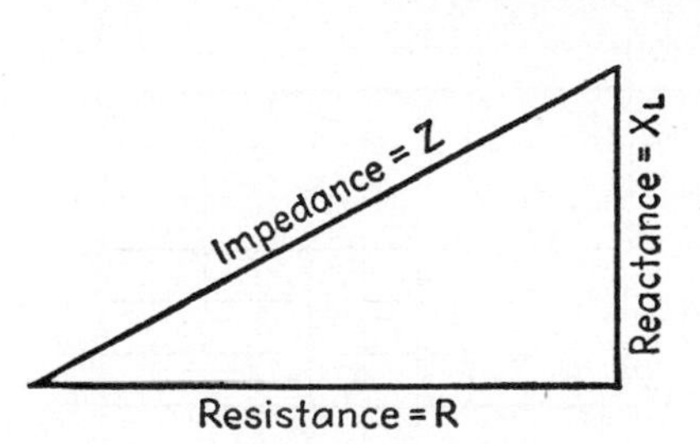

FIG. 60.—The impedance triangle.

$$Z = \sqrt{R^2 + X_L^2} \text{ ohms} \quad (27)$$

Next, in Fig. 61 (which extends the analysis of Fig. 59) it should be observed that the current I is shown in phase with the voltage across the resistance V_R and lagging behind the voltage V_X by 90 deg. In other words, when the resistance is considered separately, the current I and its voltage V_R are in phase, whereas when the reactance is considered independently, the *same* current I is 90 deg. behind *its* voltage V_X. This means that V_X must be 90 deg. ahead of V_R. Now, since $V_R = I \times R$ and $V_X = I \times X_L$, it follows that

$$E = \sqrt{V_R^2 + V_X^2} \quad (28)$$

But the total impressed voltage E must equal the current flowing I multiplied by the total impedance Z, so that

$$I = \frac{E}{Z} \quad (29)$$

From above

$$IZ = \sqrt{(IR)^2 + (IX_L)^2} = I \times \sqrt{R^2 + X_L^2}$$

Therefore, $$Z = \sqrt{R^2 + X_L^2} \qquad (27)$$

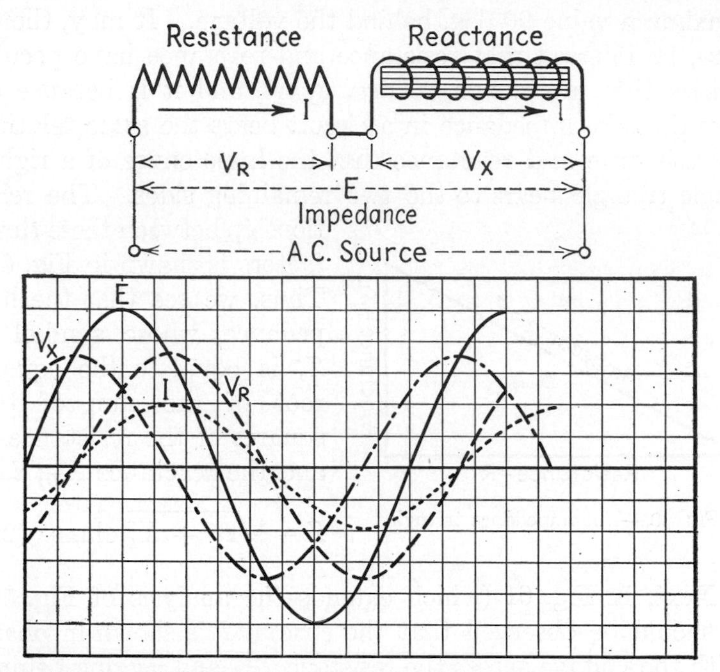

FIG. 61.—Voltage and current waves for the series *R-L* circuit.

Several examples will now be given to illustrate the principles discussed above.

Example 1.—A 60-cycle alternating current has an effective value of 8 amp. (*a*) What is the maximum value, assuming a sine wave? (*b*) What is the time between the positive and negative maximum values of one cycle? (*c*) What is the time between *f* and *d* of Fig. 56?

Solution:

a. $I_{\max} = \frac{8}{0.707} = 11.3$ amp.

b. Time $= \frac{1}{2} \times \frac{1}{60}$ sec. $= \frac{1}{120} = 0.00833$ sec.

c. Time $= fb + bd = \frac{60}{360} \times \frac{1}{60} + 0.00833$
$= 0.00278 + 0.00833 = 0.01111$ sec.

Example 2.—If insulating materials are stressed by the *maximum* impressed voltage, what effective value must *not* be exceeded between two sides of a 15-mil thickness of paper if breakdown occurs above 300 volts per mil?

Solution:

$$300 \times 0.707 \times 15 = 3{,}180 \text{ volts}$$

Example 3.—A coil of wire is wound with 344 turns and has an inductance of 0.0035 henry. (*a*) What will be the inductance of a similar coil if wound with 516 turns? (*b*) How many turns must a similar coil have if the inductance is to be 0.00175 henry?

Solution:

$$a.\ L_2 = L_1 \times \left(\frac{\text{turns}_2}{\text{turns}_1}\right)^2 = 0.0035 \times \left(\frac{516}{344}\right)^2$$

$$= 0.0035 \times (1.5)^2 = 0.00788 \text{ henry}$$

$$b.\ \left(\frac{\text{Turns}_2}{\text{Turns}_1}\right)^2 = \frac{0.00175}{0.00350} = \frac{1}{2}$$

$$\text{Turns} = \frac{\text{turns}_1}{\sqrt{2}} = \frac{344}{1.414} = 243 \text{ turns}$$

Example 4.—An impedance coil has a resistance of 1.3 ohms and an inductance of 0.0035 henry. When it is connected to a 120-volt, 60-cycle source, determine (*a*) the reactance, (*b*) the impedance, and (*c*) the current.

Solution:

$$a.\ X_L = 2\pi f L = 2\pi \times 60 \times 0.0035 = 1.32 \text{ ohms}$$

$$b.\ Z = \sqrt{R^2 + X_L^2} = \sqrt{\overline{1.3}^2 + \overline{1.32}^2} = 1.85 \text{ ohms}$$

$$c.\ I = \frac{E}{Z} = \frac{120}{1.85} = 64.9 \text{ amp.}$$

Example 5.—Neglecting the resistance of the coil of Example 4, determine the frequency at which the current will be 5 amp. for a voltage of 120.

Solution:

$$X_L = \frac{E}{I} = \frac{120}{5} = 24 \text{ ohms}$$

$$X_L = 2\pi fL \qquad f = \frac{X_L}{2\pi L} = \frac{24}{2\pi \times 0.0035} = 1{,}090 \text{ cycles}$$

Power and Power Factor.—The study of the power relations in alternating-current circuits not only is exceedingly interesting, but also clears up much of the mystery that often seems to surround the peculiar actions of electric circuits. It will, in fact, give the student a very much clearer understanding of what is taking place than can possibly be obtained by a long discussion of other characteristics of alternating-current circuits.

As was pointed out previously, the pure-resistance circuit of Fig. 57 acts no differently when connected to an alternating e.m.f. than it does when connected to a direct-current source. When the effective voltage on alternating current is equal to the direct-current voltage, the heating will be exactly the same in both cases. Power is delivered *to* the resistor at all times, varying, of course, from instant to instant when alternating current is used. True, the instantaneous powers at 0 deg., 180 deg., 360 deg., etc., are zero, and the maximum powers at points 90 deg., 270 deg., etc., are $E_{max} \times I_{max}$, but the *average* power involved in the circuit is equal to $E_{eff} \times I_{eff}$. At no time is the flow of power reversed; power is delivered *by the source to the resistor*, never by the resistor to the source. And since the average power is the same whether $(E_{d.c.} \times I_{d.c.})$ or $(E_{eff} \times I_{eff})$ is used, assuming of course that the two voltages are equal to each other as are the two currents, it is customary to say the *power factor* of the alternating-current circuit is 100 per cent, or unity. The term *power factor* merely represents the extent to which the product of E_{eff} and I_{eff} is useful power. It is a term very much like *efficiency,* which indicates the percentage of the total power delivered to a machine that is made available as useful output. Power factor has a range from zero to 100 per cent (or 0 to 1.0), as in the case of efficiency.

Now let us examine the situation with regard to a pure-reactance circuit, *i.e.*, an impedance with negligible resistance. This is the case shown in Fig. 58, where it was seen that the current lags behind the impressed voltage by 90 deg. If the wave of power is plotted through a series of instantaneous values obtained by multiplying E by I at several points in the cycle, it will be observed (see Fig. 62) that

1. The power wave is a sine wave having a frequency equal to *double* the voltage or current frequency.

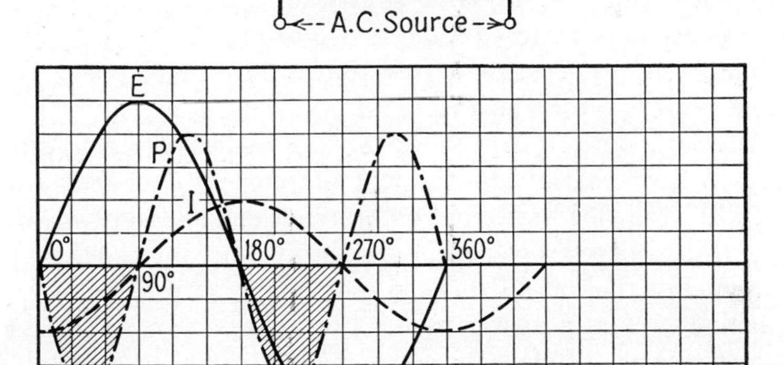

FIG. 62.—Current, voltage, and power waves in a pure-inductance circuit.

2. The instantaneous power is zero *four* times per cycle, at 0, 90, 180, and 270 deg.

3. The average power delivered *to* the reactor, indicated by the two positive loops *above* the horizontal axis, is exactly equal to the average power returned *by* the reactor to the source, indicated by the two negative loops (shaded areas) below the axis.

Note particularly that the average exchange of power between source and reactor is zero; just as much power is delivered to the reactor as is returned to source. This interesting feature is brought about in this way: (1) During one quarter of a cycle the source furnishes energy to the reactor, and inasmuch as there is no resistance to use this energy it must be stored up in the magnetic field of the reactance. (2) During the next quarter of a cycle the magnetic energy is discharged or returned to the generator. (3) During the third quarter of the cycle the same storage of magnetic energy takes place as in (1). (4) Finally, during the fourth quarter of the cycle the energy is again returned to the source. Thus, a circuit containing reactance only is one in which there is a pulsation of power first from the source to the reactor and a little later from the reactor to the source, *the average power furnished by the source per cycle being zero.* It should be obvious, therefore, that a pure-reactance circuit has a power factor of zero.

Although pure-resistance circuits are rather common, especially where heating devices are employed, pure-reactance circuits have very few practical applications. However, circuits that possess both resistance and reactance properties have many uses in all sorts of electromagnetic devices and machines. These, as was pointed out previously, are classed as impedances. When the power wave is plotted for such a circuit, as shown in Fig. 63, it resembles Fig. 62 to a very large extent. In this combination of resistance and reactance (R was arbitrarily selected equal to X_L), the current lags behind the voltage by 45 deg. Note particularly that the power wave is exactly like that of Fig. 62 with the single difference that the amount of negative energy (the shaded area) has been greatly reduced, whereas the positive energy has been correspondingly increased. It is just as though the power wave were shifted bodily upward, but in such a way that the negative energy occurs between 0 and 45 deg., between 180 and 225 deg., and again between 360 (0) and the next 45 deg. In this circuit only a part of the energy is stored in the magnetic field of the reactor and later returned to the source; the rest of the energy is consumed by the resistor. Calculation would show that under the conditions indicated the average power is 0.707 times the product of E_{eff} and I_{eff}.

Because of the fact that the alternating-current source does not furnish a continuous supply of energy to the circuit

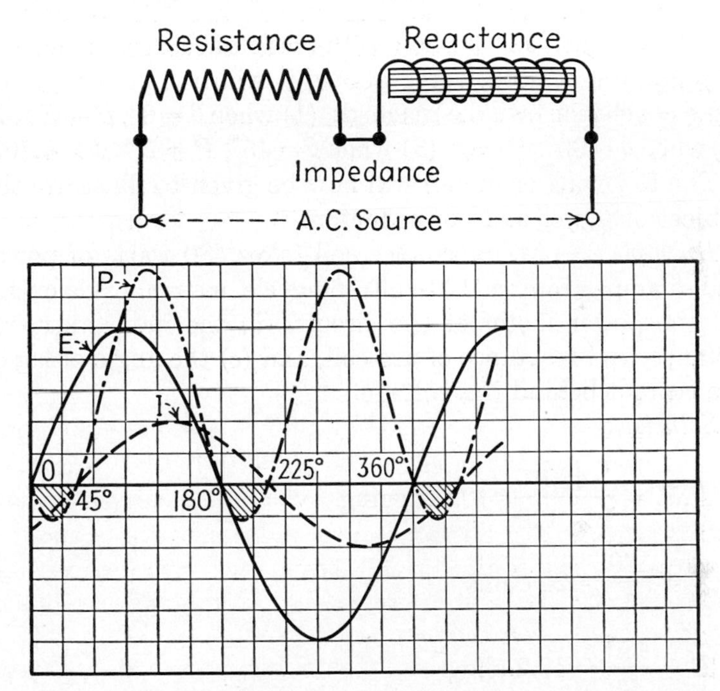

Fig. 63.—Current, voltage, and power waves in a series R–L circuit.

and sometimes even receives energy from the circuit, it is frequently said that a single-phase circuit is one of pulsing power.

In our discussion it should have become apparent that *the average power delivered to a circuit is a function of the angular displacement between the voltage and current.* Further analysis shows that this function is a cosine, whereupon the power may be calculated by the equation

$$P = E \times I \times \cos \theta \tag{30}$$

where P is the *average power* delivered to the circuit, E and I are *effective* values of *volts* and *amperes*, and $\cos\theta$ is the cosine of the phase angle between the voltage and current.

The $\cos\theta$ term is generally represented as the power factor, whence

$$P = E \times I \times P.F. \tag{30a}$$

If this equation is applied to the resistance, reactance, and impedance cases considered above, it will be found that the same conclusions will be reached: (1) when $\theta = 0°$, $P = E \times I$; (2) when $\theta = 90°$, $P = 0$; (3) when $\theta = 45°$, $P = E \times I \times 0.707$.

The following examples will now be given to illustrate the subject of power and power factor:

Example 6.—An impedance coil takes 480 watts of power and 5 amp. from a 120-volt, 60-cycle source. Calculate (*a*) the power factor of the circuit, (*b*) the impedance, resistance, and reactance of the coil, and (*c*) the angle of lag of the current behind the voltage.

Solution:

a. $P.F. = \dfrac{480}{5 \times 120} = 0.8$ lagging

b. $Z = \dfrac{120}{5} = 24$ ohms

$R = \dfrac{480}{5^2} = 19.2$ ohms

$X_L = \sqrt{\overline{24}^2 - \overline{19.2}^2} = 14.4$ ohms

c. Angle of lag = angle whose cosine equals 0.8 = 36.9°

Example 7.—An impedance coil having negligible resistance is connected in series with a group of incandescent lights, the purpose being to make the latter burn dimly. By regulating the amount of iron inserted into the coil, the "dimmer" (impedance coil) adjusts the brilliancy of the lights (see Fig. 64). If a 60-cycle, 120-volt source is connected to the circuit and adjustment is made so that the current is 0.5 amp.

when the lamp voltage is 40, calculate (*a*) the inductance in henrys of the "dimmer," and (*b*) the circuit power factor.

Solution:

$$a.\ R\ \text{(of lights)} = \frac{40}{0.5} = 80\ \text{ohms}$$

$$Z\ \text{(of circuit)} = \frac{120}{0.5} = 240\ \text{ohms}$$

$$X_L = \sqrt{\overline{240}^2 - \overline{80}^2} = 227\ \text{ohms}$$

$$L = \frac{227}{2\pi \times 60} = 0.602\ \text{henry}$$

$$b.\ \text{Power} = \overline{0.5}^2 \times \overline{80} = 20\ \text{watts}$$

$$P.F. = \frac{20}{120 \times 0.5} = 0.333$$

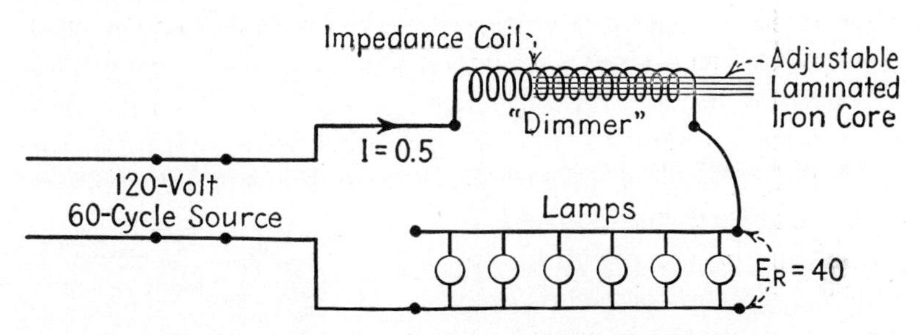

FIG. 64.—The "dimmer" circuit for incandescent lamps.

Example 8.—A washing-machine motor takes 4.3 amp. and 290 watts when connected to a 115-volt, 60-cycle source. At what power factor does the motor operate?

Solution:

$$P.F. = \frac{290}{115 \times 4.3} = 0.585$$

Example 9.—If the motor of Example 8 could be modified so that it would take the same power (290 watts) from the same source (115-volt, 60-cycle) at unity power factor, what would be the motor current?

Solution:

$$I = \frac{\text{watts}}{E \times P.F.} = \frac{290}{115 \times 1.0} = 2.52 \text{ amp.}$$

Examples 8 and 9 illustrate an extremely important point, namely, that the current taken by a circuit diminishes to a minimum as the power factor is increased toward unity.

The Capacitance Circuit.—Besides the elementary type of circuit in which the current always lags behind the voltage, there is another type of elementary circuit in which the current leads the voltage. The first type, as was pointed out previously, must always be an electromagnetic device, *i.e.*, a coil of wire generally wrapped around a magnetic core; such a circuit always possesses inductance. The second type produces just the reverse effect inasmuch as its action makes the current *lead* the voltage. The simple device that causes the current to *lead* the voltage is called a *capacitor* (or condenser), and the circuit in which this occurs is known as a *capacitance* circuit. A capacitor (or condenser) in its simplest form is merely a pair of metallic plates separated, or insulated, from each other by a nonconductor of electricity. The plates are commonly aluminum or tin (or any other nonmagnetic substance), while the insulating material, called the *dielectric*, is any of a large variety of substances such as air, mica, glass, oil, waxed paper, rubber, fiber, etc.

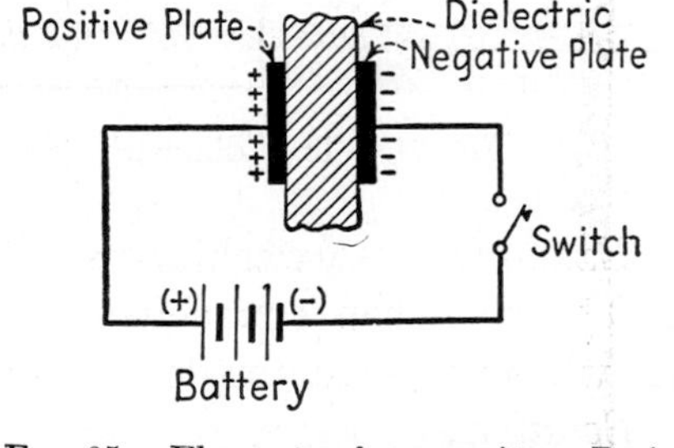

Fig. 65.—Elements of a capacitor. Positive and negative charges when connected to a battery.

When a direct-current source is connected to a capacitor, *current flows only to charge it; the current does not flow through it.* The plate that is connected to the positive terminal of the source becomes positively charged, while the other plate is negatively charged (see Fig. 65). At the instant the switch is closed, there is a sudden rush of current to charge the capacitor; but as its potential increases with increasing charge, the current falls until it is zero when the capacitor is charged to the potential of the source. In other words, as the capacitor continues to acquire more and more charge, its electric potential increases. Note that the capacitor potential is always such as to *tend* to send a current back into the battery, which, of course, it can never do because its voltage

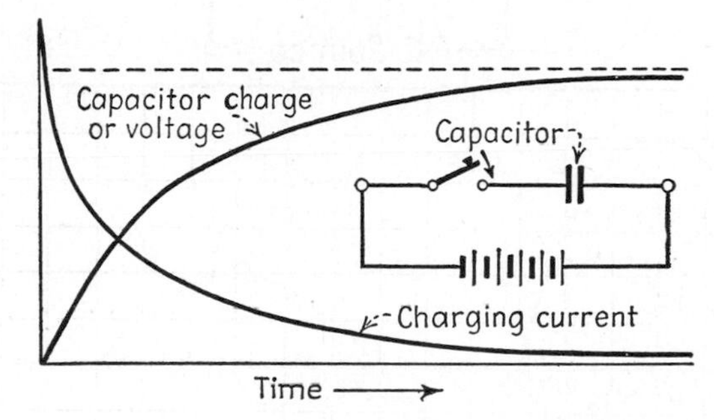

FIG. 66.—*Current-time* and *voltage-time* curves for a charging capacitor.

can never exceed the battery voltage. However, when the capacitor voltage, owing to its charge, becomes equal to the battery voltage, no charging current flows. This means obviously that the current flowing in the circuit to charge the capacitor is a maximum at the instant the switch is closed and is zero after the capacitor is completely charged.

Or, to put it another way, when the voltage of the capacitor is zero, the current flowing to charge it is a maximum; when the voltage of the capacitor is a maximum, the current flowing to charge it is zero. Figure 66 shows graphically the relation between the charging current and the voltage of the capacitor in a simple circuit and indicates how the current (to charge the capacitor) *leads* the voltage.

When an alternating-current source is impressed across the terminals of a capacitor, the same general effect of charging current leading the capacitor voltage will be produced. There is, however, one very important difference between the two types of sources, direct and alternating, namely, that the direct-current voltage is constant, whereas the alternating-current voltage varies sinusoidally (like a sine curve). With the direct-current source, therefore, the charging current rises instantly to a maximum value and then drops off rather quickly as it tapers toward zero. The shape of the current curve (Fig. 66) is concave upward and

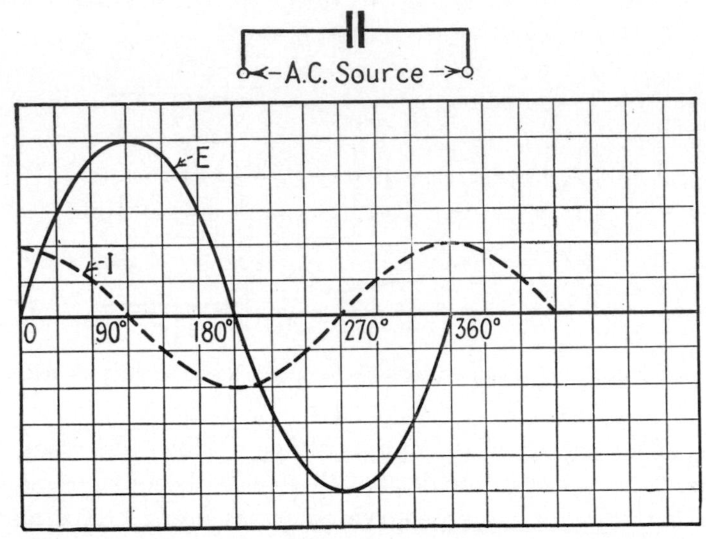

FIG. 67.—Current and voltage waves in a pure-capacitor circuit.

is known as an *exponential.* Note that the current never reverses its direction. With the alternating-current source, the charging current follows a cosine curve if the voltage varies sinusoidally. In this case the current does reverse its direction. In Fig. 67, which shows how the charging current I varies with respect to the sine wave of voltage E, it is seen that the current leads the voltage by 90 deg. Note that the current is a maximum at 0 deg. while the voltage is zero. At 90 deg. the current has dropped to zero, at which instant the voltage has risen to its maximum value. And as the current continues to charge the capacitor in the reverse direction from 90 to 180 deg., the voltage drops to zero. The completion of the cycle then proceeds in the same way from the maximum negative value as it did from the maximum positive value.

Thus, we see that capacitance is in every way similar but opposed to the effect of reactance. In other words, while reactance produces a lag, capacitance produces a lead in the current. In both cases the power factor is zero because the angle of lag (reactance) or the angle of lead (capacitance) is 90 deg. Furthermore, both inductance and capacitance affect the amount of current flowing in a circuit, but again in different ways. Whereas the current diminishes as the inductance increases ($I = E/2\pi fL$), an increase in the capacitance produces a rise in current. If the capacitance of a capacitor is expressed in microfarads, the current will be

$$I = 2\pi fCE \times 10^{-6} \text{ amp.} \tag{31}$$

Example 10.—(*a*) What charging current will flow in a capacitor circuit of 80 microfarads (80μf) if it is connected to a 120-volt, 60-cycle source? (*b*) At what voltage will the same charging current flow as in (*a*) if the frequency is 25 cycles?

Solution:

a. $I = 2\pi \times 60 \times 80 \times 120 \times 10^{-6} = 3.62$ amp.

b. $E = \dfrac{I \times 10^6}{2\pi \times f \times C} = \dfrac{3.62 \times 10^6}{2\pi \times 25 \times 80} = 288$ volts

If a circuit consists of a resistance and a capacitance in series, the current will lead the voltage by an angle less than 90 deg. but more than 0 deg. Thus, when the resistance and the capacitance are so proportioned that the voltage necessary to overcome the resistance is exactly equal to that required across the capacitor terminals, the current will lead the voltage by 45 deg. This is shown in Fig. 68. A careful study of this diagram, which is typical of the resistance-capacitance series circuit, should make it clear that both the zero and maximum values of the current occur 45 deg. *before* the corresponding values of the e.m.f. Also, the power curve P is similar in every way to that shown in Fig. 63 for a circuit containing resistance and reactance in series, except that it is displaced to the left a distance of 45 plus 45, or 90 deg. The meaning of that portion of the power curve below the hori-

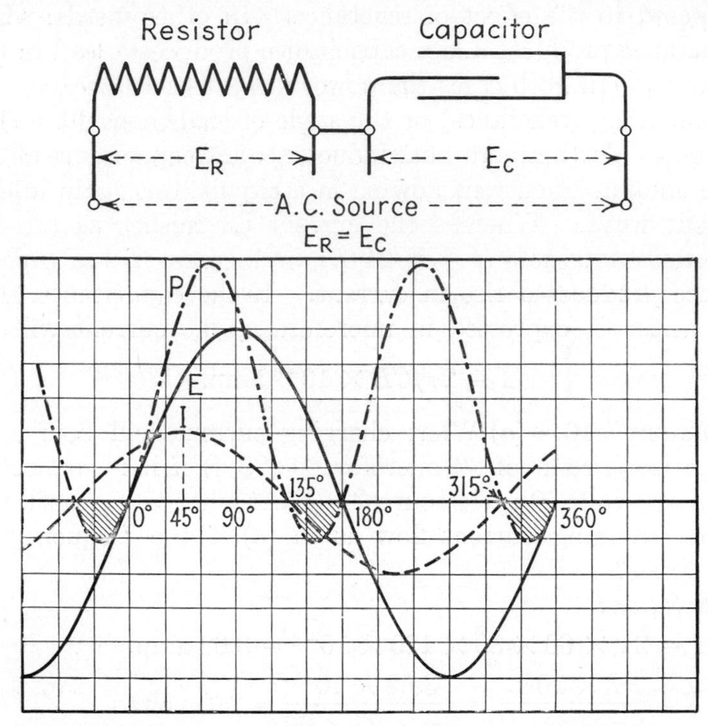

FIG. 68.—Current, voltage, and power waves in a series *R-C* circuit.

zontal axis, or negative power insofar as the generator is concerned, is that it represents the discharge of the energy stored up in the capacitor. This energy is stored up in the electrostatic field instead of in the electromagnetic field, as in the case of the reactance. Here again the power delivered by the generator to the resistance-capacitance load is of a fluctuating character.

This curve represents conditions that might exist in an unloaded long transmission circuit in which the charging current is due largely to the capacitance of the lines. (The two wires represent the plates, and the air between them is the dielectric.) As the current due to the load increases, the current curve shifts to the right with respect to the voltage curve until it is finally in phase with the e.m.f. As such lines are usually loaded with a partially inductive load, this shifting of the phase will continue as more load is applied and until the current lags behind the voltage. It frequently happens that the charging current of the line is so great that, as an inductive load is applied, the ammeter actually shows a decrease in current, because of the fact that the power factor of the complete circuit approaches unity.

The Series Resistance-inductance-capacitance Circuit.—An interesting circuit is one containing all three elements in series, namely, resistance, inductance, and capacitance, and one in which the values of the inductance and the capacitance may be varied. If such a circuit is set up, as shown in Fig. 69, so that the inductance can be changed by moving

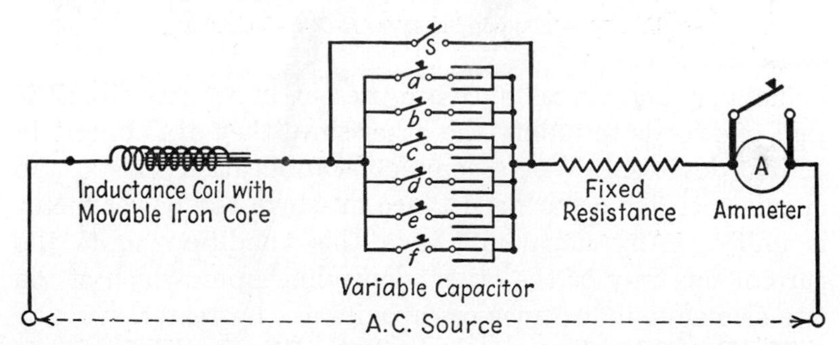

FIG. 69.—The series *R-L-C* circuit with a variable capacitor.

the iron core in or out of the coil (the greatest inductance occurs with the iron core completely *in*) and so that the capacitance can be increased by opening switch *S* and then closing switches *a*, *b*, *c*, *d*, *e*, and *f* successively, the current may be made to lead or lag behind the voltage and also take on many values. For example, if the voltages across the inductance and the capacitance are equal, the current will be a maximum as indicated on the ammeter and will also be in phase with the total impressed voltage; in fact, it will be E/R under this condition. The circuit is then said to be *resonant*. When the voltage across the inductance is greater than that across the capacitance, the current will be less than that existing for the resonant circuit and will lag behind the voltage. And when the voltage across the capacitance is greater than that across the inductance, the current will also be less than for the resonant condition but will lead the voltage. What happens, of course, when both

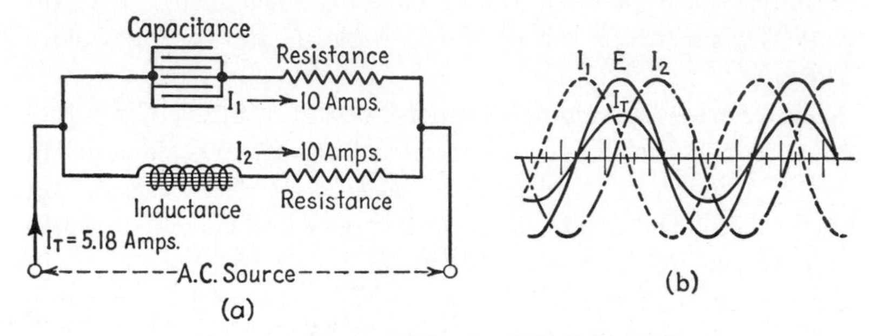

FIG. 70.—The parallel-series *R-C*, *R-L* circuit.

inductance and capacitance are present in a series circuit is that one tends to nullify the other since they are oppositely acting devices. When complete nullification exists, the circuit acts like a pure resistance in which the power factor is unity. Any departure from this condition shifts the current one way or the other, depending upon which of the two elements, inductance or capacitance, is greater.

The Parallel Inductance-capacitance Circuit.—Before leaving this subject it may be worth while to consider a circuit in which a resistance-inductance circuit is connected in parallel with a resistance-capacitance circuit. Without attempting to make the subject appear too difficult a simple illustration will be considered. Referring to Fig. 70*a*, assume a resistance-capacitance branch to be in parallel with a resistance-inductance branch. If the currents in both are then adjusted to equality, 10 amp. in each circuit, and the current in the inductance branch is made to lag behind the voltage by 75 deg., while the current in the capacitance branch is made to lead the voltage by 75 deg., the total line current will be only 5.18 amp. [(10 cos 75° + 10 cos 75°) = (2 × 10 × cos 75°) = 5.18 amp.] In other words, *the current in either branch of the circuit is greater than the current in the wire leading to the two branches.* This would appear at first sight to be a little difficult to explain, but the fact is that the capacitor discharges into the inductance, while the inductance discharges into the capacitor. The result is that the local discharging circulating currents are very large compared with the actual current in each of the two circuits. Figure 70*b* shows how the two current waves I_1 and I_2 are related to the impressed voltage and indicates, too, how the total current wave for I_T is plotted point by point from the sum of the two currents I_1 and I_2. Note particularly that the maximum value of I_T is considerably less than the maximum value of I_1 or I_2; it is, in fact, 51.8 per cent as much (5.18 amp. is 51.8 per cent of 10 amp.).

Power Measurements in Alternating-current Circuits.—When direct-current measurements are made, it is generally sufficient to use only two types of instrument, namely, voltmeters and ammeters, from which all the required information can be calculated. Power and resistance values can be determined by applying the equations of Chap. III. In alternating-current circuits a third type of instrument must be used if complete information is to be obtained. This is the wattmeter and is the only instrument that will indicate the true power in watts in an alternating-current circuit. The product of volts and amperes is *not* equal to the power as in direct-current circuits unless the power factor is unity. Furthermore, the equivalent resistance in an alternating-current circuit cannot be calculated by dividing E by I as in direct-current circuits but by dividing the power by the square of the current. Thus,

$$R_{eq} = \frac{\text{power}}{\text{amperes}^2} = \frac{P}{I^2} \tag{32}$$

The above equation was used in the solution of Example 6, page 154. The wattmeter is in reality a sort of combination voltmeter-ammeter, designed and calibrated so that it indicates watts directly. It contains two sets of coils of wire one of which, carrying a pointer, moves with respect to the other. One set of coils is connected *in series* in a circuit and carries the line current just as would any ammeter; the other set of coils is connected directly *across* the circuit as would any voltmeter. Figure 71 shows how a wattmeter is connected into a circuit to measure the power taken by a

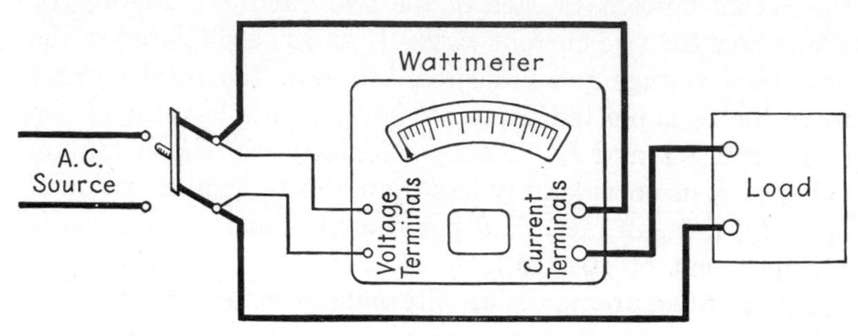

FIG. 71.—Sketch showing how a wattmeter is connected in an alternating-current circuit to measure power.

load. Note particularly that the heavy lines represent the wires that carry the load current and are shown connected in series with the current terminals of the wattmeter, whereas the voltage terminals are joined to the source by a pair of relatively fine wires because the current in these is very low and is independent of the load current. In many cases wattmeters are arranged for two or more current ranges and two or more voltage ranges, the purpose being to extend the usefulness of the instrument to varying circuit conditions. The proper selection of the current and voltage ranges will also permit the experimenter to obtain a deflection to a readable portion of a calibrated scale that is not uniformly divided. Manufacturers' instructions should, however, be followed carefully when such instruments are used, not only to avoid damage to them when connected improperly but also to provide the experimenter with the most accurate information.

Power-factor Adjustment in Series Circuits.—It is sometimes necessary to adjust the power factor in an inductive circuit by connecting a capacitor in series with it. As was pointed out previously, the *inductance in henrys* may be converted into *inductive reactance in ohms* by Eq. (26), page 144, where $X_L = 2\pi fL$. The capacitance in microfarads can likewise be converted into ohms by applying the equation

$$X_C = \frac{10^6}{2\pi fC} \text{ ohms} \qquad (33)$$

where X_C = capacitive reactance, ohms
f = frequency
C = capacitance, microfarads

This equation may be derived directly from Eq. (31), page 159, in which

$$I = 2\pi fCE \times 10^{-6}$$

or

$$E = I \times \frac{10^6}{2\pi fC}$$

where voltage (E) equals amperes (I) × ohms ($10^6/2\pi fC$).

Since any capacitive reactance X_C in ohms nullifies an equal value of X_L in ohms, it should be clear that when $X_C = X_L$ the circuit acts exactly like a pure resistance in which the power factor is unity. This is exactly the situation in Fig. 69 when the current reaches its maximum value.

In order to determine the true *value* of C in microfarads which, when connected in series in an inductive circuit, will make the power factor become unity, it is only necessary to measure the current, voltage, and power in the original inductive circuit. This may be done as indicated in Fig. 72.

From the values of E, I, and P registered by these instruments, calculations can then be made as follows to determine C in microfarads:

1. Determine R from P/I^2[Eq. (32)].
2. Calculate Z from E/I [Eq. (29)].
3. Then compute $X_L = \sqrt{Z^2 - R^2}$ [Eq. (27)].

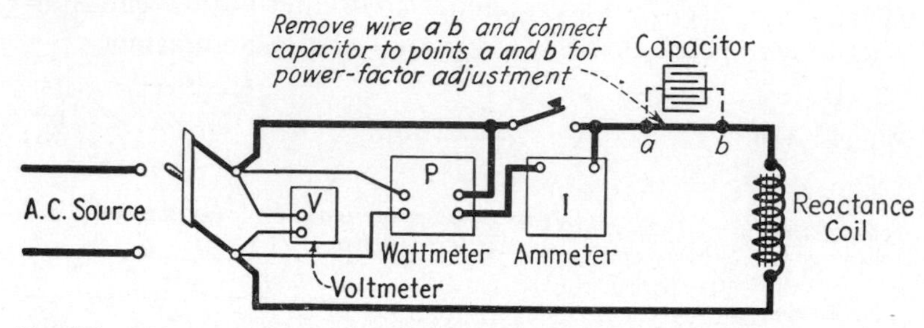

FIG. 72.—Wiring diagram showing how a capacitor is connected in series in an inductive circuit to improve the power factor.

The value of X_L is then equated to $X_C = 10^6/2\pi fC$ [Eq. (33)], from which

$$C = \frac{10^6}{2\pi f X_C}$$

Example 11.—What value of C in microfarads should be connected in series in a 60-cycle inductive circuit in which the current, voltage, and power were measured to be 4 amp., 120 volts, and 240 watts, respectively, if the resulting power factor is to be unity?

Solution:

$$R = \frac{240}{16} = 15 \text{ ohms}; \; Z = \frac{120}{4} = 30 \text{ ohms}$$

$$X_L = \sqrt{\overline{30}^2 - \overline{15}^2} = \sqrt{675} = 26 \text{ ohms}$$

$$C = \frac{10^6}{26 \times 2\pi \times 60} = 102 \; \mu\text{f}$$

In the above example, a capacitor having a capacitance less than 102 microfarads would change the power factor to a value lower than 1.0 lagging, whereas a larger capacitor than 102 μf would change the power factor to a value less than 1.0 leading.

Power-factor Adjustment in Parallel Circuits.—The power factor of an inductive circuit is more often adjusted by connecting a capacitor across (in parallel with) a device than by inserting it in series. This is particularly true of electric machines such as induction motors, to be discussed in a subsequent chapter. In order to determine in advance what the capacitance should be, a different calculation procedure from that followed in the last paragraph must be used, although exactly the same measurements should be made. Referring to Fig. 73, assume that the values of P, E, and I are measured

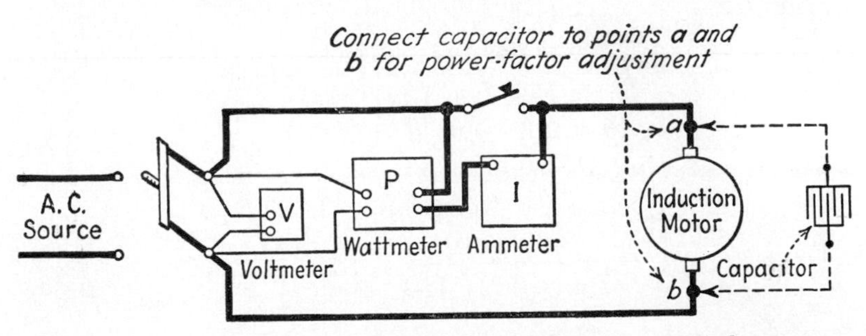

FIG. 73.—Wiring diagram showing how a capacitor is connected across an induction motor to improve the power factor.

for the motor input. The power factor can then be calculated in the usual way by dividing watts input to the motor by the product of volts and amperes [see Eq. (30a) where $P = E \times I \times P.F.$]. The current I may then be said to be made up of two components, or parts, one of which is in phase with the voltage and represents the power component, and the other of which "kicks" the actual current behind the voltage. Since it is the latter of the two components that must be annulled by the capacitor if unity power factor is to result, the latter must be selected so that it will take just this value of current. Analysis shows that it will be equal to $I \times \sin\theta$, where $\sin\theta$ is the sine of the angle represented by the power-factor angle. Thus, if the power factor is 0.866, the angle is 30 deg., and the sine of 30 deg. is 0.5. After determining $I \times \sin\theta$, the capacitance can then be calculated from the formula $I \sin\theta = 2\pi fCE \times 10^{-6}$ [Eq. (31), page 159].

In order to illustrate the method, let us solve a typical example.

Example 12.—In Fig. 73, an induction motor was tested under load and was found to take 332 watts and 4.6 amp. when operated from a 120-volt, 60-cycle source. What should be the capacitance of a capacitor when connected across the motor terminals for a combined power factor of unity?

Solution:

$$P.F. = \frac{\text{watts}}{E \times I} = \frac{332}{120 \times 4.6} = 0.6$$

$$\cos\theta = 0.6 \quad \text{Angle} = 53°$$

$$\sin 53° = 0.8$$

$$I \times \sin\theta = 4.6 \times 0.8 = 3.68 \text{ amp.}$$

$$C = \frac{3.68 \times 10^6}{2\pi \times 60 \times 120} = 81.4\ \mu\text{f}$$

Experiment 11. Current-time Relations in Inductive Circuits

Objectives: To study the relation between current and time in a highly inductive direct-current circuit in which (*a*) *the current rises to its ultimate E/R value* when the switch is closed; (*b*) *the current decays to zero from its E/R value* when the switch is opened.

Procedure: For the purposes of this experiment it will be necessary to use an electromagnet having a relatively high inductance, *i.e.*, one in which there are a great many turns of wire wrapped around a good quality of magnetic steel. Furthermore, if the current rise or fall is to be delayed sufficiently long, say, 20 to 40 sec., the resistance of the coil must be comparatively low. It will be well to remember in selecting the inductance that the larger the value of L/R, the longer will be the time period for the current change from zero to E/R or from E/R to zero. If a 5-kva., 2,300-230/115-volt distribution transformer is available, its primary or high-voltage winding will be found to be quite satisfactory as the testing unit.

A circuit should be connected as shown in Fig. 74. Note that the test circuit, consisting of an inductance, a 100-

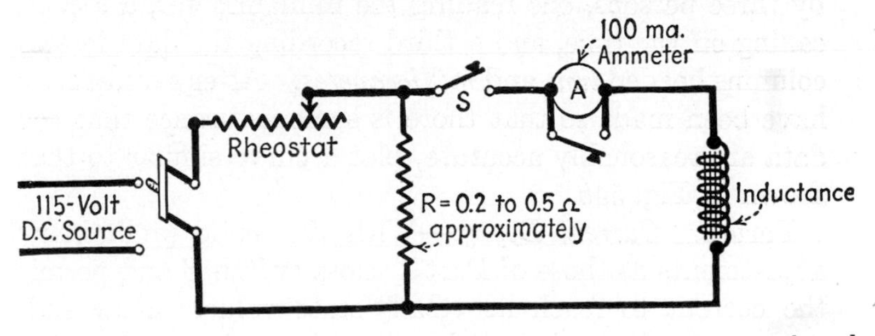

Fig. 74.—Wiring diagram showing method of determining the growth and decay of current in an inductive circuit.

milliampere ammeter, and a switch S in series, is connected across a very low resistance of approximately 0.2 to 0.5 ohm, the combination then being connected in series with an adjusting rheostat to a 115-volt direct-current source.

Preliminary adjustments and test runs should first be made before actual testing and data taking begin. This should be done in the following manner: (1) Close the main switch and switch S, setting the rheostat *all in*. After the ammeter has reached its final value, adjust the rheostat until the ammeter registers about 50 milliamperes. (2) Open switch S and make sure the needle drops to zero. (3) With a stop watch, time the current from the instant the switch S is closed until the ammeter returns to the setting made in (1) of about 50 milliamperes. (4) Do this several times for a number of values of R from 0.2 ohm to 0.5 ohm, in each case making the final adjustment with the rheostat. (5) When the experimenter is finally satisfied that the current can be read accurately every 3 sec. as the needle swings up to its ultimate value in about 20 to 40 sec., data should then be recorded as indicated below.

Part 1. *Current Rise.*—With the main switch closed, suddenly close switch S, and rapidly begin taking readings of current every 3 sec. (with a stop watch) as the needle swings up to its ultimate E/R value. This should be done by three persons, one reading the milliammeter, a second calling off the time, and a third recording the data in two columns headed *time* and *milliamperes*. After several runs have been made so that there is some assurance that the data are reasonably accurate, plot a curve similar to that shown in Fig. 54*b*.

Part 2. *Current Decay.*—With the same preliminary adjustments as those of Part 1, close switch S and permit the current to reach its steady-state value. Now suddenly open the *main switch only* and rapidly start taking readings of current every 3 sec. as the needle drops to zero. Note that the energy of the inductance discharges into the resistance R plus the resistance of the coil. Again make several runs, after which a curve should be plotted like that shown in Fig. 54*c*.

Experiment 12. Resistance and Impedance in Series

Objective: To study the voltage, current, power, power factor, and inductance relations in a *series circuit* consisting of a resistor and an impedance coil.

Procedure: A circuit should be connected as shown in Fig. 75, in which a variable resistance is wired in series with an impedance coil and the necessary instruments (wattmeter, ammeter, and voltmeter). The variable resistance may conveniently be six or more 60-watt incandescent lamps connected in parallel. The impedance coil may be about

1,000 turns of No. 14 wire wound over a 3-in. cylinder of fiber or Bakelite about 12 in. long, with a tight bundle of laminated sheets of steel or ordinary iron baling wire inserted into the coil.

The source of supply should, of course, be alternating current, 50 to 60 cycles, 110 to 120 volts. With the iron

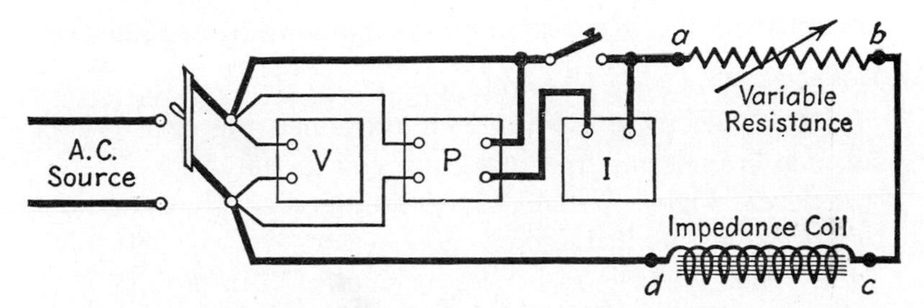

FIG. 75.—Wiring diagram showing how a wattmeter, a voltmeter, and an ammeter are connected in a series R-L circuit.

core of the impedance coil completely *in*, the variable resistance should be adjusted until the ammeter registers a reasonable value within the range of that instrument, after which a record should be made of volts E, amperes I, and watts P. These values should be repeated two or three times for other current settings by adjusting the variable resistance and *without disturbing the impedance coil.* Data should be recorded in a table similar to that shown below in the first three columns.

Calculations: Make calculations of the items indicated in the last five columns of the table.

Amperes	Volts	Watts	P/EI	E/I	P/I^2	$\sqrt{Z^2 - R_{eq}^2}$	$X_L/2\pi f$
I	E	P	$P.F.$	Z	R_{eq}	X_L	L

The results of the test should show that

a. The power factor increases as the current is reduced in the circuit, by resistance adjustment.

b. The inductance remains substantially constant and is unaffected by the reasonably small changes in current in the circuit.

Experiment 13. Resistance and Impedance in Parallel

Objective: To study the voltage, current, power, and power factor relations in a *parallel* circuit consisting of a resistor in one branch and an impedance coil in the other.

Procedure: Figure 75 should be modified so that, without disturbing the instrument connections to the left of *a* and *d*, the variable resistance is connected in parallel with the impedance coil. This can be done very simply thus: (1) remove the wire joining *b* and *c*; (2) join *b* and *d*; (3) join *a* and *c*.

The student should make a complete neat wiring diagram showing these connections.

With the iron core of the impedance coil completely *in*, adjust the variable resistance for several values of total current, taking readings of amperes, volts, and watts for each adjustment. Note that as the resistance is decreased, the total current will increase, just the reverse of the conditions existing in the series circuit, Experiment 12.

A record of the data and the calculations should be made in a table similar to that given below.

Calculations:

Amperes	Volts	Watts	Power factor	Total equivalent		
I	E	P	$P.F.$	Z	R	X_L

The results of the test should show that

a. The power factor increases as the total current increases, and vice versa.

b. The equivalent impedance (representing a single impedance coil that would take exactly the same current and power at the same power factor, from the same source of supply as the existing parallel circuit) decreases as the current increases.

c. The equivalent resistance (representing a single resistance as part of a single impedance coil) is the only part of the circuit that consumes power. To prove this, show that

$$P\ (\text{measured}) = [I\ (\text{measured})]^2 \times R_{eq}$$

Experiment 14. Resistance, Inductance, and Capacitance in Series

Objectives: (*a*) To study the voltage, current, power, and power-factor relations in a *series* circuit consisting of resistance, inductance, and capacitance. (*b*) To observe how the power factor and current vary as the capacitance is increased.

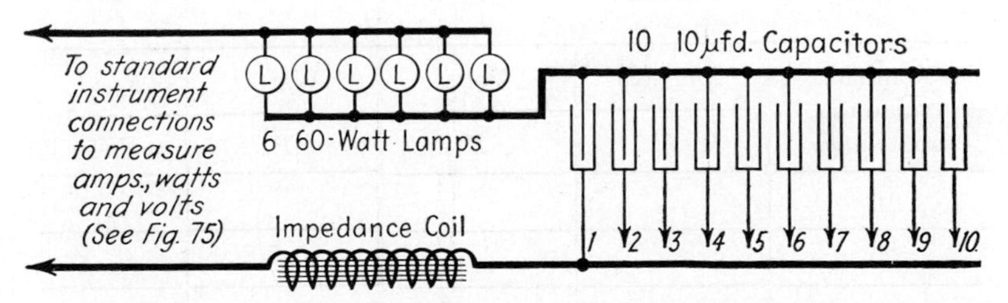

Fig. 76.—Wiring diagram showing the series *R-L-C* circuit with a variable capacitor.

Procedure: A circuit similar to that shown in Fig. 76 should be connected in which, it will be observed, a resistance (six lamps in parallel) is in series with a 100-μf capacitor and an impedance coil (like that used in Experiments 12 and 13). The instrument connections and the source of supply are omitted for simplicity, but these will be included exactly as was done previously in Experiments 12 and 13. Note that provision is made to increase the total capacitance of the capacitor to 100 μf or more by connecting, in succession, points 2, 3, 4, 5, 6, 7, 8, 9, and 10 to point 1. (When capacitors are connected in parallel, the total capacitance is equal to the sum of the individual capacitances.)

Without disturbing either the resistance (lamps) or the iron core of the impedance coil (iron core completely in) measure amperes, watts, and volts for successively increasing values of capacitance. As readings are taken and recorded in a table similar to that given below, the experimenter will notice the interesting fact that the current and power increase progressively to a maximum as more capacitors are added, until unity power factor is reached; after this point is attained, both the current and the power factor will diminish.

Calculations and Curves:

Nominal value of capacitance	Amperes	Volts	Watts	P/EI
	I	E	P	P.F.
10				
20				
30				
40				
50				
60				
70				
80				
90				
100				

After the power-factor calculations have been made, plot two curves: (1) capacitance versus amperes (Fig. 77*a*), and (2) capacitance versus power factor (Fig. 77*b*).

The results of this test should verify several important facts concerning series *R-L-C* circuits. As progressively increasing values of capacitance are used,

a. The power factor increases to a maximum of unity and then diminishes.

b. Before unity power factor is reached, the circuit power factor is lagging; after that it becomes leading.

c. Maximum current in the circuit occurs at unity power factor.

d. Before maximum current is reached, the current lags

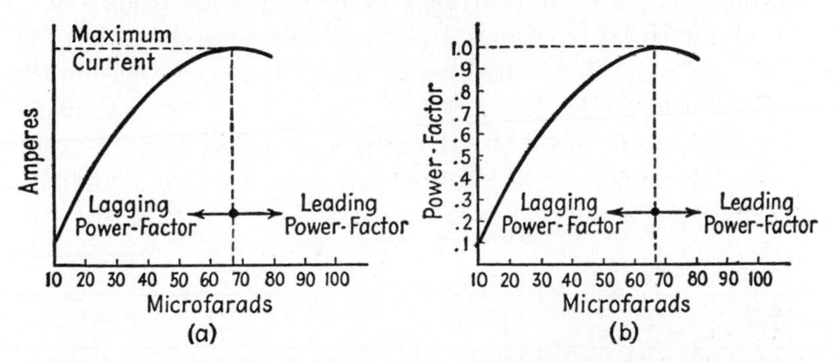

FIG. 77.—Curves showing how the current and power factor vary with increasing values of capacitance in a series *R-L-C* circuit.

behind the line voltage; after maximum current has been passed, the current leads the line voltage.

e. At unity power factor the circuit acts like a simple direct-current circuit in which $I = E/R$.

EXPERIMENT 15. POWER-FACTOR ADJUSTMENT

Objectives: (*a*) To determine the power factor of a small induction motor running idle, (*b*) to calculate the capacitance of a capacitor that should be connected across the motor terminals to raise the total power factor to unity, (*c*) to verify condition (*b*) by connecting a capacitor of this value across the motor terminals.

Procedure: Obtain a small split-phase motor (about $\frac{1}{4}$ hp. rating like that used in a washing machine or small grinder) and connect it as shown in Fig. 73 without the capacitor. Measure the input to the motor as it runs without load, recording amperes, volts, and watts. *Be sure the short-circuiting switch across the ammeter coil of the wattmeter and the ammeter is closed when the motor is started.* Open this switch only when the meters are being read, closing it immediately thereafter. Proceed next to calculate the size of a capacitor that should be connected across the motor terminals to raise the total power factor to unity. Follow the method outlined in Example 12, page 168.

After the capacitance has been determined, obtain one of approximately this value and connect it across the motor terminals.

Again test the motor, with its attached capacitor, recording amperes, volts, and watts as before, verifying the calculations made above.

Calculations:

Test		*E*	*I*	*P*	*P.F.*
1	No capacitor				
2	Capacitor (_____ μf)				

From Test 1

$$\cos\theta = \_\_\_\_\_\_\_\_$$
$$\text{Angle} = \_\_\_\_\_\_\_\_$$
$$\sin\theta = \_\_\_\_\_\_\_\_$$
$$I\sin\theta = \_\_\_\_\_\_\_\_$$

$$C = \frac{I \times \sin\theta \times 10^6}{2\pi f \times E}$$

SUMMARY

1. When a direct-current source is suddenly applied to or removed from an electromagnetic device, the current will not rise instantly to its E/R value or fall to zero.
2. An electromagnetic device is *inductive*. This implies that any change in magnetism results in an *induced* voltage in the coil that opposes the change.
3. The current in an inductive circuit lags behind the impressed voltage.
4. When an electromagnetic device is energized, magnetic energy is stored in the magnetic substance. Since the energy storage takes time, the current cannot rise instantly to its final value.
5. The *property* of an electric circuit that opposes a *change* in the value of the current is known as *self-inductance.*
6. The property of inductance is analogous to the property of inertia.
7. Inductance always manifests itself when the current or magnetism is *changed.* When there is no change, inductance cannot affect the circuit conditions.
8. A circuit has an inductance of 1 henry if a change in current of 1 amp. per second results in an induced e.m.f. of 1 volt to oppose the change.
9. The inductance in henrys of a circuit is determined primarily by its physical construction, *i.e.*, number of turns of wire, area and length of coil of wire, kind of magnetic core. It is unaffected by the size of the wire used in the coil.
10. Alternating current has several important advantages not possessed by direct current, among which are the following: (*a*) the voltage can be changed easily by transformer action; (*b*) generators can be built in large sizes and are thus less costly per kilowatt; (*c*) induction motors can be used, these being ideal for many applications.

11. The alternating-current ampere produces heat at exactly the same rate as a direct-current ampere when flowing through the same resistance.
12. Alternating-current amperes and volts are always expressed in terms of effective values. These are 70.7 per cent of their respective maximum values, a sine wave being assumed.
13. A pure-resistance circuit (no inductance) acts exactly the same whether direct current or alternating current is used.
14. The current in a pure-inductance circuit lags behind the voltage by 90 deg.
15. The inductive reactance in ohms equals $2\pi fL$.
16. A pure-inductive circuit does not consume power.
17. The current in a series R-L circuit lags behind the voltage by an angle that is less than 90 deg. and more than 0 deg. The only part of the circuit that takes power is the resistance.
18. A circuit containing both resistance and inductance is known as an *impedance.*
19. Impedance in a circuit bears the same relation to resistance and reactance that the hypotenuse of a right triangle bears to the two remaining sides. Thus,

$$Z^2 = R^2 + X_L^2$$

20. Ohm's law for the alternating-current circuit is $I = E/Z$.
21. Power factor may be defined in several ways: (*a*) it is the factor, between 0 and 1, which, when multiplied by the product of $E \times I$, represents the real power taken by a circuit; (*b*) it is the cosine of the angle between the voltage and current; (*c*) it is a *measure* of the power taken by a circuit.
22. The power taken by a single-phase alternating-current circuit is pulsing. It is not constant from instant to instant as in a direct-current circuit with a constant load. The power in alternating-current circuits is always determined on the basis of the *average* value.

23. The total power taken by a single-phase circuit is $P = E \times I \times \cos\theta$, where P is average watts, E and I are effective volts and amperes, and $\cos\theta$ is the power factor.
24. A capacitance is simply a pair of metallic plates insulated by a nonconductor of electricity called a *dielectric.*
25. A capacitance causes the current to lead the voltage, and therefore its action is just the reverse of an inductance.
26. Current *never* flows through a perfect capacitor. It flows only in the wires connected to the capacitor plates to charge or discharge it.
27. The capacitive reactance of a capacitor, X_C in ohms, is equal to $10^6/2\pi fC$ where C is given in microfarads.
28. The current flowing to charge or discharge a capacitor is equal to $2\pi fCE \times 10^{-6}$ amp.
29. A series circuit consisting of R, L, and C may have any power factor from zero to unity, lagging or leading. It will be unity when $X_L = X_C$. It will be lagging when X_L is greater than X_C. It will be leading when X_C is greater than X_L.
30. When a capacitor is connected across an inductive circuit, the current flowing in the capacitor branch tends to neutralize the lagging component of the current in the inductive branch. When the current in the capacitor branch neutralizes *all* of the lagging component in the inductive branch, the total power factor becomes unity.
31. Power in alternating-current circuits is measured with a wattmeter. If it is definitely certain that the power factor is unity, a voltmeter and ammeter may be used as in direct-current circuits.

TABLE X.—BASIC ALTERNATING-CURRENT FORMULAS FOR CALCULATING VALUES IN SERIES CIRCUITS

To determine	Formula—when given					
	$E, I, \& P$	$E, P, \& P.F.$	$P, I, \& P.F.$	$P, R, \& Z$	$I, R, \& Z$	$E, R, \& Z$
E (volts)	....	....	$\frac{P}{I \times P.F.}$	$Z \times \sqrt{\frac{P}{R}}$	$I \times Z$	
I (amperes)	....	$\frac{P}{E \times P.F.}$	....	$\sqrt{\frac{P}{R}}$	....	$\frac{E}{Z}$
P (watts)	....	....	....	....	$I^2 \times R$	$\left(\frac{E}{Z}\right)^2 \times R$
$P.F.$ ($\cos \theta$)	$\frac{P}{E \times I}$	....	....		$\frac{R}{Z}$	
Z (ohms)	$\frac{E}{I}$	$\frac{E^2 \times P.F.}{P}$	$\frac{P}{I^2 \times P.F.}$			
R (ohms)	$\frac{P}{I^2}$	$\frac{(E \times P.F.)^2}{P}$	$\frac{P}{I^2}$			

From above: X_L or $X_C = \sqrt{Z^2 - R^2}$; $L = \frac{X_L}{2\pi f}$; $C_{\mu fd} = \frac{10^6}{2\pi f X_C}$

QUESTIONS

1. When a direct-current circuit is closed, does the current rise instantly to its E/R value if the device is (*a*) a lamp? (*b*) an electromagnet? Give reasons for your answer.
2. What is an inductance? How does it manifest itself?
3. To what mechanical property can inductance be compared?
4. Why does the current lag behind the voltage in an inductive circuit?
5. Define a henry.
6. Upon what factors does the inductance of a coil depend?
7. Give several advantages possessed by direct-current circuits; by alternating-current circuits.
8. Define the alternating-current ampere.

9. What is meant by the frequency of an alternating current? What is the time required by one cycle?
10. What is the relation between the effective and the maximum values of a sine wave of current?
11. How many degrees are there in one cycle? one-quarter of a cycle?
12. What is the angular relation between the current and the voltage in a pure-resistance circuit? a pure-inductive circuit?
13. How is inductance in *henrys* converted into inductive reactance in *ohms*?
14. Explain why the average power delivered per cycle to a pure-inductance circuit is zero.
15. By how many degrees does the current lag behind the voltage in a series *R-L* circuit?
16. What is meant by impedance?
17. How is impedance determined from the values of R and X_L in a series circuit?
18. What is Ohm's law for the alternating-current circuit?
19. Define power factor in several ways.
20. Under what conditions will the total power in an alternating-current circuit be equal to $E \times I$?
21. Give several practical examples of pure-resistance devices; of impedances containing both resistance and inductance.
22. What is the general expression for the average power delivered to a single-phase circuit?
23. What is a capacitor? What materials are used to construct it?
24. What is the relation between the current and the voltage in a pure-capacitance circuit?
25. How does the action of a capacitor compare with the inductance property?
26. What does the current do in a capacitor circuit? Where does it flow? Where does it *not* flow?
27. How is the capacitance in microfarads converted into capacitive reactance in ohms?

28. Explain why the average power delivered per cycle to a perfect capacitor is zero.
29. By how many degrees does the current lead the voltage in a series *R-C* circuit?
30. Explain the conditions that exist in a series circuit containing *R*, *L*, and *C*. Under what conditions will the circuit power factor be unity?
31. What is the effect upon the total power factor when a capacitor is connected across an impedance? Under what condition will the total power factor be unity?
32. Why is a high power factor generally desirable?
33. Why is it generally necessary to use a wattmeter to measure the power in an alternating-current circuit?
34. Why is the power taken by an alternating-current circuit often referred to as *pulsing power*?

PROBLEMS

1. Calculate the inductive reactance of a coil having an inductance of 0.106 henry at 60 cycles; 30 cycles; 25 cycles; 120 cycles; 1,200 cycles.
2. Determine the time required per cycle in a 60-cycle circuit; a 25-cycle circuit; a 50-cycle circuit.
3. Assuming sine waves, what are the maximum values of the current and voltage in a circuit in which an ammeter and a voltmeter register 6 amp. and 115 volts, respectively?
4. A 60-watt incandescent lamp is connected to a 120-volt, 60-cycle circuit. What current does it take, and at what power factor does it operate?
5. A loudspeaker has a resistance of 6,000 ohms and an inductance of 1.6 henrys at 796 cycles. What current and power will it take if the impressed voltage is 40?
6. In Prob. 5, what current and power will the loudspeaker take if a capacitor is connected in series with it so that the inductive reactance is completely neutralized?
7. An impedance coil has a resistance of 30 ohms and an inductive reactance of 40 ohms. (*a*) What current will flow if it is connected to a 60-cycle, 120-volt source?

(*b*) If it is connected to a 25-cycle source, what should be the voltage if the current is to be the same as in (*a*)?

8. A small fan motor takes 124 watts and 1.6 amp. when operating from a 60-cycle, 115-volt source. What is the power factor of the motor?
9. Referring to Fig. 63, draw the current, voltage, and power waves for effective values of 14.14 amp. and 112 volts, respectively, and a power factor of 0.5 lagging.
10. Repeat Prob. 9 for a power factor of 0.5 leading.
11. Repeat Prob. 9 for power factors of zero lagging and leading.
12. An alternating-current electromagnet takes 1.8 amp. and 108 watts when connected to a 120-volt, 60-cycle source. What are its resistance and inductance?
13. Two coils A and B are exactly identical physically except that coil B has 1.5 times as many turns as coil A. If the inductance of coil A is 0.222 henry, calculate the inductance of coil B.
14. A group of lamps (in parallel) is connected in series with an impedance coil having negligible resistance and an inductance of 0.0318 henry. If the current is 10 amp. when the voltage is 130 at a frequency of 60 cycles, determine (*a*) the total impedance, (*b*) the inductive reactance, (*c*) the resistance, (*d*) the power delivered to the circuit, and (*e*) the power factor.
15. A group of incandescent lamps ($P.F. = 1$) is connected in series with an impedance coil having negligible resistance. For what value of inductance will the power delivered to the lamps be 40 watts at 20 volts? The line voltage and frequency are 120 volts and 60 cycles, respectively.
16. A refrigerator motor is connected to a 60-cycle, 120-volt source and takes 226 watts and 3.14 amp. when operating at full load. (*a*) At what power factor does it operate? (*b*) If a capacitor is connected across the motor and raises the line power factor to unity, what is the current in the capacitor circuit? (*c*) What is the capacitance of the capacitor in (*b*)?

17. A series circuit consists of a resistance of 8 ohms, an inductance of 0.0531 henry, and a capacitance of 189.7 μf. If a 115-volt 60-cycle source is applied to the circuit, calculate (*a*) the current, (*b*) the voltage drop E_R, E_L, and E_C across each of the circuit elements, (*c*) the circuit power, (*d*) the circuit power factor.
18. A 220-volt 60-cycle motor takes 24.3 amp. at a power factor of 0.83 when operating at rated load. What is the power input to the motor?
19. If the motor of Prob. 18 is connected in parallel with a load of 8 kw. at 0.8 power factor lagging, calculate (*a*) the total kilowatt load, (*b*) the total line current, (*c*) the over-all power factor.
20. Using the proper formula in Table X calculate the resistance in a series circuit that takes 1,620 watts at a power factor of 0.866 from a 240-volt 60-cycle source.
21. A capacitor is to be connected across (in parallel with) the motor of Prob. 18. What should be its value, in microfarads, if the over-all power factor is to be unity?
22. A series circuit consists of a 15-ohm resistor and an inductive reactance of 36 ohms at 60 cycles. (*a*) What will be the current and power if the circuit is connected to a 117-volt 60-cycle source? (*b*) What should be the voltage of a 25-cycle source if the current and power are to have the same values as in (*a*)?

CHAPTER 6

MAGNETISM AND ELECTROMAGNETISM

Natural and Artificial Magnets.—The ancients first discovered the remarkable property that certain substances attracted other materials when the two were brought close together. In the case of *amber*, called by the Greeks *elektron*, its ability to attract bits of *paper* or *chaff* is created only when "electrified" by *rubbing*. Sealing wax and hard rubber can also be "electrified" in the same way. These substances, therefore, acquire the attractive property artificially, *i.e.*, by being rubbed. The lodestone, however, possesses the property of attracting *iron* particles naturally, *i.e.*, just as soon as it is dug out of the ground; it need not be rubbed or treated in any way. Note that, although amber and lodestone act similarly inasmuch as they both have the power of attraction, they differ in two important respects: (1) one acquires the property artificially while the other has it naturally, and (2) one attracts bits of paper or chaff while the other acts only upon iron.

The lodestone, an oxide of iron, is a natural magnet, the word "magnet" doubtless being derived from its place of first discovery, the town of Magnesia in Lydia, Asia Minor. The material has little practical value today except as a museum or laboratory curiosity, because the force of attraction that it can exert is feeble compared with the more powerful artificially made permanent magnets. There are actually only three known practical elements that can be magnetized, namely, iron, nickel, and cobalt. Although iron is far superior to the other two as a magnetic element, it is nevertheless rather weak when compared with certain alloys containing iron and either or both of the others, or even elements which themselves are not magnetic. Thus, for example, *permalloy*, an alloy containing 22 per cent iron and 78 per cent nickel, or the tungsten steels, the cobalt steels, and the *al*uminum-*ni*ckel-*co*balt alloys known as *Alnico* have permanent-magnet properties that are truly astounding. Still more recently other more costly alloys such as the iron-nickel-titanium-cobalt group known as the new *K.S. magnet steels*, or the copper-nickel-cobalt group, or the alloys containing precious metals have been developed and are expected to add further to the usefulness of these magnetic substances in the construction of modern electrical machines and devices.

Artificial magnets may be created in several ways, their attractive power and permanency depending among other things upon the kinds and proportions of the elements used in their manufacture and the extent to which they are magnetized. Generally, it is best to magnetize a magnetic substance by wrapping a coil of wire around it, after which a direct current is passed through the former for a short time. Less effective methods involve stroking the substance with a strong magnet or placing the substance in contact with a powerful magnet. These procedures will be discussed fully and treated from the point of view of experiment later in the chapter.

The Magnetic Field.—For over a thousand years before the invention of the battery by Alessandro Volta in 1801, magnetic effects and electric currents had been known and regarded as similar although distinct phenomena. Moreover, it was thought they bore no relationship to one another. But in 1820, Hans Christian Oersted, the Danish scientist, showed experimentally that a compass needle is deflected when brought under the influence of a current-bearing wire. This important discovery of the dependence of one phenomenon upon another was taken up by a great many people who immediately began a series of experimental investigations that resulted in further important discoveries. It was indeed the beginning of the science of electromagnetism and electrodynamics.

A compass needle (which is merely a permanent magnet carefully shaped and accurately pivoted and balanced on a vertical stem) always tends to set itself at right angles to the length of a wire that carries a current. This means obviously that the space surrounding the wire acts exactly like the space surrounding a permanent magnet. This space is arbitrarily referred to as the *magnetic field,* since it is the *field* in which magnetic effects are created. For convenience it is also assumed that the magnetic field is a region of stress. In order to visualize this *fictitious* magnetic field in a state of stress, Michael Faraday invented the term "lines of force" and pictured the latter as uniformly distributed lines surrounding magnets and current-bearing wires and coils. Considerable study has since demonstrated the great usefulness of the conception *lines of force,* because it has revealed the beautiful symmetry of magnetic-field patterns and has given us an extremely powerful tool for the calculation of magnetic forces.

The fact that a compass needle points directly north and south (or very nearly so) implies that the earth is itself a sort of magnet. This property of the earth was discovered about the tenth century when a lodestone was freely suspended; in fact, the name "lodestone" was applied to the natural magnet because it was a *leading* stone for the ancient navigators. The end of a compass needle that points *north* is arbitrarily called its *north pole*; it is the *north-seeking* pole. If the north ends of two compass needles are brought close together, they are found to repel. But if the north end of one compass is brought near the south end of another compass, they are found to attract. This extremely important observation is the basis for the first law of magnetism:

(1) *Like poles repel,* (2) *unlike poles attract*

The magnetic fields surrounding a bar magnet, a U-shaped magnet, and an E-shaped magnet are shown in Fig. 78. In studying these sketches the following points should be noted: (1) the magnetic fields surrounding *uniformly* constructed magnets are always *symmetrical* unless they are disturbed by the presence of another magnetic substance somewhere in the field; (2) the lines of force have direction and are always represented as *leaving the north pole and entering the south pole*; (3) a compass needle placed anywhere in the magnetic

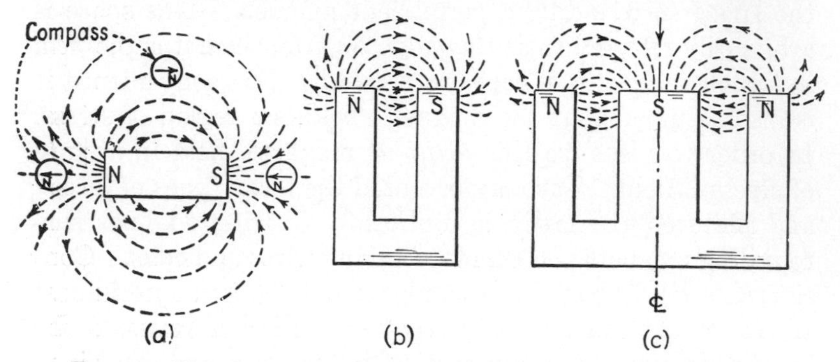

FIG. 78.—Flux distributions around straight-core, U-core, and E-core permanent magnets.

field will always be deflected so that its north end will point in a direction along the lines of force (Fig. 78*a*); (4) the greatest field intensity, *i.e.*, lines of force per unit of area, always occurs near the pole surfaces and diminishes with increasing distances from the poles; (5) a symmetrically constructed E-shaped magnet may conveniently be considered as two U-shaped magnets with the side faces of identical poles brought in contact (Fig. 78*c*).

Whenever a piece of iron is brought into the magnetic field produced by a magnet, the lines of force are urged away from their normal uniform distribution and are drawn to the magnetic substance. The reason for this may be attributed to the fact that iron is a better conductor of magnetic lines of force than air; it is, in fact, very much better, as will be pointed out later in connection with the discussion of the term "permeability." As a result of such concentration of flux, *the iron is actually drawn toward the magnet.* The iron thus becomes a magnet by induction, its polarity being determined by whether the flux enters or leaves it; if the flux leaves it as shown in Fig. 79, it becomes a north pole and is thus attracted to the south pole of the original magnet. This leads us to a very important law concerning magnetic fields, namely, *that a magnetic field always tends to arrange itself so*

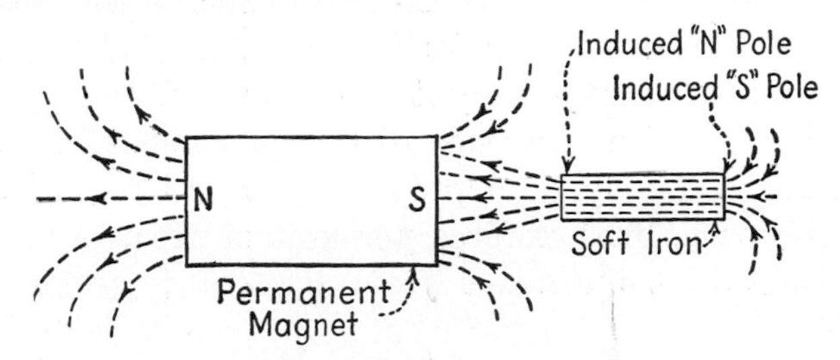

FIG. 79.—Unsymmetrical flux pattern around a permanent magnet, owing to a soft iron bar.

that the greatest number of lines of force can be created. Thus, if the ends of the U-shaped magnet of Fig. 78*b* or the E-shaped magnet of Fig. 78*c* are bridged by straight pieces of iron placed over their ends, the magnetic flux will actually be increased. Moreover, the smaller the air gap between the surfaces, the greater will the attractive force become.

One of the best ways to show visually the various magnetic-field patterns is by sprinkling fine, clean iron filings on a sheet of cardboard placed over the magnet or magnets. Sufficient iron filings should be dropped carefully, as though they were bits of salt, after which the cardboard is gently tapped. Each iron particle then becomes a miniature magnet and aligns itself, with others, along the imaginary lines of force. Many interesting patterns can be made in this way if bar magnets, U magnets, and E magnets are placed in various positions. In all this the student should thoroughly understand that the iron filings merely *represent* the stressed field; the greatest stress always exists where the filings are most thickly bunched together.

The Electromagnet.—The discovery by Oersted that a magnetic field *encircles* a straight wire carrying a current of electricity soon led to further discoveries concerning the manner in which magnetic effects are created not only by wires but by coils, as well as the laws governing their strength and direction.

When a current of electricity is sent through a straight wire, the magnetic field is produced in such a way that *the lines of force surround the wire in concentric circles.* These lines of force are most dense at the surface of the wire and become weaker with increasing distances from the wire. In fact, it has definitely been proved by experiment that *the flux density,* i.e., lines of force per unit of area, *is inversely proportional to the distance from the center of the wire.*

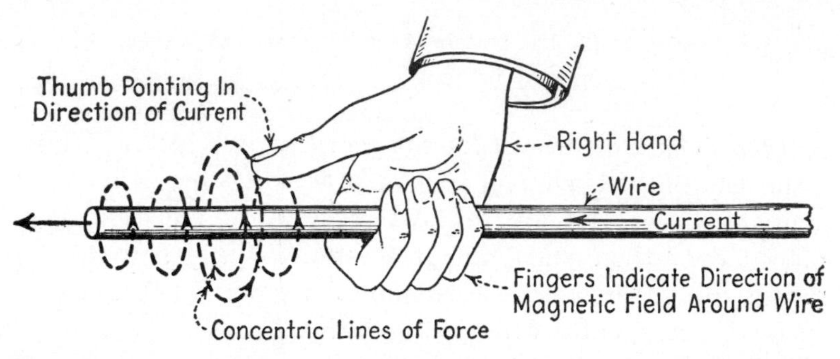

FIG. 80.—Sketch illustrating method of determining the direction of the field around a current-carrying wire.

Furthermore, it has also been shown that the *direction* of encircling lines of force may be determined by *the right-hand rule,* which may be stated thus: *Grasp the wire with the right hand so that the thumb points in the direction of the current; the encircling fingers will then indicate the direction of the lines of force around the wire* (see Fig. 80).

In order to produce appreciable magnetic effects with straight wires the current must be very large. However, if the wire is coiled as shown in Fig. 81, the lines of force are confined to the inside of the coil before they spread out into space, the result being that the flux density is greatly increased at both ends as well as within. It is, therefore, possible to magnify the effect of a given current, insofar as flux is concerned, by using coils of wire instead of straight wires. Such coils, called *solenoids*, are always employed when it is desired to develop very dense magnetic fields, the

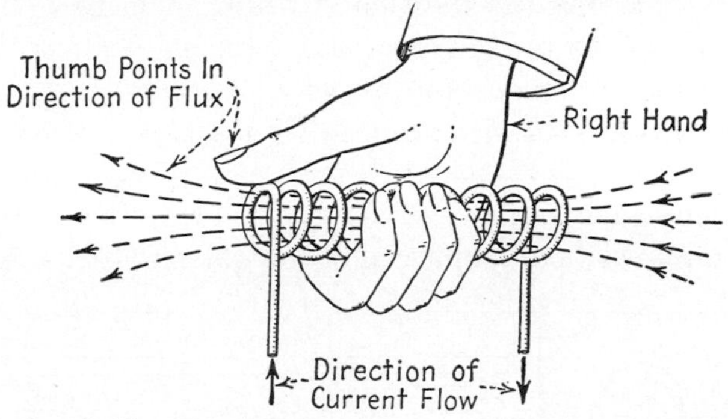

FIG. 81.—Sketch illustrating the method of determining the polarity of a solenoid.

latter being directly proportional to the number of turns of wire. Still further increase in the flux density at the ends of the coil, where it is most useful, can be produced by inserting an iron core, or other good magnetic substance, within the solenoid. The iron core thus becomes a magnet; and since *the magnet* is created by the passage of a current of electricity through the coil, it *is called an electromagnet.*

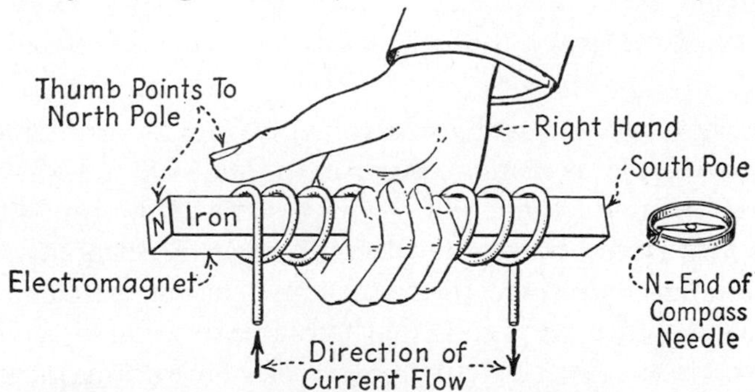

FIG. 82.—Sketch illustrating the method of determining the polarity of an iron core.

Referring to Fig. 82, the polarity of an electromagnet may be determined in one of two ways:

1. By bringing a compass near one end of the core of an

electromagnet. The end to which the north pole of the compass points is the south pole; the end to which the south pole of the compass points is the north pole.

2. By applying the right-hand rule, which may be stated thus: *Grasp the coil of wire with the right hand so that the fingers point in the direction in which the current flows in the coil; the thumb will then point to the north pole of the electromagnet.*

Electromagnets are very widely used in practice in many kinds of power equipment and control circuits. And be-

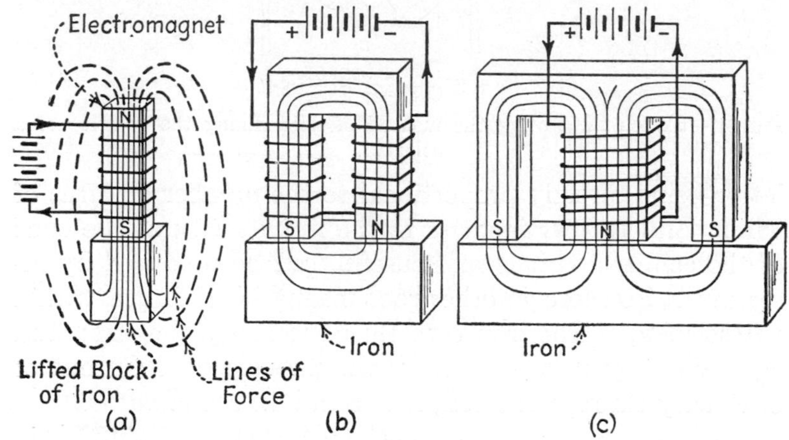

FIG. 83.—Flux distributions in straight-core, U-core, and E-core electromagnets.

cause they can be readily controlled by simple adjustments, they may often be made to perform unique and unusual operations. Some of these will be discussed at the proper time.

Factors Determining the Strength of an Electromagnet.—The strength of an electromagnet may be measured in several ways, but a very good method is to determine the force of attraction between it and a block of iron (or any magnetic substance) placed in close contact with the magnetic pole or poles. If the electromagnet is a straight bar as in Fig. 83*a*, it will not be particularly strong because the magnetic lines of force must pass through a considerable distance *in air* from the north pole of the magnet to the bottom of the block of iron. Since air is the poorest of all conductors of magnetic lines of force, the effectiveness of the current passing through the coil of wire is greatly diminished. A U-shaped electromagnet like that of Fig. 83*b* is very much better than a bar electromagnet for the reason that the lines of force are confined very largely to a good magnetic circuit consisting almost entirely of iron; the only air spaces are at the contact surfaces between the electromagnet and the lifted block of iron. A still better arrangement is that shown in Fig. 83*c*, in which an E-shaped electromagnet is used to lift a block of iron. In this construction there are two magnetic paths for the lines of force with only one coil of wire. Thus, it is seen that the strength of an electromagnet is, first of all, determined by its general construction or design.

A second factor, obvious of course, is the size of the electromagnet. The larger the surface area in contact with the block of iron to be lifted, the greater will be the force of attraction. Thus, in Fig. 83*a*, the electromagnet is weak for two reasons: (1) the flux must pass through a considerable space through air, and (2) only one surface area is in contact with the block of iron. In the E electromagnet of Fig. 83*c* there are three surfaces exposed to the lifted block, whereas a force of attraction exists at two surfaces in the U electromagnet of Fig. 83*b*.

A third factor is a term represented by the product of the *number of turns* in the coil (or coils) and the *current* passing through it (or them). This product is so important in work dealing with electromagnets that it is generally referred to as *ampere turns*, or NI, where N indicates turns and I, as before, is amperes. Strictly speaking, the same force of attraction will be produced by a given electromagnet if 1,000 turns carry 1 amp., or if one turn carries 1,000 amp., or if 5,000 turns carry 0.2 amp. In all cases the total number of ampere turns is 1,000.

Finally, the strength of an electromagnet is dependent upon the quality or grade of the magnet steel used for the core. There are so many different grades of material used in general practice that a designer of electromagnets must depend to a large extent upon the services of specialists or must refer to handbooks for information concerning his particular requirements. His choice of the proper core material will depend upon such factors as cost, whether the source of supply is direct or alternating current, permissible size, what it is to be used for, etc. Generally speaking, the "goodness" of the magnet steel is determined, among other things, by its *permeability*, a term that will be discussed fully later.

Summarizing the foregoing, the strength of an electromagnet depends upon four factors: (1) its design and construction, (2) its size, (3) the number of ampere turns (NI), and (4) the grade of the core material.

Electromagnet Strength and Wire Size.—*If the voltage impressed across the coil of a given electromagnet is fixed by a definite, constant source of supply, the force exerted by the core will be determined* almost entirely *by the size of the wire used* in constructing the coil. The smaller the wire used, the less will be the pull, and vice versa. To understand why this is so it is only necessary to remember that *the force exerted by the core of a given electromagnet depends upon the number of ampere turns* (see previous paragraph). Now then, if the resistance of a coil of N turns is R ohms, the number of ampere turns will be $(E/R) \times N$. Assuming that all turns of wire have exactly the same length, and therefore the same resistance per turn, it follows that if twice as many turns of the *same* wire are used, the number of ampere turns would still be $(E/2R) \times 2N$, or $(E/R) \times N$. The number of ampere turns would still be the same if half the number of turns were used, because the current would be twice as much while the number of turns would be halved. Thus

$$\frac{E}{(R/2)} \times \frac{N}{2} = \frac{E}{R} \times N \text{ amp. turns}$$

However, if the size of wire is *changed*, the number of ampere turns will change almost in direct ratio to the cross-sectional area because the resistance of the coil is inversely proportional to the area of cross section of the conductor. For example, an electromagnet wound with No. 17 wire will exert a greater pull than (though not exactly twice as much as) the same magnet would with No. 20 wire, the same voltage being applied in both cases. Assuming for simplicity (though this is not necessary) that both coils have the same number of turns of wire, it follows that

$$NI \text{ for No. 17 wire}^1 = \frac{E}{R} \times N$$

$$NI \text{ for No. 20 wire}^1 = \frac{E}{2R} \times N$$

This shows that the number of ampere turns developed by No. 17 wire is theoretically twice as much as that for No. 20. In fact, it may be shown that

1. For every change of wire size by one gauge number the number of ampere turns changes in the ratio of approximately $1\frac{1}{4} : 1$.

2. For every change of wire size by three gauge numbers the number of ampere turns changes in the ratio of approximately $2 : 1$.

When the number of turns of wire in the coil of an electromagnet is changed, however, the power input will change, and this will obviously affect the heating. If, for example, the number of turns of a given size of wire is increased, the resistance will increase. Assuming the same impressed voltage, this change in resistance will cause the current to diminish, which in turn will lower the power input and finally the temperature rise. Thus it is seen that, from the standpoint of heating, it is desirable to wind the coil or coils of an electromagnet with as many turns of wire as possible. On the other hand, if cost is a factor that must be considered, it is generally necessary to determine the fewest number of

[1]See Table II, p. 28.

turns to be used for the maximum allowable temperature rise. In some applications of electromagnets the problem of keeping the unit reasonably cool may present difficulties, so that it is well to bear the foregoing in mind along with such points as (1) the cycle of operation of the electromagnet, (2) the temperature of the surrounding air, (3) the ability of the various surfaces to dissipate heat, (4) the thickness of the winding coil, which will control "hot-spot" temperatures.

The following examples will now be given to illustrate the discussion under this heading:

Example 1.—The coil of an electromagnet is wound with No. 21 copper wire and has a resistance of 80 ohms. When connected to a 120-volt source it develops a pull of 35 lb. If design calculations indicate that the number of ampere turns must be increased 60 per cent to cause the magnet to lift 45 lb., (*a*) what size wire should be used in the new coil, (*b*) what will be the approximate resistance of the new coil, and (*c*) what will be the approximate power input to the new coil? (Assume that the physical dimensions of both coils are the same.)

Solution:

a. Since the number of ampere turns is practically proportional to the cross-sectional area of the wire, the new size of wire must be 1.6 times as large as the No. 21 wire.

$$C.M._2 = 1.6 \times C.M. = 1.6 \times 810 = 1{,}295$$

The nearest wire size is one having 1,288 *C.M.*, or No. 19 wire.

b. The new coil will be wound with No. 19 wire whose cross-sectional area is $\frac{1{,}288}{810} = 1.59$ times as much as No. 21 wire. Therefore, it will have $\frac{1}{1.59} \times 100 = 63$ per cent as many turns. Its resistance will be

$$80 \times 0.63 \times 0.63 = 31.7 \text{ ohms}$$

(The first 0.63 is used because the turns are reduced, while the second 0.63 is used because the area of the wire is increased.)

$$c.\ I_2 = \frac{120}{31.7} = 3.79 \text{ amp.}$$

$$P_2 = 120 \times 3.79 = 455 \text{ watts}$$

This means an increase of 455 − 180 = 275 watts.

Example 2.—The coil of an electromagnet is wound with 800 turns of wire and takes 180 watts when energized. Assuming that additional turns of the same size of wire will increase the resistance in direct proportion, how many turns should be added to the coil in order to reduce the power input to 120 watts? The impressed voltage is the same in both cases.

Solution: Using the equation for power, $P = E^2/R$,

$$P_1 = 180 = \frac{E^2}{R_1};\ P_2 = 120 = \frac{E^2}{R_2}$$

Dividing P_1 by P_2,

$$\frac{180}{120} = \frac{E^2/R_1}{E^2/R_2} = \frac{R_2}{R_1} \qquad R_2 = \frac{180}{120} \times R_1 = 1.5R_1$$

Therefore, 400 turns should be *added*.

Force Action between Parallel Wires.—When two parallel wires carry currents, a force will be created tending to move them apart or together. Whether the force will be one of repulsion or attraction will depend upon the direction of the currents in the wires with respect to each other.

In the simple electric circuit in which one wire carries current to the load while the other wire, close to the outgoing one and parallel to it, carries the return current, the force will be one tending to separate the wires. To understand why this is so, consider Fig. 84. When the right-hand rule is applied to determine the *direction* of the magnetic field around each wire separately, it is seen that the lines of force are clockwise around the left wire, which carries current away from the observer (cross ⊕), while the lines of force are counterclockwise around the right wire, which carries current toward the observer (dot ⊙). The result of these two fields is to create an area of greater flux density *between* the wires than that which exists on either side. And since one of the important laws of the magnetic field states that the resultant field tends to adjust itself so that a maximum number of lines of force are created, the wires try to

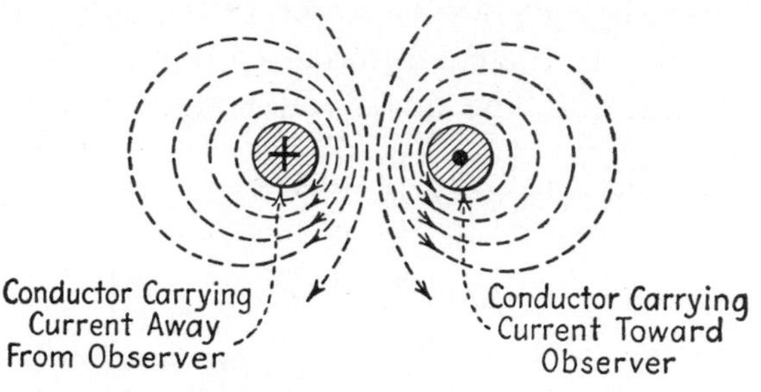

FIG. 84.—Flux pattern around two parallel conductors carrying currents in opposite directions.

separate because the area between the wires would thereby be increased.

On the other hand, if two parallel wires carry currents in the same direction, as indicated in Fig. 85, the force between them will be one of attraction. Here again the resultant magnetic field tends to conform itself so that a maximum number of lines of force are produced. As the wires move closer together, the nullifying effect of the two oppositely directed lines of force *between* the wires is diminished. In fact, the two wires *tend* to merge, under which condition they would act as a single conductor carrying a current equal to the sum of the two currents, and thereby produce the greatest possible flux.

The actual force existing between two parallel wires carrying currents either in the same direction or in opposite directions may be determined by applying the equation

$$F \text{ (pounds)} = \frac{5.4}{10^7} \times \frac{I_1 \times I_2}{d \text{ (inches)}} \times l \text{ (ft.)} \qquad (34)$$

where I_1 and I_2 are the currents in amperes in wires 1 and 2, d is the distance between the wires *in inches*, and l is the length of the line *in feet.*

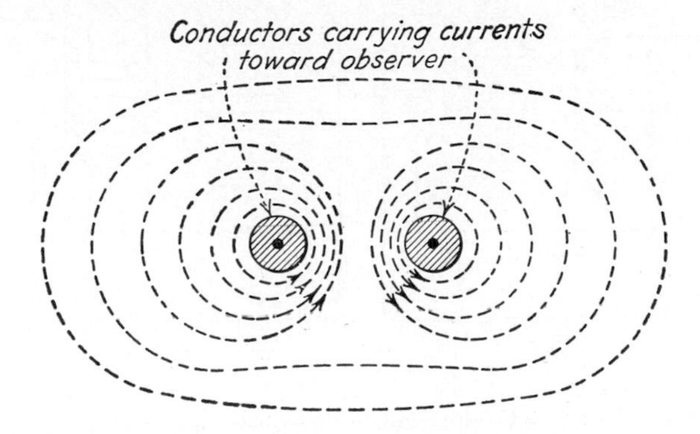

FIG. 85.—Flux pattern around two parallel conductors carrying currents in the same direction.

Example 3.—What force, in pounds, will exist between the conductors of a 200-ft. transmission line if the wires are 3 in. apart and each one carries 800 amp.?

Solution:

$$F = \frac{5.4}{10^7} \times \frac{800 \times 800}{3} \times 200 = 23 \text{ lb.}$$

Force Action between Two Bar Electromagnets.—If one electromagnet is brought under the influence of another, a force will be created tending either to push them apart or to bring them close together. Whether or not the force will be one of repulsion or attraction will obviously depend upon the *polarities* of the magnet ends that are *nearest each other.*

Thus, for example, in Fig. 86*a* the action will be one of attraction, whereas in Fig. 86*b* the electromagnets will repel each other. Note particularly that in the second case the two north poles (or the two south poles) are nearest each other—like poles repel; in the first case a north pole of one electromagnet is closest to the south pole of the other electromagnet—unlike poles attract. Further study of the two sketches should also make it clear that, when two electromagnets are parallel but not collinear, a force of

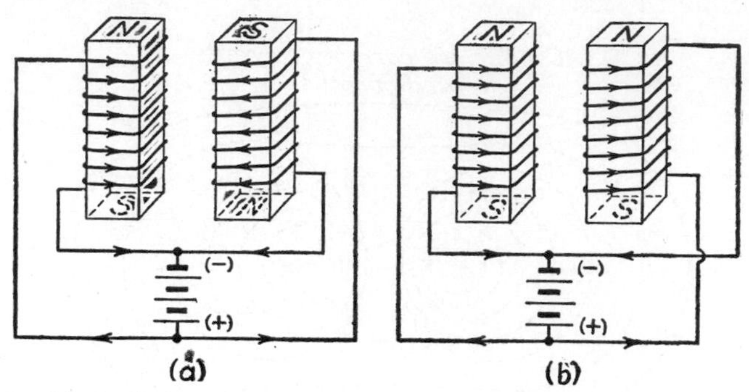

Fig. 86.—Method of connecting coils to obtain different polarities, to verify the first law of magnetism.

repulsion will exist when the currents in both coils are in the same direction (Fig. 86*b*), while a force of attraction will be created if the currents in the two coils flow in opposite directions (Fig. 86*a*).

An interesting difference from the case discussed above exists when the two electromagnets are lined up so that their axes are collinear, *i.e.*, in the same straight line. This is shown in Fig. 87*a* and *b*. Although the same universal laws of attraction and repulsion apply equally well here (unlike poles attract and like poles repel), it will be noticed that in Fig. 87*a*, where the currents in the coils are in the same direction, the force is one of attraction, whereas a force of repulsion exists in Fig. 87*b* where the currents in the two coils are oppositely directed.

Iron Core Magnetized by Two or More Current-carrying Coils.—Electromagnets are frequently constructed so that several current-carrying coils are used to magnetize the iron core. The latter may have almost any convenient shape, although it is usually desirable for the best results to make it perfectly symmetrical; generally, figures such as the U, the E, or the T are commonly employed. The coils are usually wound in advance upon wooden forms having the same dimensions as the core legs over which they will finally

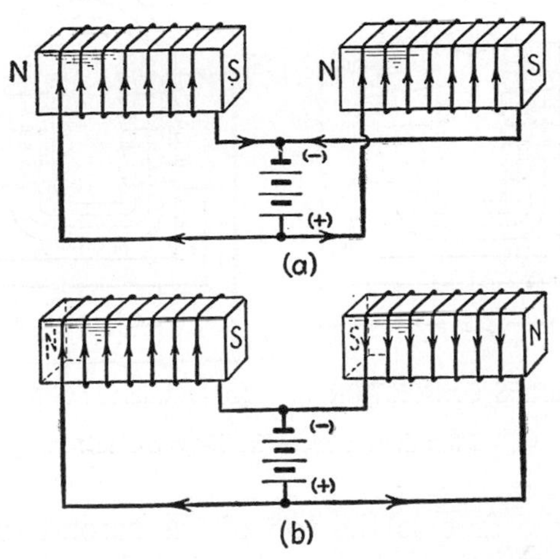

FIG. 87.—Methods of connecting coils to obtain different polarities, to verify the first law of magnetism.

be placed. After the coils are completed, they are carefully removed from the forms, dipped in an insulating varnish, and baked. This treatment makes them mechanically and electrically strong. The coils are then slipped over the upright legs and connected so that the currents in the several units flow in the proper directions to *aid* one another in developing correct polarities at the core ends. Furthermore, the coils may be connected in series or parallel; or, where many coils are used, they may be connected in one of several series-parallel or parallel-series combinations. In any case, the point to remember is that, when the *right-hand rule* is applied to the individual coils, the magnetic polarities must always be the same for all of them.

Consider Fig. 88*a* and *b*, which represents a U-shaped core with one coil on each upright leg. With both coils wound in exactly the same manner (counterclockwise when the electromagnet is viewed from above), it is necessary to connect the bottom two ends together for a series connection, or the top of the first to the bottom of the second and the

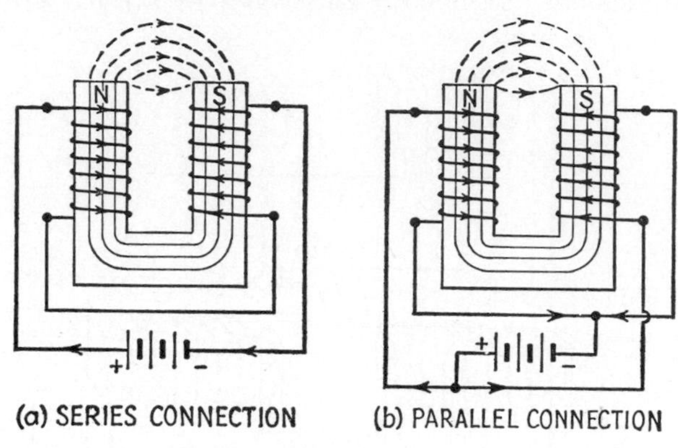

FIG. 88.—Flux distributions in U-type electromagnets.

bottom of the first to the top of the second for a parallel connection. In the common electric-bell electromagnet the series connection is generally used. For both arrangements the two coils will *aid* each other to produce the polarities shown. Should the electrical connections be made incorrectly, the iron core would not become magnetized, since the magnetizing action of one coil would be nullified by that of the other; under this condition the two coils would be said to *buck* one another.

Another common electromagnet construction is the E-core arrangement, illustrated with a single exciting coil in Fig. 83*c* and with two or three coils in Fig. 89*a* and *b*. In the two-coil type it will be observed that, with the coils on the outside upright legs, the current is in the *same* direction through both of them. Thus, two magnetic flux paths will be created so that one half of the center leg acts as the south pole for the left north pole, while the other half of the center leg acts as the south pole for the right north pole. Although this electromagnet looks as though it has only three poles, it really has four if it is remembered that the center south pole is actually a sort of merger of two south poles. In fact, it is always true that every electromagnet has an *even* number of poles, half of them north and the other half south.

In Fig. 89*b* the same E-core electromagnet is shown with the three energizing coils. Note particularly that the two outside coils have the same current directions as in the first case, but that the current in the center coil is reversed. Another point of importance is the fact that the center core leg carries twice as much magnetic flux as each of the outer two core legs, for which reason it is customary to make the former twice as wide as each of the latter. With this construction the flux density (lines per square inch) is exactly the same for every part of the magnet core.

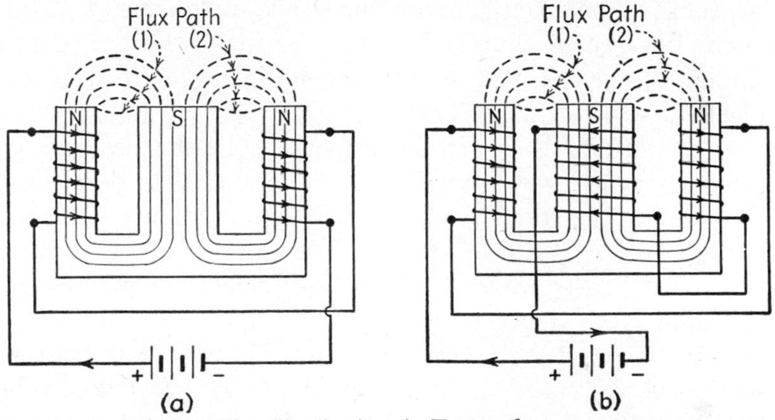

FIG. 89.—Flux distributions in E-type electromagnets.

The Magnetization of Iron and Steel.—As was previously pointed out, the strength of an electromagnet, in terms of the number of lines of force it creates, will depend, among other things, upon the number of ampere turns developed by the exciting coil or coils. In a given electromagnet having a fixed number of turns the flux will therefore depend upon the value of the current. If the electric circuit is provided with a rheostat or a potential divider so that the current can be adjusted, it is possible to vary the flux (or flux density) within certain limits. Starting with a completely unmagnetized iron core, it is found experimentally that the flux density will increase in direct proportion with an increase in ampere turns *within a certain limited range*; beyond the range where the flux density is proportional to the magnetizing force, the flux density increases less rapidly with further increases in the magnetizing force. And although the experimental procedure for obtaining data indicating the relationship between ampere turns and flux density is beyond the scope of this book, it is found that a curve similar to that of Fig. 90 will be obtained if such data are plotted.

Such a curve is extremely important to the designer of electromagnets, because with its aid he is able to determine in advance the dimensions of the core, its shape, and the number of turns and the size of wire required for the exciting coil. The procedure for this will be covered in a subsequent section. Note that the curve is a straight line from zero to a region where it gradually bends toward the X axis; in this section of the curve the flux density changes in direct proportion with the magnetizing force. Above this region where the bend seems to be most pronounced, the *knee*, the iron is said to become saturated, though, of course, only slightly so at first and more completely at high values of ampere turns. It must be understood that *saturation is a condition of the magnetic core* that indicates that the flux increases only slightly with further increases in magnetizing force. In practice, an electromagnet is rarely operated so that it is completely saturated, since this would mean an inefficient use of the power supplied to it. Furthermore, it is nearly always operated at densities above the knee because the iron tends to remain more or less stable; this means the flux does not change appreciably when the exciting current changes slightly for one reason or another. In the generator, for example, where the generated voltage depends directly upon the flux density, the iron must be worked in the region above the knee, for otherwise the voltage would fluctuate annoyingly as the normal operating conditions affect the magnetizing current.

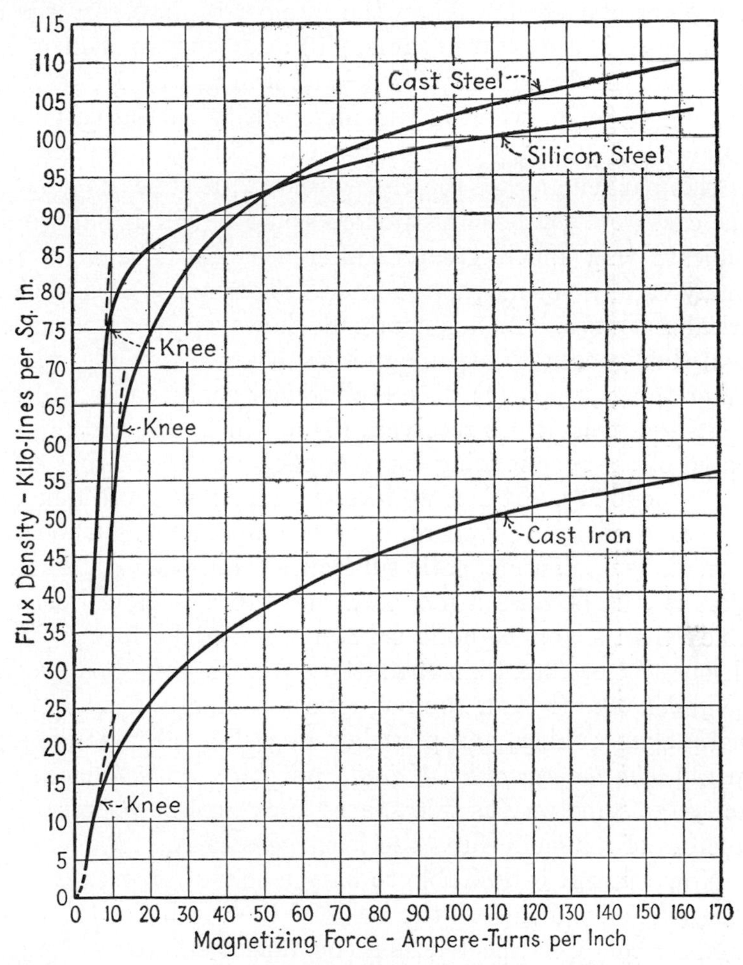

FIG. 90.—Magnetization curves.

All irons and steels behave in essentially the same general way when they are magnetized, since they follow the same curve pattern as that indicated in Fig. 90. But different *grades* of material differ widely when comparison is made between specimens on the basis of the *extent* to which they become magnetized for the same value of magnetizing force. To illustrate, consider two electromagnets similar in every respect except that the core of one is cast iron and that of the other cast steel. When the number of ampere turns in both cases is exactly the same, 110 amp. turns per inch, for example, the flux density in the cast iron will be 50,000 lines per square inch, whereas the flux density in the cast steel will be 104,000 lines per square inch. Thus, it is seen that in this particular case the cast steel is 2.08 times as good as the cast iron. Other illustrations could be cited that would indicate that much greater differences exist between the many varieties of magnetic materials commonly used in electrical machines. As a general rule, however, it can be stated that the "goodness" of a magnetic substance depends, among other things, upon (1) its metallurgical composition, (2) the heat-treatment it has received, (3) its thickness, and (4) the value of the magnetizing force applied to the exciting coil.

Permeability.—It is a well-known fact that more flux can be produced by a given number of ampere turns when the latter acts upon a magnetic substance than when it does not. This is true because a magnetic substance is more "permeable" than a nonmagnetic substance; *i.e.*, the former "lets through" more flux than the latter. In this respect it should be understood that all nonmagnetic substances such as wood, slate, glass, rubber, and porcelain as well as all metallic elements *with the exception of iron, nickel, and cobalt* act in exactly the same way as free space; they are the poorest conductors of magnetic flux, the least permeable.

Now, since it is desirable to have a sort of rating scale for magnetic substances on the basis of their abilities to create flux, air has been selected as a convenient standard of reference. Thus, for example, if cast iron is 150 times "as good" as air, and cast steel is 1,500 times "as good" as air, it follows that cast steel is 10 times better than cast iron. Or, to state this example in more practical terms, an electromagnet constructed with a cast-iron core will require 10 times as many ampere turns *to produce the same flux* as one similar in every respect except that a cast-steel core is used. The term used to express this "goodness factor" is "permeability." The permeability of all nonmagnetic materials is *one*, whereas that of magnetic substances varies from 100 or so to several thousand. In the case of special alloys, used only where the extra cost is justified, the permeabilities may reach values well over 50,000.

From what has been said, it might be thought that the permeability of a given material is constant. This is distinctly *not* the case, because *the permeability depends not only upon the material but also upon the flux density* at which it operates. In the case of cast steel, for example, the permeability is 1,500 when the flux density is 64,000 lines per square inch and only 200 at 110,000 lines per square inch. Thus, we see that the harder the material is worked, the "worse" it gets. The same situation exists with regard to cast iron and silicon steel, two other commonly used materials. It is also a fact that the permeabilities of most substances increase to a sort of maximum as the flux density is reduced; below this flux density the permeability begins to fall off again. In Fig. 91, which shows the flux-density versus permeability curve for three common magnetic core materials, these relationships are clearly indicated.

An efficient, well-proportioned electromagnet should fulfill the following requirements: (1) it should develop the desired flux density; (2) it should not be too heavy for the job it must perform; (3) it must not get too hot; (4) its cost must not be excessive; (5) it must be easy to assemble. And these requirements are not difficult to meet if one has a working knowledge of electric and magnetic circuits and materials and the fundamental laws that govern them. It is, of course, true that the *accurate* design of electromagnets is beyond the scope of this book, but it is nevertheless a fact that the student can do a creditable job in constructing a fairly good piece of equipment if he masters the subject matter covered in this chapter.

The data for plotting the permeability curves of Fig. 91 were obtained from the magnetization curves of Fig. 90. To convert flux density and ampere turns per inch for any point

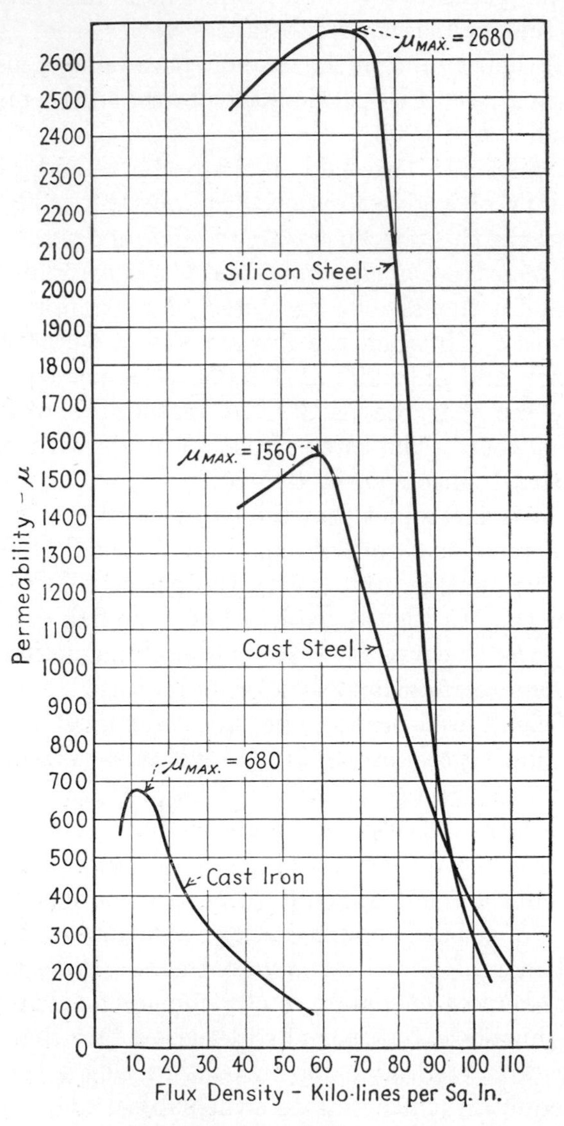

Fig. 91.—Permeability curves.

on such a curve to permeability it is only necessary to use the equation

$$\mu = 0.313 \times \frac{\mathcal{B}}{\mathcal{H}} \tag{35}$$

where μ = permeability
$\mathcal{B}$ = flux density in lines per square inch
$\mathcal{H}$ = magnetizing force in ampere turns per inch

Points were arbitrarily picked at convenient intervals on each of the curves of Fig. 90 and their corresponding values of $\mathcal{B}$ and $\mathcal{H}$ noted, after which the permeabilities were calculated by Eq. (35). To illustrate how this was done, the following example is given:

Example 4.—Using the curves of Fig. 90, determine the permeabilities of cast iron, cast steel, and silicon steel for flux densities of 40,000, 70,000, and 80,000 lines of force per square inch, respectively. Check your results with the curves of Fig. 91.

Solution:

$$\mu_{(\text{cast iron})} = 0.313 \times \tfrac{40,000}{57} = 220$$
$$\mu_{(\text{cast steel})} = 0.313 \times \tfrac{70,000}{17.5} = 1,255$$
$$\mu_{(\text{silicon steel})} = 0.313 \times \tfrac{80,000}{12.5} = 2,000$$

Pull Exerted by an Electromagnet.—An electromagnet such as that shown in Fig. 83 will exert an attractive force upon a block of iron when the open ends of the former are placed flat against the latter. Since there is always an air space, usually called *air gap*, between the surfaces, the lines of force must cross it in passing from one iron section to the other. *And it is in this air gap that the attractive force is created.* To explain this action it is necessary to assign an important property to the imaginary lines of force, namely, that property which tends to make them contract and become as short as possible. Obviously, since the air gap is the only place in the magnetic circuit where the lines can become shorter by pulling the surfaces together, a force of attraction exists there.

Theory and experiment have shown that the pull is proportional to two factors, these being (1) the square of the air-gap flux density, and (2) the total contact area between the electromagnet and lifted iron surfaces. When practical units are used, the equation is

$$\text{Pull (pounds)} = \frac{\mathcal{B}^2 \times A}{72{,}000{,}000} \tag{36}$$

where $\mathcal{B}$ = air-gap flux density in lines per square inch
A = total surface area in square inches

In order to illustrate how the above equation is applied, three examples will be given.

Example 5.—Referring to Fig. 83*b*, determine the total pull exerted by the U-type electromagnet if the air-gap flux density is 50,000 lines per square inch and each of the pole faces is 2 × 3 in.

Solution:

$$\text{Pull} = \frac{\overline{50{,}000}^2 \times 6 \times 2}{72{,}000{,}000} = 417 \text{ lb.}$$

Example 6.—Referring to Fig. 83*c*, determine the total pull exerted by the E-type electromagnet if the air-gap flux density is uniform throughout at 70,000 lines per square inch and the two outer faces are 1.5 × 2 in. while the center face is 3 × 2 in.

Solution:

$$\text{Pull} = \frac{\overline{70{,}000}^2 \times (3 + 3 + 6)}{72{,}000{,}000} = 817 \text{ lb.}$$

Example 7.—It is desired to construct a U-type electromagnet like that shown in Fig. 83*b* with silicon-steel sheets to produce a pull of 160 lb. Standard laminations are to be used where pole ends have a width of 0.75 in. Assuming that the exciting coil can be designed to produce an air-gap density of 80,000 lines per square inch, determine how many sheets must be used if the laminations can be stacked 36 to the inch.

Solution:

$$\text{Pull} = \frac{\mathcal{B}^2 A}{72{,}000{,}000}; \quad 160 = \frac{\overline{80{,}000}^2 \times A^*}{72{,}000{,}000}$$

$$A = \frac{160 \times 72{,}000{,}000}{\overline{80{,}000}^2} = 1.8 \text{ sq. in.}$$

Area of one pole face $= \frac{1.8}{2} = 0.9$ sq. in.
Stacking length $= \frac{0.9}{0.75} = 1.2$
Number of laminations $= 1.2 \times 36 = 43$

Determining the Number of Ampere Turns for an Electromagnet.—The exciting coil or coils on an electromagnet magnetize *three* parts of a magnetic circuit: (1) the electromagnet core, (2) the lifted block of iron, and (3) the air gaps. In order to determine the total number of ampere turns required for this excitation it is necessary to consider each part separately, after which a simple addition is made. Refer to Fig. 92, and assume that the flux densities in the electromagnet core, the air gaps, and the lifted iron are known. It is further assumed that the grades of iron are known and their magnetization curves are available. With this information the procedure should be as follows:

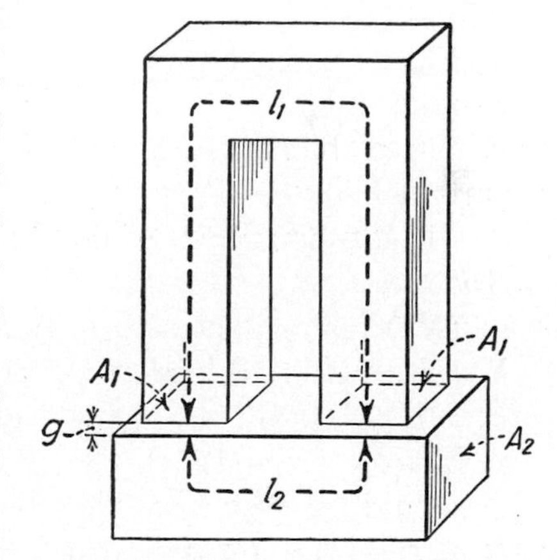

Fig. 92.—U-type core and crosspiece.

1. Determine the average length of the flux path l_1 in the electromagnet core.

2. Determine the average length of the flux path l_2 in the lifted block of iron.

3. Determine as accurately as possible the length of the air gap g—if this is difficult to measure make a reasonable estimate.

*A is the area of both pole faces.

4. Refer to the magnetization curve for the material used in the electromagnet core and pick off the number of ampere turns per inch for the known flux density; multiply this number by l_1.

5. Do the same thing for the lifted block as in (4).

6. To determine the number of ampere turns required for the air gaps, use the equation

$$(NI)_g = 0.313\ \mathcal{B}_g \times 2g \qquad (37)$$

where $(NI)_g$ = total ampere turns for both air gaps
$\mathcal{B}_g$ = air-gap flux density
$2g$ = length of both air gaps

7. Add together the ampere turns calculated in (4), (5), and (6).

Example 8.—It is desired to determine the total number of ampere turns required for an electromagnet such as that shown in Fig. 92, given the following information:

a. $l_1 = 8$ in., $l_2 = 3$ in., $g = \frac{1}{64}$ in. (0.016 in. approximately).

b. Electromagnet core is silicon steel and $\mathcal{B} = 85{,}000$ lines per square inch.

c. Lifted block is cast steel and $\mathcal{B} = 75{,}000$ lines per square inch.

d. Air-gap density is 85,000 lines per square inch.

Solution:

a. (NI) for magnet core $= 19 \times 8 = 152$
b. (NI) for lifted block $= 21 \times 3 = 63$
c. $(NI)_g = 0.313 \times 85{,}000 \times (2 \times 0.016) = 853$
d. Total $(NI) = 152 + 63 + 853 = 1{,}068$

It should be clear from the above example that the major part of the total ampere turns are required for the air gaps, and this is especially true when high grades of magnetic steel are used in the magnetic circuit.

Determining the Wire Size and the Number of Turns for an Electromagnet.—After the total number of ampere turns that must be used for an electromagnet is calculated, as outlined in the previous section, the next step is to determine the size of wire and the number of turns. To do this it is necessary to know four things: (1) the number of ampere turns per coil, (2) the voltage impressed across the coil, (3) the average length of each turn of wire, and (4) the actual dimensions of the winding space of the coil. In Fig. 93, which represents a coil of wire wound over a rectangular form, the winding space is $h \times w$, where h is the height of each winding layer and w is the width or thickness of the coil. The average length of each turn can be readily estimated as indicated in the sketch. The size of the wire in circular mils may now be calculated by using the formula

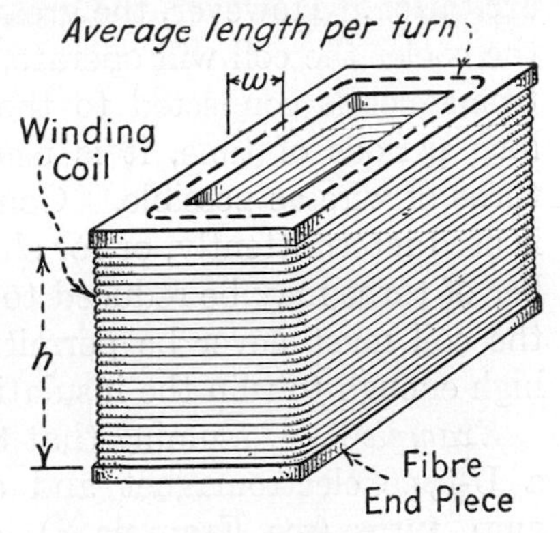

FIG. 93.—Exciting coil for an electromagnet.

$$C.M. = \frac{(NI) \times (\text{A. T. L.})}{E_c} \tag{38}$$

where $C.M.$ = circular-mil area of wire required
NI = ampere turns per coil
A.T.L. = average length per turn
E_c = volts impressed across the coil

After the circular-mil area has been found, Table II (page 28) should be consulted and the nearest wire size to this area selected, although it is usually customary to choose the next larger wire when the calculated size does not fall near a standard number. After the wire is chosen, the next step is to look up the column giving the number of turns that can be placed in each square inch of winding space (Table II, column 7 or 12) when the wires are carefully placed side by side and in uniform layers. This number from the table, then multiplied by the winding space area $h \times w$, will give the number of turns of wire in the coil.

Actually, the size of the wire and the voltage across the coil are the only factors that will affect the ampere turns. The *number of turns* of wire has practically no effect upon the excitation. However, the greater the number of turns used, the cooler the coil will operate, and vice versa. If the electromagnet is connected to the source continuously, or for long periods of time, it is usually safer to wind as many turns of wire as possible. Conversely, if the electromagnet is used intermittently, or for short periods of time, the number of turns may be reduced to save copper. In any event, the coil must never be permitted to attain a temperature high enough to ruin the insulation.

Example 9.—Assuming that two coils are to be wound for a U-type electromagnet and each one must develop 534 amp. turns (see Example 8), calculate the size of wire to be used and the number of turns of wire for a battery voltage of 6 volts. The average length of each turn is 7 in., h is 2.25 in., and w is 0.5 in.

Solution:

$$a.\ C.M. = \frac{534 \times 7}{3} = 1{,}250$$

Use No. 19 wire, which has 1,288 *C.M.*

b. Total turns per coil

Plain enamel = $718 \times 2.25 \times 0.5 = 810$

Formex wire = $660 \times 2.25 \times 0.5 = 745$

Designing and Constructing an E-type Electromagnet.—An E-type electromagnet is extremely interesting because it can be used in a variety of ways to demonstrate the fundamental laws of magnetism and electromagnetism. Furthermore, if the core is laminated and of a good grade of magnetic sheet steel, it can be used to illustrate inductive effects and transformer action as well as generator and motor principles. It is for this reason that this section will be devoted to the complete design of a good electromagnet that will serve not only when connected to a direct-current source of supply but also when operated from any 60-cycle, 115-volt convenience outlet.

The author has designed and constructed many excellent electromagnets but has usually found it most convenient to purchase standard laminations from manufacturers of electrical equipment. These are accurate, die-cut sheets, usually of high-grade silicon steel, the saturation curves for which are likewise obtainable. Figure 94 shows several

FIG. 94.—Several sizes of E-type laminations punched by users of electrical sheets. (*Carnegie-Illinois Steel Corp.*)

typical E-type laminations of various sizes that are readily obtainable from electrical manufacturers and supply houses. The one selected for this project, and around which the design calculations will be made, has the dimensions indicated in Fig. 95. It is No. 28 gauge, having a thickness

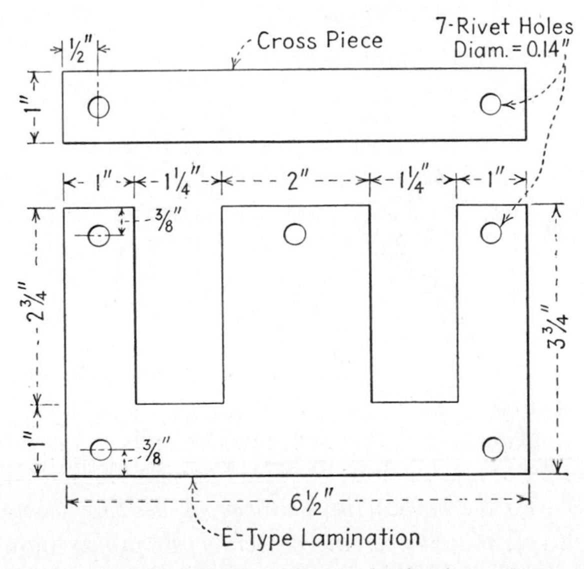

FIG. 95.—Dimensioned sketch of E-type lamination and crosspiece.

of 0.0155 in. The saturation and permeability curves are those labeled silicon steel in Figs. 90 and 91.

Let us proceed to design an E-type electromagnet that will exert a force of 600 lb. on a laminated crosspiece, with an air gap of 0.017 in., using a 12-volt storage battery for a source of supply. The problem will be divided into the five following major parts:

1. To determine the stacking length of the iron core.
2. To determine the number of laminated sheets required.
3. To determine the number of ampere turns needed.
4. To determine the size of wire to be used.
5. To determine the number of turns of wire in the coil that will be placed over the center section of the E core.

Part 1. *To determine the stacking length of the iron core.*

$$\text{Since } P \text{ (pounds)} = \frac{\mathcal{B}^2 A}{72{,}000{,}000} \text{ [Eq. (36)]},$$

$$\text{Total pole-face area} = \frac{P \times 72{,}000{,}000}{\mathcal{B}^2}$$

Assuming an air-gap flux density of 80,000 lines per square inch at all three pole faces,

$$A_{\text{total}} = \frac{600 \times 72{,}000{,}000}{6{,}400{,}000{,}000} = 6.75 \text{ sq. in.}$$

Since the center pole face has one-half of the total area and each of the outer pole faces has one-fourth of the total area, it follows that the center pole face has an area of 3.375 sq. in. Therefore, the stacking length is

$$\frac{3.375}{2} = 1.6875 \text{ in.} = 1\tfrac{11}{16} \text{ in.}$$

Part 2. *To determine the number of laminations (Fig. 95) required.*

Laminations stack 59 sheets to the inch. Therefore, the number of laminations required equals $1.6875 \times 59 = 100$.

Part 3. *To determine the number of ampere turns needed for a coil placed over the center leg to produce an air-gap density of 80,000 lines per square inch.*

In Fig. 95 there are two magnetic paths, like those shown in Fig. 83*c*. The estimated average length of each path is 12 in. Since the two magnetic paths are in parallel, the same ampere turns act on both. Assuming a stacking factor of 0.92, *i.e.*, 8 per cent spaces between laminations, the *iron* flux density will be

$$\frac{80{,}000}{0.92} = 87{,}000 \text{ lines per square inch}$$

From Fig. 90, NI per inch at 87,000 lines per square inch for silicon steel is 24. Therefore, NI for the iron is

$$12 \times 24 = 288 \text{ amp. turns}$$

NI for the two air gaps [Eq. (37)] is

$$0.313 \times 80{,}000 \times 0.034 = 852$$

The total number of ampere turns required is

$$288 + 852 = 1{,}140$$

Part 4. *To determine the size of wire required.*

When the average length of each turn is estimated, as in Fig. 93, by assuming that the coil thickness w is 1.25 in. and that the core dimensions, around which the coil must fit, are 2×1.75 in., it is found that A.T.L. = 12.5 in. From Eq. (38),

$$C.M. = \frac{1{,}140 \times 12.5}{12} = 1{,}190$$

Part 5. *To determine the number of turns for the coil.*

From Table II, it is found that No. 19 Formex wire can be wound 660 turns to the square inch. Assuming h to be 1.5 in. and w to be 1.25 in. (see Fig. 93), it is found that the total number of turns that can be wound in this space is

$$1.5 \times 1.25 \times 660 = 1{,}235$$

However, allowing for insulating paper between the layers and for final taping, the coil should have about 1,100 *turns*. The number of feet of wire in the coil will be approximately

$$\begin{aligned} \text{A.T.L.} \times \text{number of turns} &= 12.5 \times 1{,}100 \\ &= 13{,}700 \text{ in.} = 1{,}150 \text{ ft.} \end{aligned}$$

The assembly of the core should be done carefully. The laminations must be squeezed tightly in a press before the rivets are flattened down securely. If this is not done, the laminations will vibrate noisily when the exciting coil is connected to an alternating-current source. Finally, the core should preferably be placed on a surface grinder and the faces ground perfectly flat. A glass-smooth finish for both the E core and the crosspiece will improve the electromagnet

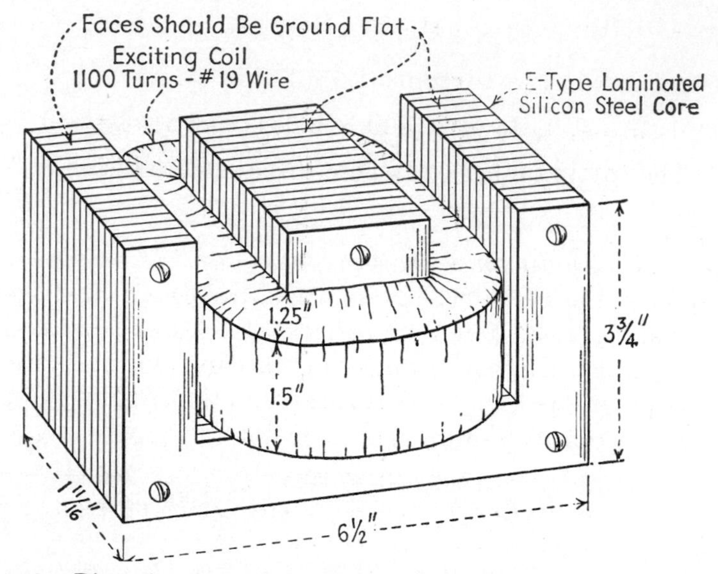

Fig. 96.—Dimensioned sketch showing assembled E-type core electromagnet with exciting winding on the center leg.

tremendously and make it superior to one having rough, uneven surfaces. In fact, it is not advisable to use the assembly unless this procedure is followed. Figure 96 is a sketch showing the assembled electromagnet.

The Alternating-current Electromagnet.—When the exciting coil of an electromagnet is connected to a constant direct-current source, the only heating that takes place is that due to the wire resistance, *i.e.*, I^2R. There is practically no heating of the iron except that which is conducted from the coil to the core. However, if the exciting coil is connected to an alternating-current source, the iron *does* become hot. There are two reasons for this heating, namely, magnetic action and electromagnetic action (Chap. 8). It is obvious, therefore, that *the iron-core heating must be directly traceable to energy losses within the iron itself.* The first heat loss results because the tiny magnetic molecules are being rapidly jerked around from one direction to the opposite direction as the polarity changes with the changing current direction; this is called *hysteresis loss,* and that which causes it is known as *hysteresis.* The second heat loss is due to the fact that the iron core is itself in a magnetic field that is continually changing in direction and magnitude, as a result of which voltages are generated in the iron. And since these induced voltages act upon closed, low-resistance iron paths, currents will flow in eddies very much like the whirling eddies in a whirlpool. Such currents are known as *eddy* currents.

Because both hysteresis and eddy currents occur in the iron core only where the flux is created and only when alternating current is used, it is logical to expect that the values of the frequency and the flux density will largely determine the *amount* of heating. In fact, experiment has shown that the heat loss due to hysteresis is practically proportional to the *square* of the flux density in the iron core in lines of force per square inch[1] and *directly* proportional to the frequency; the heat loss due to eddy currents is proportional to the square of both the flux density and the frequency. One other factor, the quality or grade of iron, is responsible for a part of the hysteresis loss only, while another, the thickness of the laminations, partially influences the eddy currents only. The latter point is an extremely important one, because it indicates very definitely that *eddy currents are absolutely independent of the quality of the core material* (it may even be a nonmagnetic substance), whereas *laminating the core has no effect whatsoever upon the hysteresis loss.* Or, to put it another way, eddy currents are reduced by laminating, whereas

[1]Actually, the hysteresis loss is proportional to $\mathcal{B}^{1.6}$.

hysteresis is minimized by employing high-quality magnetic steel.

In most well-designed alternating-current electromagnets the hysteresis loss represents about two thirds of the total heat loss in the core (called *core loss*), while one third goes into eddy-current heating. For 60-cycle service, where a fairly good grade of silicon-steel sheets is used (thickness of laminations about 0.015 in.), the loss per pound of iron may vary between 1 and 3 or 4.

Two very interesting experiments can be performed with an electromagnet similar to that shown in Fig. 96 to demonstrate the effects of both hysteresis and eddy currents. If a solid crosspiece of iron is placed over the upright leg of the laminated E-type core, it will be noted that the latter remains comparatively cool, whereas the former will become very hot in a few minutes; the wetted finger will sizzle if it is touched for an instant to the heated block of iron. Both hysteresis and eddy currents are responsible for this heating. However, if a copper trough containing some water is placed over the upright legs, the copper will become very hot and the water will soon begin to boil; this heating is due to eddy currents only.

There are several important differences in operation between alternating-current electromagnets and those connected to a direct-current source. First, there is this iron-core heating, already discussed, which exists only when alternating current is used. It is for this reason that the cores of alternating-current electromagnets *must* be laminated; they need not be if direct current is used, although they often are. In the second place, alternating-current electromagnets vibrate, chatter, or "hum" and frequently do so quite annoyingly; this is never so when the coil is energized with direct current. There are generally two reasons for this noise: (1) the laminations vibrate because it is difficult to rivet them tightly together, and (2) the lifted piece vibrates in the small air gap as the value of the alternating current passes through zero twice per cycle. A third difference is the fact that an alternating-current electromagnet requires a much higher voltage to produce a given flux density than that necessary for direct-current operation. For example, the electromagnet illustrated in Fig. 96 will operate satisfactorily when connected to a 12-volt storage battery but will draw less current and develop considerably less pull if the source is 120 volts, 60 cycles. A fourth difference is an extremely interesting one; if a nonmagnetic metal such as copper or aluminum is placed over the pole faces of the electromagnet, it is unaffected when direct current is used but becomes very hot if the coil is connected to an alternating-current supply. Furthermore, with alternating current the copper or aluminum will experience a considerable force of repulsion. In fact, it will be found rather difficult to hold down the copper trough, mentioned above, because of this repelling tendency.

Uses of Permanent Magnets and Electromagnets.—Electricity and magnetism are inseparable and are certainly responsible in large measure for the widespread use of electrical energy. Although other electrical effects, previously discussed, are indeed important and widely applied, it should be remembered that magnetic and electromagnetic phenomena are nearly always responsible for the operation of dynamic devices and machines. Magnetic and electromagnetic effects create forces, both great and small, that are under complete control of the operator. And it is because we understand the laws governing magnetism that we can build mechanisms, often quite complicated, to perform so many useful operations for us.

In order to emphasize the importance of magnets and electromagnets, the following list of applications is given. Far from complete, it illustrates, nevertheless, the great variety of uses.

TABLE XI

Permanent-magnet Uses

1. Direct-current generators (up to several kilowatts)
2. Direct-current motors (up to several horsepower)
3. Blowout for arcs
4. Polarized relays
5. Electrical measuring instruments
6. Radio loudspeakers (magnetic type)
7. Telephone receivers
8. Transmitter microphones
9. Phonograph pickups
10. Recording heads for sound recorders
11. Compasses
12. Tack hammers
13. Speedometers and tachometers
14. Magnetic chucks
15. Magnetic jigs
16. Magnetic separators
17. Magnetic detectors
18. Braking action for watt-hour meters
19. Seismograph instruments
20. Tension-producing devices (replacing springs to produce quick make-and-break in electric circuits)
21. Motion devices acting through seals (flow meters and packingless drives)
22. Magnetos
23. Oscillographs
24. Flux meters
25. Cardiograph recorders
26. Vibration pickups
27. Coin separators for vending machines
28. Clocks
29. Magnetic oil filters
30. Hearing aids
31. Voltage regulators
32. Damping devices
33. Conveyers
34. Toys and novelties

Electromagnet Uses

1. Direct-current and alternating-current generators
2. Direct-current and alternating-current motors
3. Circuit breakers
4. Relays for automatic-control equipment
5. Electrical measuring instruments
6. Radio loudspeakers (dynamic type)
7. Telephone receivers
8. Telegraph relays and sounders
9. Bells, buzzers, chimes
10. Brakes for hoists, cranes, and elevators
11. Track brakes for streetcars
12. Lifting magnets
13. Electric shavers
14. Vibrators
15. Voltage regulators (Tirrill type)
16. Cyclotrons
17. Holding coils for motor starters
18. Automatic carbon feed mechanisms for arc lights
19. Automatic selector switches in telephone exchanges
20. Magnetic chucks
21. Magnetic clutches

Experiment 16. Electromagnet Polarity

Objectives: To determine the polarity of an E-type electromagnet when it is excited with (*a*) a single coil over the center leg, (*b*) a single coil over one of the outer two legs, (*c*) two coils, one on each of the outer legs.

Procedure: For the purposes of this experiment it will be necessary to have an E-type core. If an electromagnet like that shown in Fig. 96 is available, its coil should be removed or completely disregarded. An ordinary good

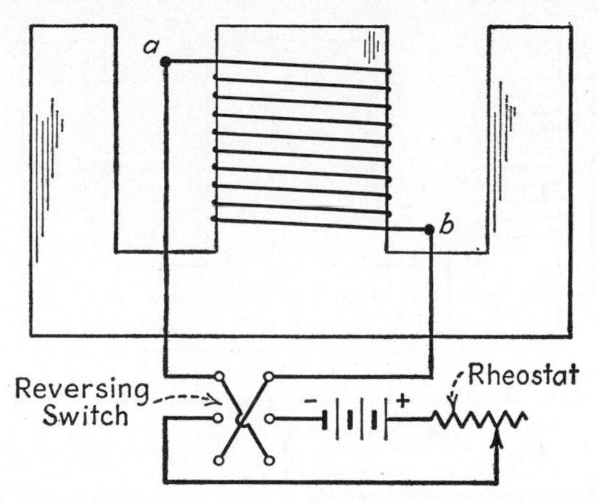

Fig. 97.—E-type core with exciting coil on the center leg.

pocket compass will also be needed, which should be tested to determine its *north pole.* (The point of the compass that points in a northerly direction is the *north-seeking* or *north pole.*)

Part 1. Wrap about 20 turns of insulated copper wire (No. 18 bell wire is satisfactory) around the center leg of the E core. Be sure to note carefully the direction in which the wire is wrapped so that the current direction may be readily traced after the coil is connected to a battery. The ends of the coil should next be connected to a three-cell battery and a rheostat through a reversing switch (see Fig. 97).

With the switch closed in one direction, *up,* for example,

the positive terminal of the battery would be connected to *a*; when the switch is closed in the opposite direction, *down*, *b* would be connected to the positive terminal. For each switch position, slowly and carefully bring the compass first near the center pole face, then to each of the outer pole faces in turn. Note particularly that when the center leg is *north*, both of the outer legs will be south; when the center leg is south, both of the outer legs will be *north*.

To test the relationship between magnet polarity and direction of current flow, apply the right-hand rule

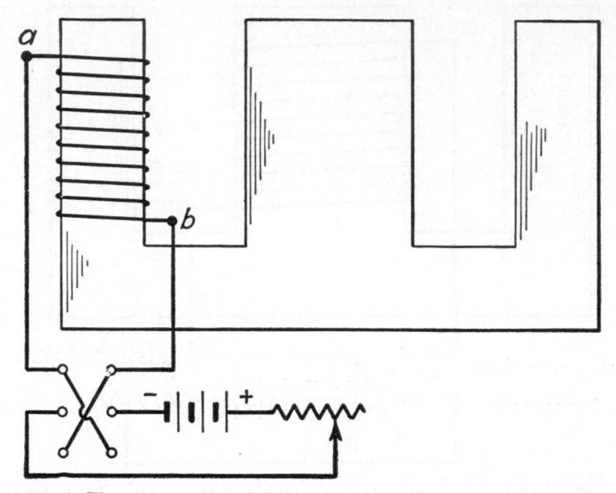

Fig. 98.—E-type core with exciting coil on one outside leg.

(pages 191–192), verifying the law for both positions of the switch.

Part 2. Remove the coil from the center leg, straighten the wire, and proceed to wrap about 24 or more turns around one of the outer legs. Similarly, connect this coil to a reversing switch, a rheostat, and a three-cell battery (see Fig. 98).

Again determine the polarity of the three pole faces, first for one position of the reversing switch and then for the other position. And, as before, check the polarity of the pole around which the coil is wound by the right-hand rule.

It will be interesting to observe that, when the pole around which the coil is wrapped is *north*, the center leg and the other outer leg will be *south poles*; when the pole around which the coil is wound is *south*, both of the other two poles will be *north*. Furthermore, the center pole will be stronger than the unwrapped outer pole.

Part 3. Without disturbing the outer coil of Part 2, wrap an identical coil around the other outer leg. Next, connect both of these coils to the three-cell battery through a reversing switch as shown in Fig. 99. With this arrangement both coils will be in series with either position of the reversing switch, but in one position, to the left, the left leg will be north while the right leg will be south; in the other position, to the right, both outer legs will become north poles. Again test the polarities of the electromagnet with the compass and verify these observations by applying the right-hand rule.

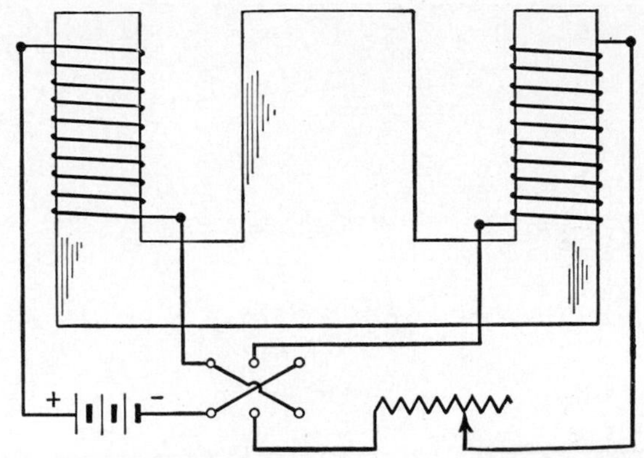

FIG. 99.—E-type core with exciting coils on the two outside legs.

As a further extension of this important experiment it will be worth while to draw sketches showing the flux paths for all six combinations, two for each part. Consult Fig. 89 as a guide for such procedure.

EXPERIMENT 17. FLUX-DISTRIBUTION PATTERNS

Objective: To observe and study the flux patterns surrounding the poles of an E-type electromagnet, using iron filings carefully sprinkled on a sheet of cardboard placed over the pole faces.

Procedure: Following exactly the same arrangements as those described in Experiment 16, performing Parts 1, 2, and 3 in order, place a sheet of heavy cardboard or glass on top of the pole faces before the switch is closed. Adjust the current in the circuit to a comparatively low value, using the rheostat for this purpose. Next sprinkle dry,

FIG. 100.—Arrangement of apparatus to observe flux patterns produced by E-type electromagnet. Exciting coil placed on center leg. Iron filings carefully sprinkled on sheet of paper placed on top of E core.

finely divided iron filings over the sheet, carefully dropping small bits in much the same way as one would sprinkle salt with the thumb and forefinger. After covering the area over and near the three pole faces, gently tap the sheet and observe how the filings arrange themselves in symmetrical patterns in accordance with the fictitious lines of force discussed in this chapter. Note particularly, for all six combinations, how the filings tend to bunch themselves near the pole-face edges, being thickest near those poles where the flux densities are greatest. Figure 100 shows a photograph taken for the flux pattern surrounding the poles with a single exciting coil over the center leg.

Experiment 18. Effect of Air Gap upon Force Exerted by Electromagnet

Objective: To observe how the air gap at the pole-face surfaces affects the number of ampere turns required by an electromagnet when the latter must exert a given force.

Procedure: Using any well-constructed electromagnet having pole faces and a crosspiece ground perfectly smooth (one similar to that previously described and illustrated in Fig. 96 will give excellent results), connect a circuit like that indicated in Fig. 101. Note that a slide-wire

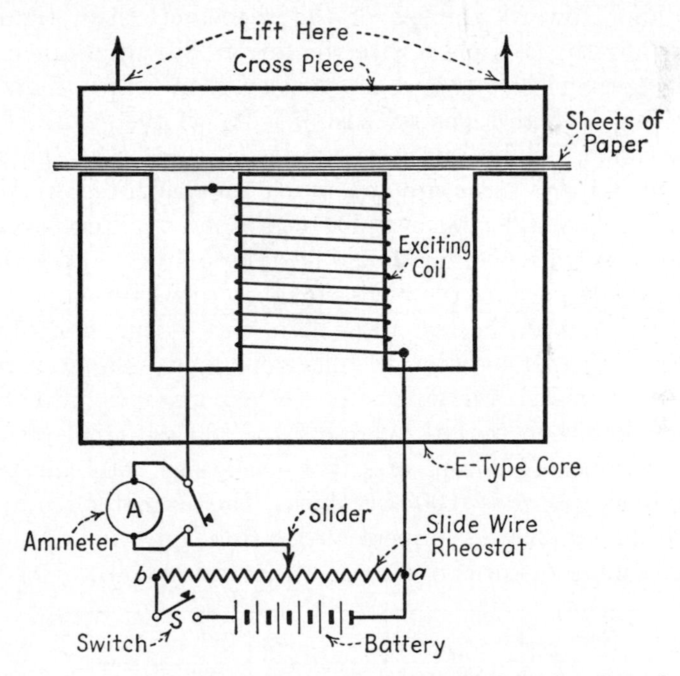

Fig. 101.—Wiring diagram for testing procedure, to show the effect of an air gap on the strength of an electromagnet.

rheostat is used so that the the current through the exciting coil can be accurately adjusted from *zero* to any desired value, this latter being determined by the battery voltage and the coil resistance. If the design of Fig. 96

is used and the coil is excited from a 12-volt battery, the current will be adjustable from zero to about 1.25 amp. Several strips of ordinary writing paper should next be cut so that each will totally cover the upper surface of the electromagnet.

With switch *S* open and the slider moved to *a* on the rheostat, place one of the sheets of paper over the pole-face surfaces. Carefully lay the crosspiece on the paper so that it lines up with the pole faces. Now close the switch *S* and open the ammeter switch. The ammeter should register zero. Very slowly move the slider a short distance toward point *b* of the rheostat; then, tightly grasping the crosspiece with the fingers, lift up an inch or so. If the electromagnet *drops down*, it indicates that the exciting ampere turns are insufficient; if the entire electromagnet can be raised *easily*, it indicates that the exciting ampere turns are too much for the lifted weight. Moving the slider one way or the other, making several trials, the experimenter should be able to find that position which *just* permits the electromagnet to be raised.

Next, repeat the test using two, three, four, and more sheets of paper between the electromagnet pole faces and the crosspiece, carrying on the experiment until the slider has been moved over to *b*. For each trial, record the number of sheets of paper used, the total air gap (ordinary paper is 0.003 in. thick), the ammeter reading, and the calculated ampere turns (multiply amperes by the number of turns of wire in the exciting coil).

No. of sheets of paper	Gap length	Amperes	Ampere turns

Since the weight lifted throughout this test was the same, it should be clear that (1) the air-gap flux density remained substantially constant during the entire experiment, and (2) for constant flux density in the air gap the number of ampere turns required for excitation must be increased as the air-gap length is increased.

Experiment 19. Adjusting the Excitations of Several Coils to Produce Complete Demagnetization of Iron Core

Objective: To adjust the excitations on the three legs of an E-type electromagnet so that those on the outer two legs *completely nullify* the effect of the coil on the center leg.

Fig. 102.—E-type electromagnet with crosspiece, shown with exciting coils placed over all three legs. All coils are wound in the same direction to simplify connections for proper polarity.

Procedure: For this experiment it will be desirable to have a good E-type core, similar to the one described previously, and three special coils. Figure 102 shows an arrangement that the author has used successfully for this and many other extremely interesting experiments. Each coil contains 344 turns of No. 17 Formex wire wound in 8 layers with 43 turns per layer. The construction of these coils, in addition to the one already suggested in Fig. 96, will prove worth while. With them it will be possible to perform many kinds of experiments, demonstrating important principles of electromagnetism, transformer action, three-wire circuits, inductance effects, generator and motor operation, and others.

Set up a circuit like that shown in Fig. 103, using one

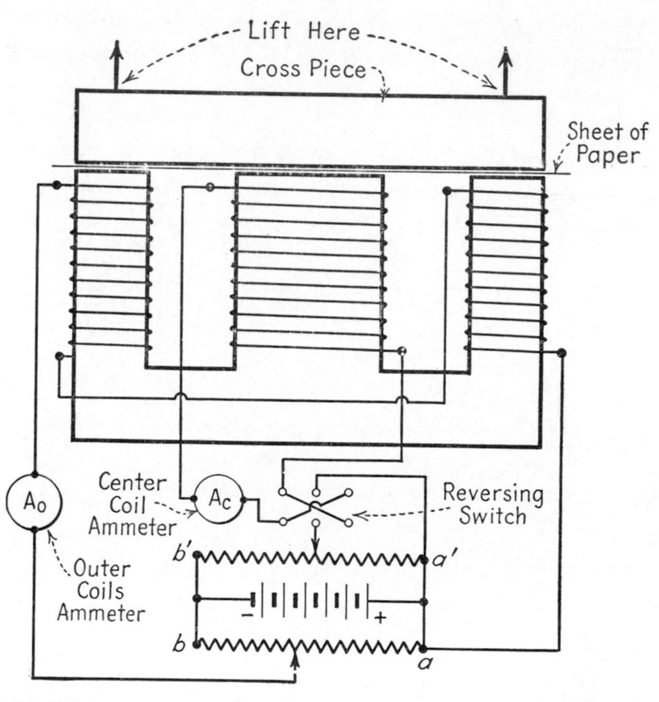

Fig. 103.—Wiring diagram showing method used to demagnetize core completely, using three coils and E-type core.

slide-wire rheostat, a reversing switch, and an ammeter A_c for the *center* coil and one slide-wire rheostat and an ammeter A_o for the *outer* series-connected coils. Note that outer coils are so connected that their polarities will always be the same (south in the sketch), and that the center pole will be either north *or* south depending upon the position of the reversing switch (south when thrown left and north when thrown right).

Move the sliders to a and a'; then close the reversing switch to either side. After placing a sheet or two of paper over the pole-face surfaces, test the electromagnet with the crosspiece to see if the former is unmagnetized; it should be possible to raise the crosspiece quite easily since the exciting current will be zero for all three coils. (The paper serves to prevent sticking due to residual magnetism.)

Next, increase the exciting current to some reasonable value, say, 0.5 amp., in the outer coils by moving the lower slider toward b. Under this condition there will be a considerable force of attraction, and it will easily be possible to raise the entire electromagnet by lifting the crosspiece. Record the value of the current in ammeter A_o and calculate the number of ampere turns.

Now increase the current in the center coil to about twice the value in the outer coils. If, for example, the outer poles become south and the center pole becomes north, the force of attraction will be much greater. However, if the center pole is also south, the force of attraction will be much less. Also, by applying the right-hand rule it will be possible to predict in advance what the polarities of all three poles will be. Proceeding next to close the reversing switch so that the *polarities* of all three legs are *alike*, make several current adjustments in the center coil, for each of which the force in the crosspiece should be tested. When the experimenter finds that the crosspiece can be raised quite easily, feeling no appreciable pull, it may be assumed that the E core is practically demagnetized. When this condition is finally achieved, record the current in the center coil A_c and calculate the total number of ampere turns.

If the center pole-face area is exactly equal to the sum of the two outer pole-face areas, it will be found that almost complete demagnetization of the E core will occur when the ampere turns on the center coil exactly equal the total ampere turns on both outer coils. In the construction of Fig. 96 such symmetry has been planned, since the width of the center leg is 2 in. while each of the outer legs is 1 in. wide.

Experiment 20. Heating Effect of Simultaneous Action of Hysteresis and Eddy Currents

Objective: To observe the heating effect of hysteresis and eddy currents upon a solid block of iron when the exciting coil is energized with alternating current.

Procedure: This experiment will require the use of a laminated U-type or E-type electromagnet with a solid crosspiece of cast iron or steel to fit across the open ends. For the best results the contact surfaces should be perfectly smooth, preferably ground flat. The design of Fig. 96 will be quite satisfactory.

Excite the coil with alternating current of any standard frequency. In the case of Fig. 96, a 115-volt, 50- or 60-cycle source is desirable. If a 25-cycle source is used, the voltage should be about 60. In a short time the solid iron crosspiece will become very hot although the laminated core will remain quite cool. A wetted finger quickly touched to the heated solid iron will sizzle in much the same way as it would if touched to a heated flatiron. Also, drops of water sprinkled on the heated iron will turn to steam instantly.

It should be clearly understood that the heating of the solid iron is due to both hysteresis and eddy currents; the hysteresis heating results because the iron is of poor magnetic quality, while the eddy-current heating takes place because the iron is not laminated.

Experiment 21. Heating Effect of Eddy Currents Only

Objective: To observe the heating effect of eddy currents upon a copper trough filled with water when it is placed on an electromagnet excited with alternating current.

Procedure: This experiment will require the use of a rectangular copper trough made to fit on the pole faces of a laminated U-type or E-type electromagnet. Such a trough can be made from a flat piece of copper, about $\frac{1}{8}$ in. thick, with corners cut out and the sides and ends turned up about $\frac{3}{8}$ in. Figure 104 shows a photograph of a satisfactory arrangement with three coils supplying the

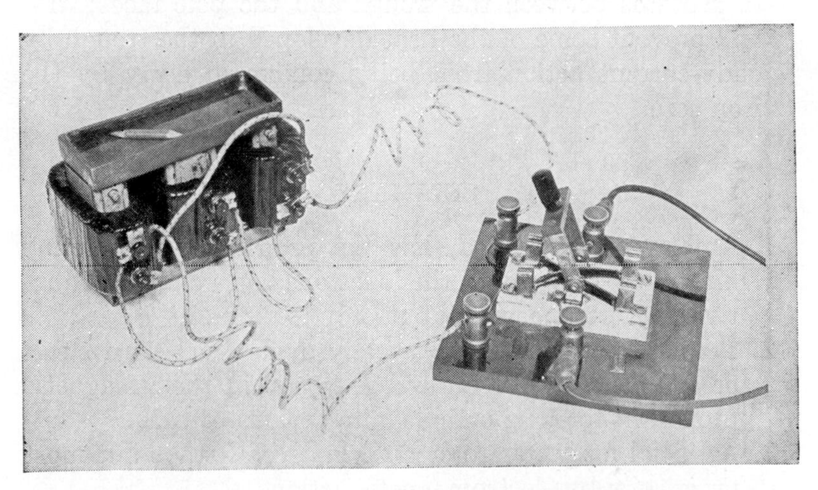

FIG. 104.—Arrangement of apparatus to perform an experiment demonstrating the effect of eddy currents upon a copper trough filled with water.

excitation. The same wiring as that used in Experiment 19, Fig. 103, can be employed here. Before proceeding it will be necessary to recognize the following important points: (1) 60-cycle alternating current should be used, although a higher frequency is preferable, if available; (2) the polarity of the outer two legs in an E-type electromagnet should be the same, and opposite to the center-leg polarity; (3) a small block of wood should be placed on top of the trough and pressed down firmly to prevent its being pushed aside by electromagnetic-force action; (4) the current in the exciting coils should be adjusted to as high a value as possible without permitting the coils to become too hot.

With everything ready and the trough about half full of water (note the pencil floating in the water in Fig. 104), switch on the current. After several minutes the trough will begin to get hot, and with it the water. Soon the water will begin to boil and steam will be seen to rise.

The above heating will take about 5 min. or more. If greater speed of heating is desired, place a thin sheet of asbestos between the trough and the pole faces; this will prevent some of the heat developed in the trough by eddy-current action from being conducted away by the iron core.

SUMMARY

1. Amber, when rubbed, has the property of attracting bits of paper or chaff; the lodestone has a similar attractive property naturally but only for iron.
2. Permanent magnets are usually made from hard steels or special alloys of steel. They retain their magnetic properties for long or indefinite periods of time.
3. Artificial magnets are created in several ways but most practically by electromagnetic action.
4. A magnetic field surrounds a current-carrying wire, its strength diminishing as the distance from the wire surface increases.
5. The earth is generally regarded as a magnet since it acts upon a compass in the same way as does a permanent magnet.
6. The term "lines of force," suggested by Michael Faraday, conveniently represents the stressed space or field surrounding magnets. Such lines of force are continuous but are called *tubes* of force within the magnetic substance.
7. Like poles of two magnets repel; unlike poles attract.
8. The greatest field intensity always occurs at the magnet pole surface where the lines of force enter or leave the surrounding space.

9. Lines of force are assumed to leave a north pole and enter a south pole.
10. Symmetrically constructed and excited electromagnets always create symmetrical field patterns.
11. A magnetic field always tends to arrange itself so that the greatest number of lines of force is created.
12. The right-hand rule for determining the direction of the lines of force around a wire is extremely important. It should be studied and remembered.
13. Solenoids produce stronger magnetic fields than straight wires. When a magnetic substance is inserted within a solenoid, still stronger fields are created.
14. The right-hand rule for determining the polarity of a solenoid or electromagnet is extremely important. It should be studied and remembered.
15. Air is the poorest of all conductors of magnetic lines of force.
16. Four factors determine the strength of an electromagnet: (*a*) design and construction, (*b*) its physical size, (*c*) the number of ampere turns used for excitation, and (*d*) the quality or grade of the core material.
17. Strictly speaking, the strength of a given electromagnet will depend only upon the size of wire used for the exciting coil, assuming a fixed impressed voltage.
18. For a given size of wire used on an electromagnet, the heat loss decreases as the number of turns is increased.
19. Two parallel current-carrying wires will exert a force upon each other. If the currents are in the same direction, the force will be one of attraction; if the currents are in opposite directions, the force will be one of repulsion.
20. If two electromagnets are parallel but not collinear, they will attract each other if the currents flow in the opposite directions in the two coils; they will repel each other if the currents in both coils are in the same direction.
21. A magnetization curve, often called a *saturation* curve, represents the relation between magnetizing force, in

ampere turns, required per inch of the material magnetized and the degree of magnetization, usually expressed in lines of force per square inch.

22. Saturation implies that further increase in magnetizing force results in little or no change in the flux density developed in a magnetic substance.
23. "Permeability" is a term used to express the value of a material as a magnetic substance when compared with air. The permeability of air is unity; that of magnetic substances may be several hundred, several thousand, or several tens of thousands.
24. The permeability of all magnetic substances changes with the flux density.
25. The pull exerted by an electromagnet is proportional to the square of the air-gap flux density and the total area of the pole faces.
26. The number of ampere turns required for the exciting coil on an electromagnet will depend upon (*a*) the air-gap flux density, (*b*) the air-gap length, (*c*) the flux densities in the various iron paths, and (*d*) the lengths of the various iron paths.
27. Alternating-current electromagnets usually chatter and "hum"; direct-current electromagnets do not.
28. Alternating-current electromagnets develop two kinds of core heating not present in direct-current electromagnets, namely, hysteresis heating and eddy-current heating.
29. Hysteresis is the property of a magnetic substance that causes the flux to lag behind the magnetizing force. Heating is caused only when the magnetizing force is changed, as with alternating current.
30. Eddy currents are created in any solid substance if it is placed in a changing or alternating magnetic field.
31. Hysteresis heating may be limited by using high grades of magnetic materials.
32. Eddy-current heating may be limited by laminating.

QUESTIONS

1. Distinguish between natural and artificial magnets; between temporary and permanent magnets.
2. In what respect is amber similar to a magnet? How do these substances differ?
3. Name the three magnetic elements.
4. Name several high-grade permanent-magnet materials.
5. How are permanent magnets made?
6. What is a magnetic field? Does such a field actually exist? What value does it possess?
7. What is the effect of a magnetic field upon a compass?
8. What is the direction of the magnetic field with respect to the polarity of a magnet?
9. What is a compass? Why is it useful? Explain its action on the earth's surface.
10. Distinguish between magnetic lines of force and lines of induction.
11. State the first law of magnetism concerning magnets.
12. Explain why the lines of force produced by a magnet are urged away from their normal distribution when a piece of iron is placed in a magnetic field.
13. State a law concerning magnetic fields that relates to the arrangement and the number of flux lines.
14. How may magnetic lines of force be represented visually? Explain.
15. What is an electromagnet? What advantages does it have when compared with permanent magnets?
16. State the rule for determining the direction of the field around a current-carrying wire.
17. State the rule for determining the polarity of an electromagnet.
18. Give four factors that determine the strength of an electromagnet.
19. Explain why the strength of an electromagnet can be increased only by a change in the size of the wire on the exciting coil, assuming a given impressed voltage.

20. Explain why the number of ampere turns doubles when the size of the wire on the exciting coil is changed by three gauge numbers.
21. What happens when two parallel wires carry currents in opposite directions? in the same direction? Explain.
22. What happens when two electromagnets are parallel (not collinear) and are excited by currents flowing through the coils in opposite directions? in the same direction?
23. Answer Ques. 22 for electromagnets placed end to end (collinear).
24. If two coils are used to excite a U-type electromagnet, how must the currents flow if a strong magnet is to be created? a weak magnet?
25. In an E-type electromagnet excited by a single coil on the center leg, what are the polarities of the three poles with respect to each other?
26. In an E-type electromagnet excited by a single coil on one of the outer legs, what are the polarities of the three poles with respect to each other?
27. What is meant by saturation when referring to a magnet?
28. What is a saturation curve? What value does it have in magnetic circuit calculations?
29. What is meant by permeability? Upon what factors does it depend?
30. Why is high permeability generally desirable?
31. Explain how the permeability can be determined from the saturation curve for a given value of flux density.
32. Upon what factors does the pull of an electromagnet depend?
33. Why is it important to have a small air gap in an electromagnet? What procedure should be followed to obtain a small air gap?
34. What effect does the number of turns of a given size of wire have upon the heating of an electromagnet?
35. Why do alternating-current electromagnets "hum"?

36. What is meant by hysteresis? Why is hysteresis heating developed in the core when alternating current is used?
37. What is generally done to limit hysteresis heating?
38. What is meant by eddy currents? Under what conditions do they exist?
39. How is it possible to limit the amount of eddy-current heating developed in the core?
40. What kind of action is responsible for hysteresis heating? for eddy-current heating?
41. Referring to Table XI, add several permanent-magnet and electromagnet uses to the list.

PROBLEMS

1. Make a sketch showing the flux distribution around a bar electromagnet.
2. Repeat Prob. 1 for a U-type electromagnet.
3. Repeat Prob. 1 for an E-type electromagnet with an exciting coil on (*a*) the center leg, (*b*) one of the outer legs.
4. An E-type electromagnet has a coil of 800 turns wound over the center leg. If its resistance is 4.5 ohms and it is connected to a 22.5-volt, direct-current source, how many ampere turns does it develop?
5. A U-type electromagnet has two similar exciting coils, each containing 240 turns. When connected in series-aiding, the two coils develop 1,200 amp. turns. (*a*) What current flows in the coils? (*b*) What is the resistance of each coil if the impressed direct-current voltage is 24?
6. Determine the number of ampere turns developed by the electromagnet of Prob. 5 if the voltage is 24 and the coils are connected in parallel-aiding.
7. In Prob. 5, what voltage should be used if the coils are to be connected in parallel-aiding and must develop 1,200 amp. turns?
8. Obtain an electric bell. Examine it carefully. Make a sketch showing the U-type core and the two exciting coils connected in series-aiding. Explain why the clapper vibrates when the coils are excited with direct current.

9. The coil of an electromagnet is wound with No. 20 wire and develops 750 amp. turns. Approximately how many ampere turns will be developed if the coils are rewound (*a*) with No. 19 wire, (*b*) with No. 22 wire? (Assume the same impressed direct-current voltage.)
10. Two wires are placed side by side, $\frac{1}{2}$ in. apart, and each one carries 500 amp. If the currents are in opposite directions, what will be the force per foot acting on the wires and what will be the direction of the force?
11. Referring to Fig. 90, determine the permeability of cast iron at 40,000 lines per square inch. Compare your result with the value given in Fig. 91.
12. Repeat Prob. 11 for cast steel at 70,000 lines per square inch.
13. Repeat Prob. 11 for silicon steel at 95,000 lines per square inches.
14. Referring to Fig. 91, determine the number of ampere turns required per inch of cast steel for maximum permeability (μ = 1,560).
15. Referring to Fig. 96, calculate the pull exerted by the electromagnet for an air-gap flux density of 60,000 lines per square inch.
16. Referring to Fig. 92, calculate the total number of ampere turns required for the electromagnet and the pull exerted, given the following particulars: $l_1 = 9$ in., $l_2 = 4.5$ in., $g = 0.003$ in., material = cast steel, flux density throughout = 60,000 lines per square inch, $A_1 = 2.5$ sq. in.
17. An electromagnet requires a total of 1,350 amp. turns to develop the proper air-gap flux density. If each turn of wire is 9 in. long and the impressed voltage is 24, determine the size of wire to be used on the exciting coil.
18. An electromagnet exerts a pull of 260 lb. when the exciting current is adjusted to yield an air-gap density of 40,000 lines per square inch. What will be the pull if the exciting current is increased to a value that establishes an air-gap density of 60,000 lines per square inch?

19. An electromagnet has two similar 5.25-ohm exciting coils, each wound with 550 turns of wire. When connected series-aiding to a 12-volt direct-current source, it develops a pull of 450 lb. (*a*) How much power is delivered to the winding? (*b*) What will be the pull and the power input if only one of the coils is connected to the 12-volt source?
20. What pull will be developed by the electromagnet of Prob. 19 if the coils are connected in parallel to a 12-volt direct-current source, assuming that the flux density increases only 20 per cent as much as the ampere turns?
21. Two long parallel conductors that are 3 in. apart carry equal currents of 600 amp. in opposite directions. Calculate the flux density $\mathcal{B}$, in lines per square inch, midway between the conductors, if it is known that $\mathcal{B}$ is proportional to the current in one wire and inversely proportional to one-half the distance, in inches, between the conductors.
22. What will be the flux density midway between the conductors of Prob. 21 if the currents in the wires are in the same direction?

CHAPTER 7

DIRECT-CURRENT MEASURING INSTRUMENTS

General Types and Uses of Measuring Instruments.—Experimental testing is undertaken to verify rules, principles, or laws or to determine how a piece of equipment behaves under operating conditions. Obviously, the information or data that are obtained from tests should be accurate and trustworthy; valid conclusions cannot be reached if the data are questionable. Many factors are responsible for the accuracy of the results of an experiment, but probably the most important of these is the precision of the electrical instruments used.

The two most commonly employed types of instrument in direct-current circuit testing are ammeters and voltmeters; from the indications on such instruments, properly inserted in circuits, it is possible to calculate the power ($P = E \times I$) and the resistance ($R = E/I$). Direct-reading instruments are sometimes used to measure the resistance of circuits; these are ohmmeters, Wheatstone bridges, and meggers, the latter for the determination of extremely high values of resistance and particularly insulation resistance. For the measurement of low values of e.m.f. with an extremely high degree of accuracy, and especially when the instrument must not draw current from the source of voltage that is measured, a potentiometer must be used. In alternating-current testing, for the measurement of power (watts), it is generally necessary to include a wattmeter; the latter, a sort of combination voltmeter-ammeter, may, and sometimes does, measure power in direct-current circuits. All electrical instruments can be made to have any desirable range, and some are constructed to have several ranges. In still other designs an instrument may be used as an ammeter *or* a voltmeter, the change from one to the other being readily accomplished by turning a selector switch.

Permanent-magnet Moving-coil Instrument.—The arrangement most common to present-day instruments for the measurement of current (amperes) and electromotive force (volts) is the *permanent-magnet moving-coil mechanism.* Generally referred to as the *D'Arsonval movement,* it represents the efforts of many persons over a period of more than 140 years of development. Based upon the application of fundamental principles of electric and magnetic circuits, it embodies numerous ingenious designs. Among those who should be cited for major contributions to this important phase of electrical instrumentation are the following:[1] Oersted (1819), who discovered the relation between a current of electricity and magnetism; Faraday (1821), who demonstrated that a current-carrying conductor would move when placed in a magnetic field; Ampère (1821), who worked out the mathematical laws that govern the strengths of currents; Sturgeon (1836), who first demonstrated that a current-carrying coil of wire would move (or rotate) if suspended in a magnetic field; Kelvin (1867), who placed a soft iron core in the center of the coil to shorten the air gap and thereby increase the sensitivity (deflection per unit current) of the device; D'Arsonval (1881), who, having developed the first practical measuring device, patented an instrument of this type; Weston (1888), who discovered that the factors that govern the permanency of a magnetic circuit are associated with the circuit rather than the magnet, added soft iron pole pieces to the magnet and current-carrying control springs, and made the first commercial permanent-magnet moving-coil instruments.

Although there have been no changes in theory and design since 1888 when Weston introduced his basically sound device, instruments of this type have been so greatly improved since then that they now give a pointer deflection of about $5\frac{1}{2}$ in. for a current of 0.005 milliampere (0.000,005

[1] See Appendix.

amp.) instead of the 1888 value of about 10 milliamperes (0.01 amp.).

Figure 105 illustrates the general constructional arrangement of the various parts of a modern type of D'Arsonval instrument. The assembly shows a coil of very fine wire wound on an extremely light aluminum frame accurately suspended in a magnetic field that is provided by a permanent magnet; the latter may be tungsten steel, cobalt steel, or Alnico. Since the degree of permanency of the magnet is

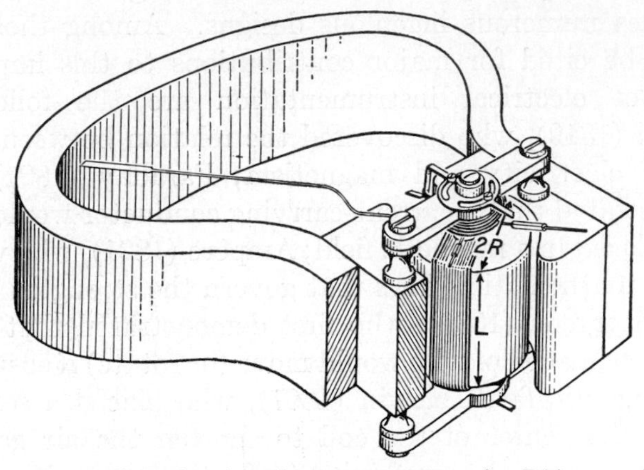

FIG. 105.—Illustration showing the construction of a D'Arsonval type of indicating instrument. (*Weston Electrical Instrument Corp.*)

an important factor in the sustained accuracy of such an instrument, this feature of the design has been thoroughly investigated. In addition to proper aging of such magnets it was discovered that the permanency is directly proportional to the length of the magnet steel and the cross-sectional area of the air gap, and inversely proportional to the cross-sectional area of the magnet steel and the length of the air gap. These basic principles are so well recognized that instrument manufacturers follow them carefully in their designs. It is customary to give the magnet its greatest length by making it follow the outside shape of the enclosing case.

The moving coil is suspended by two short pointed shafts fastened to the top and bottom of the frame, the ends of which rest in V-type sapphire bearings. In such double-pivoted instruments flat coil springs, wound in opposite directions and similar to watch hairsprings, are attached to the shaft extensions previously mentioned; the springs serve two important functions, namely, (1) as lead-in wires to conduct current into and out of the moving coil, and (2) to provide the countertorque against which the movement is

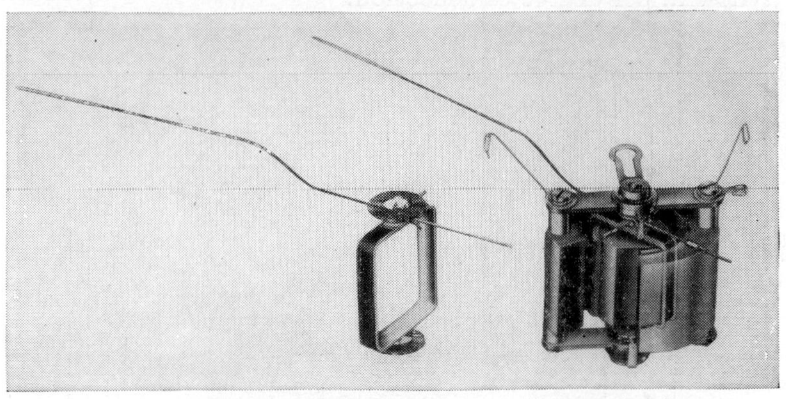

Fig. 106.—Coil assemblies for D'Arsonval type of measuring instrument. (*Weston Electrical Instrument Corp.*)

calibrated. When the zero setting is made both springs are given initial deflections so that they act against each other. Sketches showing the complete moving-coil assembly are given in Fig. 106.

When current is passed through the suspended coil, torque is developed; moreover, if the current is in the proper direction with respect to the magnetic polarities of the permanent-magnet poles, an upscale deflection will result. Since the force tending to turn the coil is proportional to the strength of the magnet and the ampere turns in the moving element, the torque, *i.e.*, turning moment, is proportional to both factors and is given by the formula

$$T = 0.2BNI \times RL \tag{39}$$

where T = torque in dyne-centimeters
B = flux density in air gap in lines per square centimeter
I = moving-coil current in amperes
R = radius of moving coil in centimeters (see Fig. 105)
L = axial length of moving coil in centimeters (see Fig. 105)

A Model 1 Weston instrument that has a movement weighing about 2 g. will develop a torque of approximately $3\frac{1}{2}$ dyne-cm. per degree of deflection.

Fig. 107.—Phantom view of direct-current instrument (ammeter or voltmeter). (*Weston Electrical Instrument Corp.*)

A phantom view of a modern permanent-magnet moving-coil (D'Arsonval type) instrument is shown in Fig. 107. It is basically a *torque motor* in which the torque developed by the moving coil (Eq. 39) is opposed by the restraining torque provided by spiral springs. In analyzing the torque actions by electromagnetic theory, assume that the polarity of the permanent magnet is *north* on the left and *south* on the right. When no current passes through the moving coil, the latter is set at rest at an angle of about 45 deg. with the vertical; in this position the light aluminum pointer, fastened to the coil, is adjusted to zero on the calibrated scale. Now then, if current is made to pass through the coil so that its direction is away from the observer at the top of the coil and toward the observer at the bottom, torque will be developed to produce *clockwise* rotation. This comes about because the two magnetic fields, *i.e.*, the permanent-magnet field and the moving-coil field, tend to combine into a single *resulting* magnetic field having the greatest possible strength; the coil, therefore, swings around in an attempt to get its lines of force parallel to, and in the same direction as, the permanent-magnet field. The moving coil will, of course, come to rest when the electromagnetic force exerted upon it is exactly balanced by the restraining force created by the loaded (wound-up) springs. The term "torque motor" is, therefore, appropriate for an electrical instrument because motor action is developed during the upswing period, and sustained torque steadies the coil against the spring tension after the pointer reaches the position that is a measure of the coil current.

Instrument Damping.—The fact that the turns of wire of the moving coil are wound upon an aluminum (a metal) frame means that the latter will exert a braking action upon the assembly as it revolves through the magnetic field. This braking or *damping* effect results from generated e.m.f's in the metal frame *as it turns* through the very field that is responsible for the original motion. Since the generated voltage in the short-circuited frame is always in such a direction as to set up an m.m.f. that tends to oppose the motion, the coil moves the pointer upscale slowly, and without overshooting its final deflected position; such damping is, therefore, effective in preventing oscillations that would normally result from the oppositely directed forces exerted by the spiral springs and the moving coil.

Direct-current Ammeters and Voltmeters.—Both types of instrument are essentially alike, being constructed from foundation assemblies previously discussed; they *differ only in the manner in which an external resistor is connected with respect* *to the moving coil element.* An extremely low value of current is permitted to pass through the suspended coil, which, with its attached pointer, turns through an angle that is directly proportional to the current; the pointer moves over a calibrated scale to indicate either amperes or volts. A good *ammeter* has an extremely *low resistance;* a good *voltmeter* has a comparatively *high* resistance. This implies, of course, that when an ammeter is placed in *series* in a circuit it incurs a low voltage drop (its resistance is low), and when a voltmeter is connected *across* (in parallel with) a circuit it draws very little current (its resistance is high); in either case, it is important to understand that when either type of instrument is inserted in a circuit for measurement purposes, *it must alter that circuit as little as possible.* In the D'Arsonval type of direct-current instrument, very widely used, full-scale deflection usually occurs when the voltage across its terminals is 0.05 volt (50 millivolts). If the moving-coil resistance is 2.5 ohms, its current must not exceed $0.05/2.5 = 0.02$ amp. Under this condition a 5-amp. ammeter, for example, must have a shunt connected *across* its terminals that must carry the difference between the 5-amp. line current and the 0.02-amp. instrument coil current, or 4.98 amp. The shunt resistance must, therefore, be $0.05/4.98 = 0.01004$ ohm, an extremely low value. If the instrument is to be used as a voltmeter having a full-scale deflection of, say, 150 volts, the moving coil must be connected in series with a resistor capable of causing a voltage drop of $150 - 0.05$ volts, or 149.95 volts. Its resistance must, therefore, be $149.95/0.02 = 7{,}497.5$ ohms, a comparatively high value. Figure 108 shows the manner in which this type of instrument is constructed to serve as an ammeter or as a voltmeter. In the ammeter (Fig. 108*a*) the resistance connected *across* the moving coil is called a *shunt.* In the voltmeter (Fig. 108*b*) the resistance connected *in series* with the moving coil is called a *multiplier.* Portable direct-current instruments are illustrated in Figs. 6 and 7.

In ammeters of the smaller ranges, up to about 25 amp., shunts are usually placed inside the case. For ranges above

25 amp. externally connected shunts are used because of their size and the heating loss. Figure 109 shows two externally applied ammeter shunts for 100- and 2,000-amp. instruments. Multipliers are nearly always placed inside the voltmeter

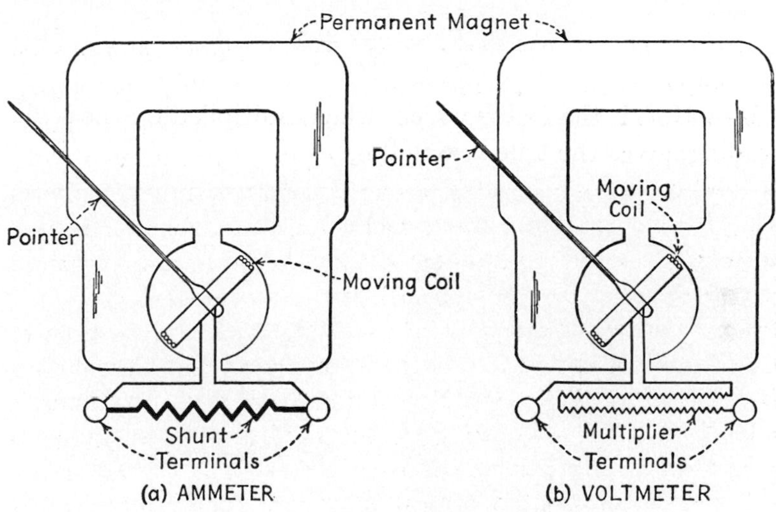

FIG. 108.—Internal wiring connections of direct-current ammeter and voltmeter. Note shunt for ammeter and multiplier for voltmeter. Calibrating resistances are omitted for simplicity.

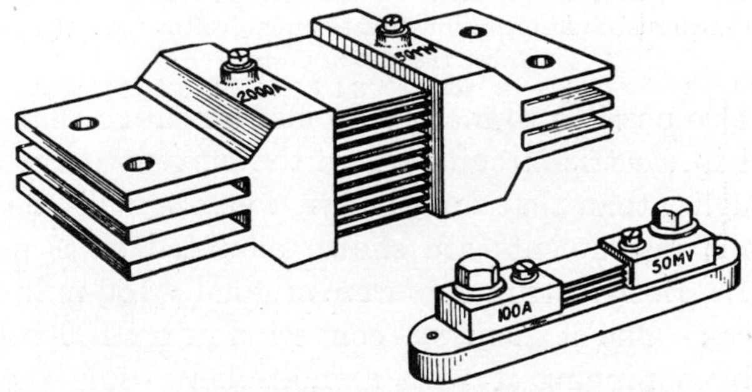

FIG. 109.—External shunts for 100- and 200-amp. ammeters. (*Weston Electrical Instrument Corp.*)

cases. It sometimes happens that the range of a given voltmeter must be increased. In such an instance an externally connected multiplier must be used. Figure 110 shows two such multiplier resistors that could be used with any voltmeter to increase its range. If a *multiplier* having a resistance R_M is connected in series with an *instrument* having a resistance R_I, then the multiplying factor $M.F.$ of the combination will become

$$M.F. = \frac{R_M}{R_I} + 1 \tag{40}$$

where $M.F.$ is the factor which, when multiplied by the scale reading, gives the true line voltage.

FIG. 110.—External multipliers for direct-current voltmeters. (*Weston Electrical Instrument Corp.*)

It is also possible to modify an instrument so that it may be used in electric circuits where the current or voltage is much higher than that for which it was originally designed. Two such instruments are shown mounted on a panel in Fig. 111. Both instruments were originally 150-milliampere ammeters. One of them was converted into a 150-volt voltmeter by equipping it with a multiplier, while the other instrument was converted into a multiscale ammeter having ranges of 1.5 amp., 6 amp., and 15 amp. Note particularly the back of the panel, in which the external shunts and the multiplier are plainly visible.

Shunts and multipliers are not particularly difficult to make for electrical instruments to extend their ranges.

After they are applied the complete assembly should, however, be properly and carefully calibrated against other instruments acting as standards.

A number of examples will now be given to illustrate the principles of ammeters and voltmeters.

Example 1.—A D'Arsonval type instrument (see Fig. 105) has a moving coil containing $60\frac{1}{2}$ turns of wire, wound over a

Fig. 111.—Panel-mounted direct-current milliammeters converted into an ammeter and a voltmeter. Rear view (at right) shows shunts for ammeter and multiplier for voltmeter.

frame having a radius R of 0.4 in. and an axial length L of 1.25 in. If the air-gap flux density is radial and uniform and has a value of 4,800 lines per square inch, calculate the torque developed for a full-scale deflection if the coil current under this condition is 15 milliamperes (0.015 amp.).

Solution: Before proceeding with a solution, using Eq. (39), it will be necessary to convert the values given in inch units to centimeter units. Thus:

$$R = 0.4 \times 2.54 = 1.016 \text{ cm.}$$
$$L = 1.25 \times 2.54 = 3.175 \text{ cm.}$$
$$B = \frac{4{,}800}{6.45} = 745 \text{ lines per square centimeter}$$

Therefore,

$$T = 0.2 \times 745 \times 60.5 \times 0.015 \times 1.016 \times 3.175$$
$$= 435 \text{ dyne-cm.}$$

Example 2.—If full-scale deflection in Example 1 occurs for a coil rotation of 75 deg., calculate the torque per degree of deflection.

Solution:

$$\frac{T}{\text{degree}} = \frac{435}{75} = 5.8 \text{ dyne-cm.}$$

Example 3.—The moving coil of a D'Arsonval type instrument has a resistance of 1.8 ohms and deflects full scale when an e.m.f. of 54 millivolts is applied to its terminals. Calculate (*a*) the resistance of a shunt that will give a full-scale deflection for a line current of 10 amp.; (*b*) the resistance of a multiplier that will convert the instrument to a 75-volt voltmeter.

Solution:

a. Moving-coil current for full-scale deflection is

$$I_I = \frac{0.054}{1.8} = 0.03 \text{ amp.}$$

The resistance of shunt is

$$R_{SH} = \frac{0.054}{(10 - 0.03)} = 0.00542 \text{ ohm}$$

b. Total resistance of instrument and multiplier is

$$\frac{75}{0.03} = 2{,}500 \text{ ohms}$$

$$\text{Resistance of multiplier } R_M = 2{,}500 - 1.8$$
$$= 2{,}498.2 \text{ ohms}$$

Example 4.—A 150-volt voltmeter has a total resistance between terminals of 15,000 ohms (100 ohms per volt). (*a*) If a resistance of 7,500 ohms is connected in series with the instrument, what is the multiplying factor *M.F.*? (This is the factor by which the instrument indication must be multiplied to give the true measured voltage.) (*b*) What resistance should be connected in series with the instrument if the multiplying factor is to be 4? (The instrument will thus be converted into a 600-volt voltmeter.)

Solution:

$$a.\ M.F. = \frac{7{,}500}{15{,}000} + 1 = 1.5 \text{ (see Eq. 40)}$$

$$b.\ M.F. = 4 = \frac{R_M}{15{,}000} + 1;\ R_M = 45{,}000 \text{ ohms}$$

Multirange Instruments.—The foregoing should make it clear that the usefulness of measuring instruments may be extended by providing them with several internal shunts or multipliers, or both; they then become *multirange instruments* because each shunt or multiplier, properly connected to the moving coil, enlarges the calibrated scale by a different amount. The important point to remember in this connection is that full-scale deflection occurs when maximum permissible current passes through the *moving coil*, and that this moving-coil current must not be exceeded whether the instrument is equipped with a shunt (in which it becomes an ammeter) or a multiplier (under which condition it serves as a voltmeter). This implies, of course, that (*a*) when used as an ammeter the shunt always bypasses a definitely exact proportion of the total current, and (*b*) when used as a voltmeter the multiplier always incurs a definitely exact proportion of the total voltage drop. For example, if full-scale deflection occurs when the instrument potential drop is 50 millivolts and its current is 0.02 amp., a shunt must bypass 4.98 amp. if the instrument is to be used as a 5-amp. ammeter, or a multiplier must incur a voltage drop of 149.95 volts when it serves as a 150-volt voltmeter.

Multirange Ammeter.—The internal wiring connections, and other details, of a triple-range direct-current ammeter are shown in Fig. 112. Note particularly that there are three shunts R_A, R_B, and R_C. When the 1.5-amp. range is used, between the plus and 1.5-amp. terminals, the series circuit consisting of the moving coil and its calibrating resistor is paralleled (shunted) by $R_A + R_B + R_C$; under this condition a maximum line current of 1.5 amp. will divide so that a major part will pass through the shunt and the remaining *correct* value of current will pass through the coil to give

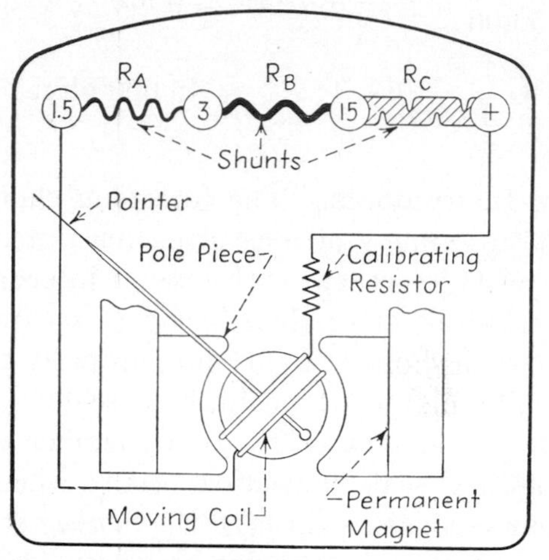

FIG. 112.—The internal wiring connections of a triple-range direct-current ammeter.

full-scale deflection. For the 3-amp. range, between the plus and 3-amp. terminals, the series circuit consisting of R_A, the moving coil and its calibrating resistor is shunted by $R_B + R_C$; under this condition a maximum line current of 3 amp. will divide so that a still larger part will pass through the shunt and the remaining *correct* value of current (exactly the same value as for the 1.5-amp. range) will pass through the coil to give full-scale deflection. Finally, for the 15-amp. range, between the plus and 15-amp. terminals, the series circuit consisting of R_B, R_A, the moving coil, and its calibrating resistor is paralleled by R_C only; under this condition a maximum line current of 15 amp. will divide so that most of the current will pass through R_C and the remaining *correct* value of current (exactly the same value as for the 1.5- and 3-amp. ranges) will pass through the coil to give full-scale deflection. For line currents smaller than 1.5 amp., 3 amp., or 15 amp. the deflections will, of course, be proportional to the current magnitudes on each of the respective ranges.

The material generally employed for ammeter shunts is the alloy *manganin;* it is ideally suited for this purpose because it has a comparatively high specific resistance, good

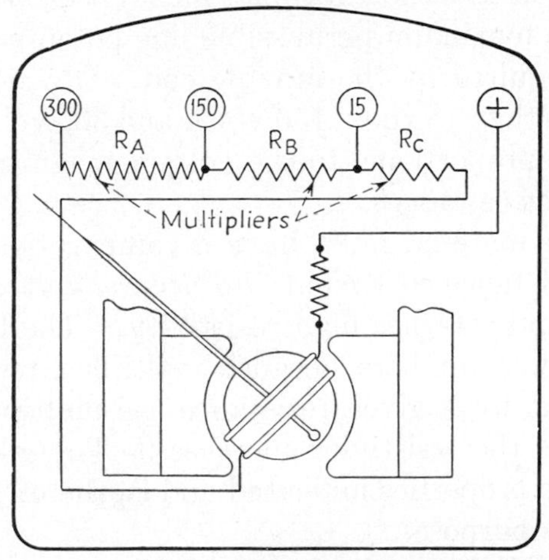

FIG. 113.—The internal wiring connections of a triple-range direct-current voltmeter.

current-carrying capacity, and a negligibly small temperature resistance coefficient. This latter property is extremely important because the accuracy of the instrument can be maintained only if the resistance of the shunt does not change with wide changes in temperature.

Multirange Voltmeter.—Figure 113 shows the internal connections for a triple-range direct-current voltmeter. Comparing it with the triple-range ammeter of Fig. 112, it will be observed that the shunts that parallel the moving coil are replaced by multipliers, *i.e.*, series resistors. Assuming that full-scale deflection occurs when the moving coil is connected to a 50-millivolt source, it should be clear that (*a*) when the instrument is to be used as a 15-volt voltmeter (plus and 15-volt terminals), the R_C multiplier must incur a 14.95-volt drop for full-scale deflection; (*b*) when the instrument is to be used as a 150-volt voltmeter (plus and 150-volt terminals), the series combination of $R_C + R_B$ multipliers must incur a 149.95 volt drop for full-scale deflection; and (*c*) when the instrument is to be used as a 300-volt voltmeter (plus and 300-volt terminals) the series combination $R_C + R_B + R_A$ multipliers must incur a 299.95-volt drop for full-scale deflection. In each case the multiplier must absorb the difference between the maximum permissible line potential and the 50 millivolts required by the moving coil. Obviously, for line voltages less than 15 volts, 150 volts, and 300 volts the deflections will be proportional to the voltage magnitudes on each of the respective ranges.

Multiplier material must have a comparatively low temperature resistance coefficient (for accuracy at varying temperatures) and a rather high resistivity. The latter is particularly important here because multiplier resistances are usually large; for a given resistance the multiplier occupies less space as the resistivity increases. The alloy *nichrome* possesses the properties indicated and is, therefore, generally used for this purpose.

Multirange Volt-ammeter.—Instruments are sometimes designed to be used either as an ammeter or a voltmeter and may, moreover, have several ranges for both the current and voltage scales. Such an arrangement is shown in Fig. 114, in which three current ranges and two voltage ranges are indicated. Connections must, of course, be made to the proper instrument terminals in compliance with maximum current (load) and voltage (source) conditions. Note particularly that amperes will be registered when the insulated button is in the normal position shown; for a voltage measurement it is necessary to press the spring-loaded button. Being a combination instrument, it is somewhat more difficult to calibrate than single-purpose measuring devices.

Ohmmeters.—For the determination of resistance in a direct-current circuit it is customary to employ the volt-ammeter method. The procedure, illustrated by Fig. 8 and outlined in Experiments 3 to 8 of Chap. 3, involves merely the measurement of the current *through* the resistor and the

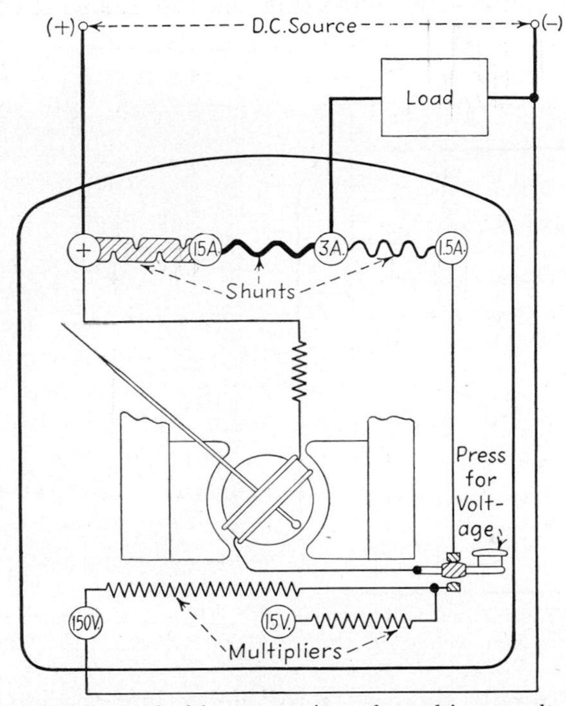

FIG. 114.—The internal wiring connections of a multirange volt-ammeter.

voltage *across* the resistor; the ratio of E to I is then equal to the circuit resistance.

A more convenient method, although a somewhat less accurate one, makes use of a direct-reading *ohmmeter*. This self-contained instrument has two externally mounted open-circuited terminals that are internally connected in series with a small dry-type battery and a fixed limiting resistor; a calibrating rheostat, directly in parallel with the movement, completes the internal connections. After the ohmmeter is calibrated, as described below, the unknown resistor is connected to the instrument's terminals, whereupon the needle is deflected to indicate the ohmic value of the unknown unit.

Figure 115 shows a wiring diagram for the instrument. Before it is put to use it must be calibrated by short-circuiting the terminals and adjusting the calibrating rheostat R_C

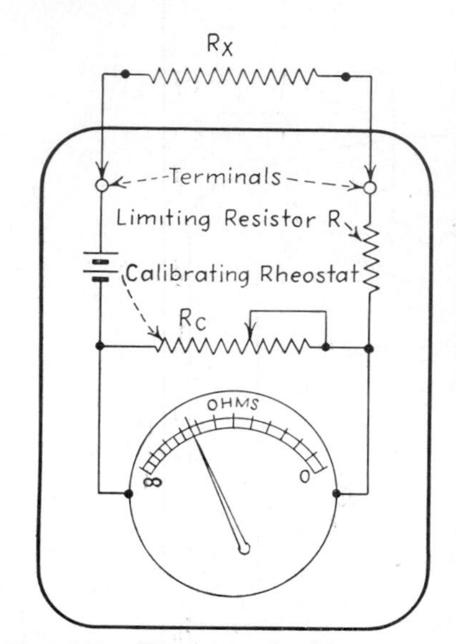

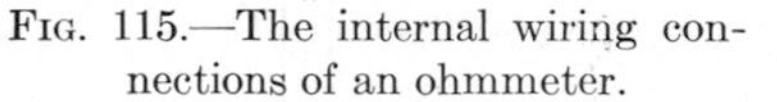

Fig. 115.—The internal wiring connections of an ohmmeter.

Fig. 116.—A wide-range ohmmeter. (*Weston Electrical Instrument Corp.*)

until the needle gives a "zero" deflection; the latter zero-resistances marking is at the extreme right because, representing maximum current, it results from an external resistance of zero ohms. Now then, if the short circuit is removed and an unknown resistor R_X is connected to the terminals, the needle will receive a smaller upscale deflection that, on the previously calibrated scale, indicates the resistance in ohms. In fact, if the terminals are left open-circuited, the needle will remain at the extreme left to indicate infinite resistance.

Since the accuracy of the deflection, for a given value of R_X, depends upon the condition of the dry cell, compensation for aging and use must be provided by the calibrating rheostat; this simple shunt rheostat merely provides an easy means of adjusting the sensitivity of the ohmmeter.

A serious disadvantage of the instrument is that its ohmic range, over a comparatively short scale, is from zero to infinity. This makes the ohmmeter quite inaccurate for deflections that are somewhat less than 10 per cent of full scale. Figure 116 depicts a widely used type of ohmmeter.

Example 5.—The moving coil of the instrument in an ohmmeter (see Fig. 115) has a resistance of 2.5 ohms and deflects full scale on 40 millivolts. When the ohmmeter terminals are short-circuited the calibrating rheostat must be adjusted to 10 ohms to give a "zero" needle deflection. If the battery e.m.f. is 3 volts, calculate (*a*) the resistance of the limiting resistor R; (*b*) the current through the moving coil and the per cent full-scale deflection if an external resistance R_X of 250 ohms is connected across the ohmmeter's terminals. Neglect the internal resistance of the battery.

Solution:

a. With the terminals short-circuited, the current through the limiting resistor R is the sum of the currents through the moving coil and the calibrating rheostat. Thus

$$I_R = \frac{0.04}{2.5} + \frac{0.04}{10} = 0.02 \text{ amp.}$$

Since the voltage drop across the limiting resistor is

$$E_R = 3 - 0.04 = 2.96 \text{ volts}$$

it follows that

$$R = \frac{2.96}{0.02} = 148 \text{ ohms}$$

b. With 250 ohms connected across the instrument's terminals, the total circuit resistance is

$$R_t = 250 + 148 + \frac{2.5 \times 10}{12.5} = 400 \text{ ohms}$$

The total circuit current will, therefore, be

$$I_R = \frac{3}{400} = 0.0075 \text{ amp.}$$

and the moving-coil current will be

$$I_{m.c.} = 0.0075 \times \frac{10}{(10 + 2.5)} = 0.006 \text{ amp.}$$

Hence

$$\text{Per cent deflection} = \frac{0.006}{0.016} \times 100 = 37.5$$

The Wheatstone Bridge.—When four resistors are connected in *parallel-series*, as shown in Fig. 117*a*, the *potential*

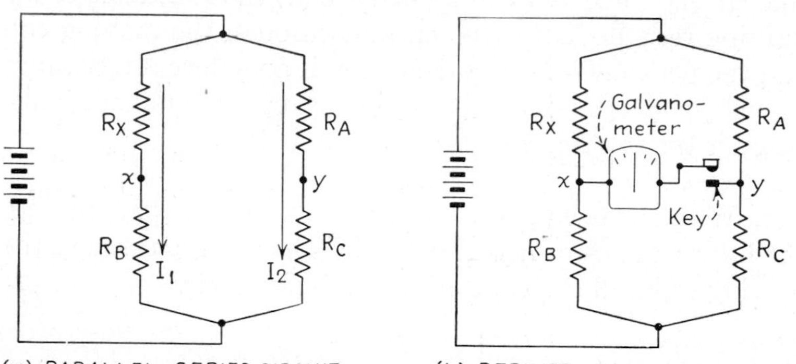

Fig. 117.—The Wheatstone bridge considered as a development of the parallel-series circuit.

difference between x and y will be zero if the voltage drops across R_X and R_A are equal; under this condition the voltage drops across R_B and R_C will also be equal. In equation form, these statements become

$$I_1R_X = I_2R_A \qquad \text{and} \qquad I_1R_B = I_2R_C$$

If the first equation is divided by the second,

$$\frac{I_1R_X}{I_1R_B} = \frac{I_2R_A}{I_2R_C}$$

from which

$$R_X = \left(\frac{R_B}{R_C}\right) R_A \tag{41}$$

Since, as indicated above, zero potential difference exists between x and y, a conductor joining these two points will carry no current. This suggests the possibility, therefore, of connecting a delicate instrument between points x and y to determine whether or not the condition given by Eq. (41) is fulfilled; the arrangement is shown in Fig. 117*b* with a *bridge*, consisting of a delicate instrument—a *galvanometer*—and a key connecting points x and y. First proposed by Wheatstone for the measurement of resistance, it is called a *Wheatstone bridge.* In practice it is customary to have one set of standard resistances that may be adjusted to give a desired *ratio* of R_B to R_C in the decimal system (*i.e.*, 0.001, 0.01, 0.1, 1.0, 10, 100, etc.) and another variable standard resistance representing R_A. By properly manipulating the dials corresponding to the *ratio arm* and the variable resistance it is possible to *balance the bridge;* the galvanometer will then show zero deflection, and the value of R_X may be determined by Eq. (41). While the bridge is being balanced, the operator should exercise care to prevent violent deflections of the pointer. As the bridge approaches a balance, when resistance R_A is varied, the needle will swing to the left or right (zero is at the center of the scale in the type of galvanometer generally used); after some practice the operator will know whether to increase or decrease R_A to obtain a balance.

Example 6.—Referring to Fig. 117*b*, determine the value of R_X if the bridge is balanced when $R_B/R_C = 0.1$ and $R_A = 68$.

Solution:

$$R_X = 0.1 \times 68 = 6.8 \text{ ohms}$$

High-resistance Measurements (Voltmeter Method).—It is sometimes necessary to determine, by measurement, the insulation resistance of electrical machines or cables, the ohmic values of high-resistance radio components, and others; many excellent precision devices, such as meggers and special bridges, have been developed for this purpose. Although descriptions and operation of the latter are beyond the scope of this book, a simple procedure that employs a high-resistance voltmeter will be considered.

For reasonably good accuracy it is necessary to have a 150- or 300-volt voltmeter that has a resistance of 1,000 ohms per volt; such voltmeters, having resistances of 150,000 ohms

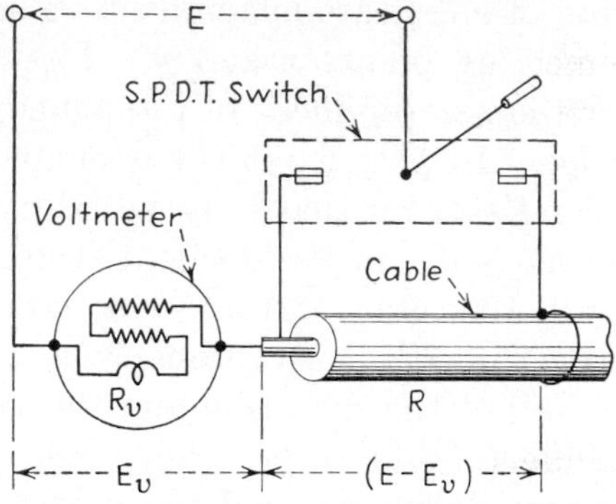

FIG. 118.—Wiring connections showing how the insulation resistance of a cable may be measured with a high-resistance voltmeter.

or 300,000 ohms, are widely used, and their internal resistances are usually given on the calibrated scale or case. Referring to the diagram of Fig. 118, which shows the wiring connections for the measurement of the insulation resistance of a cable between conductor and surrounding cover (*e.g.*, a lead sheath), the following procedure should be followed: (*a*) the blade of the s.p.d.t. switch is closed to the left to measure the line voltage E; (*b*) the switch is then closed to the right, whereupon the voltmeter registers its own voltage drop E_v. Since the voltage drop across the cable insulation resistance is $(E - E_v)$, it follows that, for a simple series circuit,

$$\frac{(E - E_v)}{E_v} = \frac{R}{R_v}$$

from which

$$R = \left(\frac{E}{E_v} - 1\right) R_v \tag{42}$$

To measure the insulation resistance between conductor and ground, of an electrical machine a similar procedure is followed; the leads shown connected to the cable in Fig. 118 would then be joined to any conductor (or commutator in the case of a direct-current armature) and the grounded frame.

Example 7.—A 150,000-ohm voltmeter is connected in series with the insulating material of a motor (between a conductor and the frame), and then to a previously measured 114-volt direct-current source. If the voltmeter deflection indicates that the voltage drop across its own 150,000-ohm resistance is 6 volts, what is the insulation resistance?

Solution:

$$R = (\tfrac{114}{6} - 1)\ 150{,}000 = 2{,}700{,}000 \text{ ohms or } 2.7 \text{ megohms}$$

Experiment 22. Making an Ammeter Shunt

Objectives: (*a*) To extend the range of a given ammeter by providing it with a shunt. (*b*) To calibrate the shunted ammeter using another higher-range instrument as a secondary standard.

Procedure: For this experiment it will be desirable to make use of two ammeters, one having a range that is twice that of the other. (Ammeters having 5- and 10-amp. ranges will be satisfactory for this purpose.) Set up a circuit similar to that shown in Fig. 119 using a suitable length of bare No. 14 (or larger) copper wire for the experimental shunt material. (If the shunt is to be used permanently it will be necessary to obtain *manganin* wire.) Loop the wire through the ammeter terminals as indicated, and fasten the extended ends to a s.p.s.t. switch, each of whose terminals is provided with double fastening holes and screws. With the loop around the ammeter terminals as short as possible, adjust the load until the secondary standard registers exactly one-half of full scale, (5 amp. on a 10-amp. instrument). Now open the s.p.s.t. switch; the shunted ammeter should show a rather small deflection. Loosen one of the ammeter terminals slightly to free the wire shunt, and carefully lengthen the loop until the shunted ammeter also gives a 50 per cent registration; then tighten the terminal. The

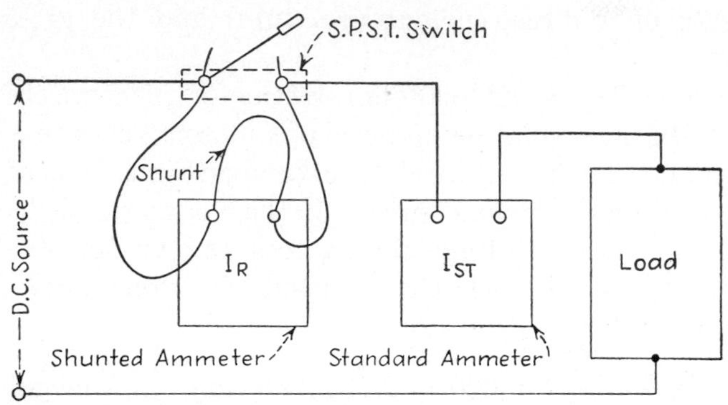

FIG. 119.—Wiring diagram showing how to calibrate a shunted ammeter.

student will be quite safe in handling the energized circuit because the voltage drop across the instrument is extremely low. After a few trials, lengthening and shortening the loop, a half-scale deflection on the shunted ammeter will exactly match a half-scale deflection on the secondary standard.

Calibration: The next step is to calibrate the shunted instrument by making a "load run" in convenient steps (1-amp. steps if the secondary standard is a 10-amp ammeter). Record values of *standard* amperes I_{ST} and shunted-instrument *registration* I_R. Data should be recorded in a table similar to that given below.

No.	I_{ST}	I_R	*S.F.**	$I_R \times$ S.F.	Error

* Scale factor.

Finally, a calibration curve should be plotted with the *error* $[I_{ST} - (I_R \times S.F.)]$ as ordinate *versus* $(I_R \times S.F.)$ as abscissa.

EXPERIMENT 23. MAKING A VOLTMETER MULTIPLIER

Objectives: (*a*) To extend the range of a given voltmeter by providing it with a multiplier. (*b*) To calibrate the multiplied voltmeter using another higher-range instrument as a secondary standard.

Procedure: For this experiment it will be desirable to make use of two voltmeters, one having a range that is twice the

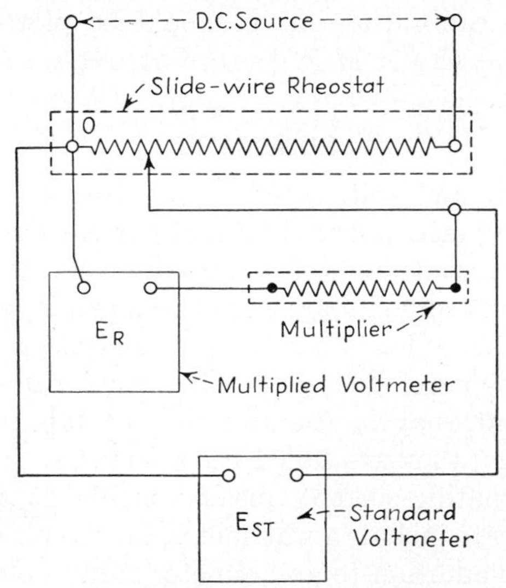

FIG. 120.—Wiring diagram showing how to calibrate a multiplied voltmeter.

other. (Voltmeters having 75- and 150-volt ranges will be satisfactory for this purpose.) Set up a circuit similar to that shown in Fig. 120; the multiplier should have a *known* ohmic value R_M that is very nearly equal to the resistance R_I of the multiplied voltmeter. If the 75-volt 150-volt instrument combination is used, energize the circuit from a 230-volt direct-current source, making sure the slider of the slide-wire rheostat is set for *zero volts* (at 0) before the main switch is closed.

Calibration: The next step is to calibrate the multiplied voltmeter by moving the slider to give a convenient number of upscale deflections (10-volt steps if the secondary standard is a 150-volt voltmeter). Record values of *standard* volts E_{ST} and multiplied-instrument *registrations* E_R. Data should be recorded in a table similar to that given below.

No.	E_{ST}	E_R	$M.F.$*	$E_R \times M.F.$	Error

* Multiplying factor $M.F. = R_M/R_I + 1$ [see Eq. (40)].

Finally, a calibration curve should be plotted with the *error* $[E_{ST} - (E_R \times M.F.)]$ as ordinate *versus* $(E_R \times M.F.)$ as abscissa.

SUMMARY

1. Ammeters and voltmeters are the most commonly used measuring instruments in direct-current circuits.
2. For the measurement of resistance several types of *direct-reading* instruments are sometimes employed; these are ohmmeters, Wheatstone bridges, and meggers.
3. Special types of precision instruments, drawing little or no current, may be used for the accurate measurement of voltage; they are called *potentiometers*.
4. In alternating-current measurements it is generally necessary to include a wattmeter, for the measurement of watts, in addition to an ammeter and a voltmeter.
5. Electrical instruments may have two or more ranges, and are sometimes designed to be used both as ammeter and voltmeter; changing from one to the other is accomplished by turning a selector switch.
6. The D'Arsonval type of direct-current electrical instrument as presently made represents the efforts of many persons over a period of more than 140 years.
7. The permanency of the magnet used in the D'Arsonval instrument depends, for the most part, upon the magnet circuit design; it is directly proportional to the length of

the magnet steel and the cross-sectional area of the air gap; it is inversely proportional to the cross-sectional area of the magnet and the length of the air gap.

8. Permanent magnets are made of tungsten steel, cobalt steel, or Alnico.
9. The moving coil, suspended by two short pointed shafts, is accurately pivoted in V-type sapphire bearings that never need oiling. Flat springs fastened to the coil assembly are wound in opposite directions and exert the necessary countertorques; the flat springs also act as lead-in and lead-out wires for the moving coil.
10. The force tending to turn the coil is directly proportional to the strength of the magnet and the number of ampere turns in the moving coil.
11. The moving coil is usually set at rest at an angle of about 45 deg. with the vertical, while the permanent magnet poles create a horizontally directed field.
12. Instrument damping is effected through the short-circuited aluminum frame over which the wire of the moving coil is wound.
13. Direct-current ammeters and voltmeters differ only in the manner in which an external resistor is connected with respect to the moving coil.
14. Normal moving-coil currents are generally very low. When an instrument is to be used to measure high currents (ammeters) the moving coil must be shunted; when used to measure high voltages (voltmeters) a multiplier (high resistance) must be connected in series with the moving coil.
15. A good instrument will not appreciably alter the conditions of the circuit into which it is placed.
16. A good ammeter has an extremely low resistance; a good voltmeter has a comparatively high resistance.
17. Shunts and multipliers may be made for given instruments to extend their ranges; such carefully made additions may be applied externally or connected internally.
18. Multirange ammeters and voltmeters are provided with

several shunts and multipliers. Each section acts with the moving coil to give the instrument a different value for the full-scale deflection.

19. Manganin is generally used for ammeter shunts and nichrome for voltmeter multipliers.
20. Volt-ammeters may be used interchangeably as voltmeters or ammeters; such instruments may be multirange for either service or for both.
21. Direct-reading ohmmeters are convenient to use for the measurement of resistance; their accuracy is generally not so good as that obtained by the voltmeter-ammeter method.
22. Ohmmeters generally have a short scale that ranges from zero ohms to infinity; they are inaccurate for deflections that are less than 10 per cent of full scale.
23. Wheatstone bridges are extremely accurate for the direct measurement of resistance. Precision units are available in many styles and sizes; in practice they generally come equipped with a ratio dial (R_B/R_C) and a set of calibrated resistances (R_A), [Eq. (41)].
24. A high-resistance voltmeter may be used to measure very high values of resistance; this is often convenient when it is necessary to determine the quality (resistance) of insulating materials.

QUESTIONS

1. What types of instrument are generally used for direct-current measurements? for alternating current measurements?
2. How is the resistance of a unit or circuit determined by the volt-ammeter method? Explain.
3. Name several types of *direct-reading* instrument used for the measurement of resistance.
4. What purpose is served by a potentiometer? Is it a precision instrument?
5. What important fundamental principles are involved in the operation of a permanent-magnet type of instrument?

6. Upon what factors does the permanency of a magnet depend? What are *directly proportional* factors? *inversely proportional* factors?
7. What materials are generally used for permanent magnets?
8. Describe the construction of the moving coil of a D'Arsonval type of instrument.
9. Upon what factors does the developed torque of an electrical instrument depend?
10. How is the moving coil set with respect to the permanent-magnet field?
11. Why is damping generally necessary in a measuring instrument? How is this effected in the D'Arsonval type of instrument?
12. How do the permanent-magnet and moving-coil fields react with respect to each other to develop torque? Explain carefully.
13. What fundamental differences exist between ammeters and voltmeters?
14. What is a shunt? a multiplier?
15. How does a shunt limit the moving-coil current in an ammeter?
16. How does a multiplier limit the moving-coil current in a voltmeter?
17. What is the relative resistance of a good ammeter? of a good voltmeter? Explain why, for each type of instrument.
18. Explain why the insertion of an instrument in a circuit tends to alter the conditions in the circuit. Indicate how such alteration may be minimized.
19. Is it possible to extend the range of a given ammeter or voltmeter? Explain carefully.
20. Make simple sketches showing how shunts and multipliers are applied in measuring instruments.
21. What materials are generally used for shunts and multipliers?
22. Explain why a very low shunt resistance greatly increases the range of an ammeter.

23. Explain why a very high multiplier resistance greatly increases the range of a voltmeter.
24. What is a multirange ammeter? a multirange voltmeter? a volt-ammeter?
25. For full-scale deflection, what current must be bypassed by the shunt of an ammeter?
26. For full-scale deflection, what voltage drop must be incurred by the multiplier of a voltmeter?
27. What is meant by the multiplying factor (*M.F.*) of a voltmeter?
28. Describe the construction of an ohmmeter.
29. Why is it possible to calibrate an ohmmeter in terms of ohm units?
30. In an ohmmeter, why is the zero-resistance marking at the extreme right?
31. In an ohmmeter, why is the marking at the extreme left given as *infinite ohms*?
32. Why must an ohmmeter be calibrated before use? Explain carefully.
33. Why is a resistance measurement, made with an ohmmeter, less accurate than one made by the volt-ammeter method?
34. How is it possible to use an ohmmeter to make a continuity test?
35. Describe a simple Wheatstone-bridge circuit.
36. What type of measuring instrument is used in a Wheatstone bridge? Where is its zero marking?
37. Is it possible to use a pair of headphones in place of a measuring instrument in a Wheatstone bridge? Explain.
38. What is meant by a ratio dial in a Wheatstone bridge? Explain why this is a convenient arrangement.
39. Describe the procedure in balancing a Wheatstone bridge.
40. Why is a high-resistance voltmeter desirable when used to measure very high values of resistance? Describe the procedure for doing this.

PROBLEMS

1. The moving coil of a D'Arsonval-type instrument has $80\frac{1}{2}$ turns of wire that are wound over a frame having an axial length of 1.5 in. and a width of $\frac{7}{8}$ in. If the permanent magnet produces a uniform air-gap flux density of 5,000 lines per square inch., and full-scale deflection of 75 deg. occurs when the current is 12 milliamperes, calculate the torque per degree of deflection.
2. If the calibrated scale of Prob. 1 is assumed correct, what per cent error will result if the permanent magnet suffers a loss of 300 maxwells per square inch?
3. A millivoltmeter has a resistance of 2.5 ohms and deflects full scale on 50 mv. (*a*) What should be the resistance of a shunt if the instrument is to be used as a 1-amp. ammeter? (*b*) Repeat part (*a*) neglecting the moving-coil current.
4. Using the given data of Prob. 3 calculate the resistance of a multiplier if the instrument is to be used as a 150-volt voltmeter.
5. Repeat Prob. 4 neglecting the voltage drop across the moving coil.
6. A D'Arsonval-type instrument has a resistance of 3.5 ohms. If a 0.0028-ohm shunt is connected across its terminals and full-scale deflection occurs when the line current is 25 amp., calculate (*a*) the instrument current; (*b*) the current in the shunt.
7. If a resistance of 3,746.5 ohms is connected in series with the instrument of Prob. 6, determine the voltage that may be impressed across the combination to give full-scale deflection.
8. A 75-volt voltmeter has a resistance of 7,500 ohms. What will be the multiplying factor of the instrument if a resistance is connected in series having a value of (*a*) 7,500 ohms; (*b*) 22,500 ohms; (*c*) 18,000 ohms.
9. A 3-volt voltmeter has a resistance of 300 ohms. Calculate the total resistance of a multiplier, and the points

at which it should be tapped, so that its range may be extended to 15 volts, 150 volts, and 300 volts.

10. A 150-volt voltmeter has a resistance of 16,000 ohms. When connected to a source of e.m.f. slightly greater than 150 volts the deflection is a little off scale. A resistance of 1,500 ohms is then connected in series with the instrument, whereupon it indicates 141 volts. Calculate the voltage of the source.
11. A 15,000-ohm 150-volt voltmeter is connected in series with a 17,500-ohm 150-volt voltmeter, and the combination is used to measure the e.m.f. of a source. If the 15,000-ohm instrument gives a deflection of 102 volts, determine the reading on the 17,500-ohm voltmeter and the line voltage.
12. What maximum source voltage can be measured by the series combination of voltmeters of Prob. 11?
13. An ohmmeter has a 1.8-ohm instrument that gives full-scale deflection on 54 millivolts. When the ohmmeter terminals are short-circuited, the calibrating rheostat (see Fig. 115) must be adjusted to 13.5 ohms to give "zero" needle deflection. If the battery e.m.f. is 1.5 volts, calculate (*a*) the ohmic value of the limiting resistor; (*b*) the per cent of full-scale deflection if an external resistance of 41.1 ohms is connected to the ohmmeter terminals.
14. What will be the per cent deflection if the external resistance in Prob. 13 is doubled, *i.e.*, is 82.2 ohms?
15. If the ratio arm of a Wheatstone bridge is set at 10 and the variable standard resistance is adjusted to 168.2 ohms, calculate the resistance of the unknown resistor.
16. A 150,000-ohm voltmeter is connected in series with the insulating materials of a direct-current armature (between the commutator and shaft). If the voltmeter registers a deflection of 4.5 volts when the line potential is 117 volts, what is the resistance of the insulation in megohms?

CHAPTER 8

ELECTROMAGNETIC INDUCTION, TRANSFORMER ACTION, AND TRANSFORMERS

The Principle of Electromagnetic Induction.—A current of electricity will flow only when an e.m.f. is established in a circuit. In the case of the dry cell (Chap. 3) or the storage battery the e.m.f. is developed by *chemical action*. A second method is to heat the junction of two dissimilar metals, as, for example, in the electrical pyrometer; in this very useful device the so-called "thermocouple" will generate a feeble voltage capable of deflecting the needle of a sensitive electrical instrument whose scale is calibrated in temperature. Still another way in which a voltage may be developed is to permit light to fall upon a special chemical substance, called *photosensitive*, in which case a current will flow in a circuit consisting of the chemical, a collecting plate, and an instrument or other electrical units. The *light meter* and the *electric eye* are practical examples of this photoelectric effect.

But the most important method of generating an e.m.f., certainly from the standpoint of commercial power generation, results from the *principle of electromagnetic induction*. This principle was discovered by one of the greatest of all scientists, Michael Faraday, in 1831. After patiently toiling for nearly 11 years to find a more satisfactory source of electricity than the crude, inefficient battery, invented in 1801 by Alessandro Volta, Faraday accidentally hit upon one of the most important discoveries of all time. And strange as this may seem, the principle is extremely simple, since he found that a voltage can be developed in one of several ways:

1. By moving a conductor in such a manner that it *cuts across* magnetic lines of force.

2. By moving lines of force in such a manner that they *cut across* a conductor.

3. By *changing* the number of lines of force that link with a wire or coil of wire.

In direct-current generators large numbers of conductors mounted upon an armature are rapidly rotated through strong magnetic fields, the latter being provided by stationary poles radially bolted to a supporting cylindrical frame; this is method 1. In alternating-current generators strong magnet poles are rotated inside a cylindrical structure upon which are placed large numbers of conductors properly connected to form an armature winding; this is method 2. In transformers two stationary windings are placed over a common laminated steel core so that they are linked magnetically. The varying flux, produced by the excitation of one coil that is connected to an alternating-current source, induces a voltage in the second coil; this is method 3. Methods 1 and 2, which require the actual motion of coils of wire or magnet poles, give rise to *generated* voltages. In method 3 where the *flux* linking with a coil of wire is *changed*, the voltage is said to be *induced.*

Faraday's discovery that a voltage may be established by *changing the direction of the flux, or the amount of flux, that links with a conductor or coil* is generally regarded as one of the greatest scientific achievements of all time. This occurred on Aug. 31, 1831. He had wound two separate coils of wire upon an iron ring, the iron ring forming a common core for the two coils. The ends of one coil were joined together by a long wire that passed over a compass needle. To the other coil he connected a battery. What he thought he might observe was a deflection of the compass needle under the wire of the second coil merely because the latter was magnetically linked to the first coil. But no such deflection was produced. However, what he did notice was something quite unexpected. It was this: when the battery circuit was *closed,* the compass needle did move, then, oscillating back and forth, finally returned to its original position of rest; also, upon opening the battery circuit the needle moved again, then, oscillating as before, likewise returned to a position of rest. This transient, that is, a momentary flow of current, was wholly unexpected; in fact, it puzzled the experimenter so much that he had some difficulty explaining the phenomenon. After considerable study Faraday was able to understand exactly what happened. He later showed that magnetic and electrical actions were truly reciprocal because

1. *It is necessary for electricity to move before a magnetic effect is produced.*
2. *It is necessary for magnetism to move (or change) before an electrical effect is produced.*

Note particularly that electricity is caused to flow in the *second coil* when the magnetism in the iron core is made to *change* as a result of the closing or opening of the electric circuit of the *first coil.* The phenomenon is known as *the principle of electromagnetic induction.*

Faraday's Law.—As Faraday continued his electromagnetic researches, he found that *the magnitude of the generated voltage is directly proportional to the rate at which a conductor cuts magnetic lines of force.* This law, called *Faraday's law,* and Ohm's law are generally regarded as the two most important laws in the whole realm of electrical science.

When a conductor moves at a constant speed across a magnetic field of uniform flux density, 1 *volt is generated for every* 100,000,000 (10^8) *lines cut per second.* The value of the developed voltage is absolutely independent of the size or kind of conductor; the only thing that counts is *rate of flux cutting.* Thus, when a wire moves parallel to a magnetic field, it cuts no flux and, therefore, no voltage is generated. Furthermore, cutting across a field at an angle less than 90 deg. will result in a lower voltage than if the wire were moved at the same speed perpendicularly to the field. If the rate at which flux is cut changes from one instant to another over a given period of time, the generated e.m.f.

(*e*lectro*m*otive *f*orce) will be an average value and may be calculated by the formula

$$E_{av} = \frac{\phi}{t \times 10^8} \text{ volts} \tag{43}$$

where E_{av} = average generated voltage in a conductor
ϕ = the total flux cut
t = the time, in seconds, during which the cutting takes place

Example 1.—Calculate the average voltage generated in each conductor of an armature as it rotates at a speed of 1,200 r.p.m., cutting 5,500,000 lines of force under each pole of a four-pole generator.

Solution:

Total flux cut per revolution = $4 \times 5.5 \times 10^6 = 22 \times 10^6$ lines

Time required for armature to make one revolution

$$= \frac{60}{1200} = 0.05 \text{ sec.}$$

$$E_{av} = \frac{22 \times 10^6}{0.05 \times 10^8} = 4.5 \text{ volts}$$

As has been previously stated, a voltage may be *induced* in a coil of wire if the flux passing *through* the coil is *changed.* It is customary to speak of lines of force that pass *through* a coil as flux that *links* with it. When the flux linking with a coil *changes* at the rate of 100,000,000 (10^8) lines per second, 1 volt is induced in *each* turn of wire. This leads to the equation

$$E_{coil} = \frac{N \times \phi}{t \times 10^8} \text{ volts} \tag{44}$$

where E_{coil} = average induced voltage in the coil
N = number of turns in the coil
ϕ = the total change in the number of lines of force linking with the coil
t = the time, in seconds, during which the flux change takes place

Example 2.—Two coils, each containing 300 turns, are placed over the legs of a U-type iron core whose ends are bridged by a crosspiece. One of the coils is connected to a 6-volt battery while a direct-current voltmeter is connected across the second coil. If the flux linking with the second coil is 400,000 lines and the battery circuit is suddenly opened, calculate the voltmeter reading, assuming that it takes 0.2 sec. for the flux to drop to a residual value of

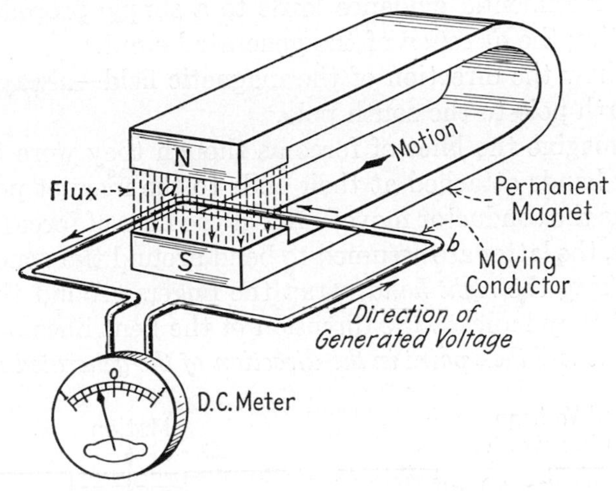

Fig. 121.—Sketch illustrating method of verifying the *principle* of voltage generation.

10,000 lines. (Note: A direct-current voltmeter registers the average voltage.)

Solution:

$$E_{\text{coil}} = \frac{300 \times 390{,}000}{0.2 \times 10^8} = 5.85 \text{ volts}$$

Direction of the Generated Voltage.—It is quite simple to show experimentally that the *direction* of the generated voltage in a conductor as it cuts lines of force depends upon two factors: (1) the direction of the magnetic field, and (2) the direction of motion of the conductor. Consider Fig. 121, which shows a permanent horseshoe magnet between whose poles a conductor *ab* is indicated. If the latter is connected to a direct-current instrument with its zero at the center of the scale, the needle will be observed to deflect in one direction if the conductor is moved away from the observer, and in the opposite direction if moved toward the observer. By carefully checking motion, magnet polarity, and meter polarity it is found that the generated voltage is from b to a when the conductor is moved away from the observer, and from a to b when moved toward the observer. Such experimental evidence leads to a simple procedure for predicting the *direction* of the generated e.m.f.:

1. Show the direction of the magnetic field—always from the north pole to the south pole.
2. Imagine the lines of force as though they were flexible rubber bands attached at their ends to the magnet poles.
3. As the conductor moves against the lines of force (rubber bands), the latter are assumed to bend around the conductor.
4. Using the *right hand*, wrap the fingers around the wire so that they indicate the direction of the bent lines of force; *the thumb will then point in the direction of the generated voltage.*

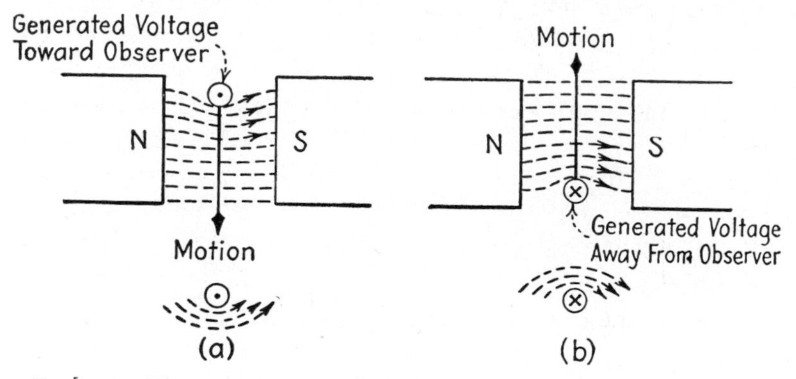

FIG. 122.—Sketches showing method for determining the *direction* of the generated voltage.

In Fig. 122, two conditions are shown for conductors perpendicular to the plane of the paper. In (a) the conductor is moved down, resulting in a voltage toward the observer, ⊙. In (b) the conductor is moved up, resulting in a voltage away from the observer, ⊕.

If the magnetic polarities of Fig. 122 were reversed, the

generated voltages in the conductors would be opposite to those indicated, being away from the observer in (*a*) and toward the observer in (*b*).

Lenz's Law and Direction of the Induced Voltage.—It is an experimental fact that any change in the existing position or motion of a body is *opposed* by a reaction that tends to prevent the change. This law was first stated by Newton in the first of his three laws of motion. When it is extended to the science of electricity and magnetism, observations lead to the same general conclusion that changes in electric and magnetic circuits are always accompanied by reactions that tend to oppose such changes. Thus, for example, when a switch is closed to energize the exciting coil of an electromagnet, the flux density does not rise to its ultimate value instantaneously but does so in some finite time. Or, conversely, if the circuit is opened, the flux density does not fall to its residual value in zero time. In either case *the change in flux is opposed only during that period of time when the conditions of the electric and magnetic circuits are being altered.* Now then, since any opposition to change must be due to an opposing force, it follows that in an electric circuit it must be an electromotive force. Such an e.m.f. is said to be induced and is always directed so that it tends to prevent the change.

Consider Fig. 123*a*, which shows two coils A and B wound around a closed iron core. Coil A is connected to a battery through a single-pole switch S, while coil B is connected to a resistor B. If switch S is suddenly closed, current will flow as indicated, and its effect will be to create the flux ϕ_A in the direction shown. But, while this flux ϕ_A is increasing, a voltage will be induced in coil B which in turn will send a current through resistor R in such a direction that flux ϕ_B will be created. Note that ϕ_B opposes ϕ_A because it tries to prevent the increase in the flux. The polarity of coil B, during and only during the period when the flux is increasing to its ultimate value, will be plus (+) at the top terminal and minus (−) at the bottom terminal.

If the switch S is now suddenly opened (Fig. 123*b*), the reverse action will take place in coil B. In this case the flux ϕ_A will try to diminish to its residual value and will be restrained by a sustaining flux ϕ_B as indicated. Thus, the induced voltage in coil B will be such that its polarity will be reversed with respect to the condition for closing the switch, so that the bottom terminal will be plus (+) and the top terminal will be minus (−). If resistor R is replaced by a meter having its zero at the center of the scale, the current through the meter will deflect the pointer; the deflection

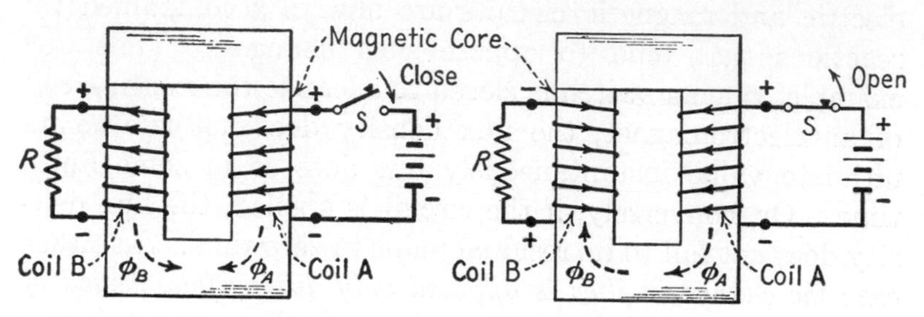

Fig. 123.—Electromagnet arrangements to verify the *laws* of induction.

will be in one direction if the switch is closed and in the opposite direction when the switch is opened. The deflections will, of course, be only momentary; *i.e.*, the needle will move to a position indicating the magnitude and direction of the current and will immediately return to its zero marking.

The above discussion can now be summed up by stating the law first given by Lenz and known as *Lenz's law: The current set up by an induced voltage always tends to create flux in such a direction as to oppose any change in the existing flux.*

If the battery of Fig. 123 is replaced by an alternating-current source, the current in the exciting coil A, called the *primary*, will be continually changing in both magnitude and direction. Under this condition *the induced voltage* in the second coil B, called the *secondary*, will be alternating and will, at every instant, be opposite in direction to the impressed voltage on the primary. When used in this way, an alternating-current electromagnet, containing a primary exciting coil and a load-delivering secondary coil, is called a *transformer*. Transformers, very widely used, are extremely important electrical units and should always be recognized as electromagnetic devices that operate by the principle of electromagnetic induction.

Mutual Induction and the Coefficient of Coupling.—The flux produced by the current flowing through a coil always spreads out more or less uniformly and symmetrically to form closed magnetic paths. Any of the flux thus created that passes directly through a second coil is said to be mutual to both coils, or briefly *mutual flux*. When the mutual flux changes in magnitude or direction, a voltage will be induced in the second coil; the e.m.f. resulting in this way is said to be a voltage of *mutual induction*. Mutual induction always implies that two coils are coupled magnetically; in other words, it is a condition that results when some or all of the magnetic flux passes *through* two coils at the same time.

The degree to which magnetic coupling exists depends upon a number of factors: (1) the closeness of the coils with respect to each other, (2) whether or not the coils are linked by a common magnetic core, (3) the permeability of the core material if the linking takes place through a common magnetic substance, (4) the angle between the magnetic axes of the two coils when no common magnetic substance links the coils. When maximum magnetic coupling exists between two coils, the implication is that all the magnetic flux created by one coil passes through the other; under this condition the *coefficient of coupling* is said to be 100 per cent, or *unity*. On the other hand, if no part of the flux created by the first coil passes *through* the second coil, the coefficient of coupling is said to be zero. Again, if only a part, say 80 per cent, of the flux produced by the first coil passes through the second coil, the coefficient of coupling is 0.8. Sometimes electrical men refer to the degree of coupling by such general terms as "close," "tight," "loose," etc. Transformer coils are generally coupled very tightly by placing them upon a common magnetic core of high permeability and as close together as insulation thicknesses permit. The reason for such construction is the fact that the value of induced voltage in the secondary coil depends, among other things, upon the number of lines of force, created by the primary, that passes *through* the secondary. In other cases, as for instance in certain communication systems, where it is desirable to prevent the feeding of electromagnetic energy from one electric circuit to another, the coils are placed as far apart as possible and with their magnetic axes at right angles. Figure 123 is a good example of two closely coupled coils; in this case the coefficient of coupling is practically unity because the coils are closely linked by a common magnetic core so that all the flux created by coil A passes through coil B.

In Fig. 124*a*, *b*, and *c* are shown three conditions of coupling between coils A and B, in no one of which is there a common

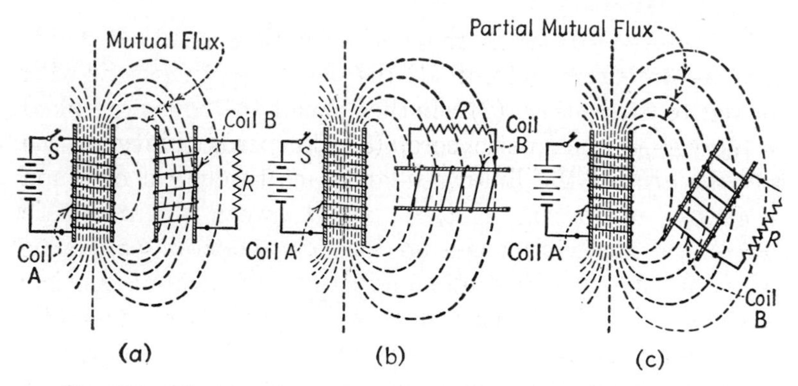

FIG. 124.—Sketches showing varying degrees of magnetic coupling.

magnetic core. Flux is created by coil A after the switch S is closed. In Fig. 124*a* with the coil axes parallel only a small part of the primary flux links with coil B. In Fig. 124*b* the two coils A and B are represented with their magnetic axes at right angles; in this case no part of the flux created by coil A passes *through* coil B, for which reason the coefficient of coupling is, for all practical purposes, zero. In Fig. 124*c* the two coils *A* and *B* are shown with their magnetic axes at an angle of 30 deg. with respect to each other. In this case it should be noted particularly that the small percentage of the flux passing through coil *B* does not even link with all of its turns. And since this mutual flux acts to link both coils only *partially*, it is called *partial mutual flux*. When the foregoing is summarized, it should be clear that in Fig. 123 the coefficient of coupling is very nearly unity because practically no flux escapes from the magnetic core that tightly links coils *A* and *B*; in Fig. 124*a* the coefficient of coupling may be about 0.2 because only about 20 per cent of the total flux created by coil *A* passes through, and links with, coil *B*; in Fig. 124*b* the coefficient of coupling may be considered zero because flux passes *across*, not through, coil *B*; in Fig. 124*c* the coefficient of coupling is very small, say 0.1, because very little flux, about 10 per cent, passes directly through coil *B*, and even that portion which does so links with a portion of the turns.

The above discussion of mutual induction is extremely important and should be thoroughly understood by the student because it is fundamental to the operation of many kinds of alternating-current apparatus, particularly transformers, induction motors, and automatic control devices.

Self-induction.—When a single coil carries a steady current, the magnetic field that is created is likewise steady and links with its own turns of wire. If the current changes, the flux changes, and in accordance with Lenz's law (page 280) a voltage is induced in the coil in such a direction that it tries to prevent the change in flux. This e.m.f. is said to be *self-induced* for the reason that it is induced in the very coil in which the current changes. The value of the self-induced voltage will depend upon the rate of change of the flux passing through the coil, which in turn will be determined by (1) the number of ampere turns in the exciting coil, (2) the type and size of the magnetic circuit, and (3) the rapidity with which the circuit conditions change. If the current changes at the rate of 1 amp. per second, and, as a result of this current change, the flux passing through the coil changes at the rate of 100,000,000 lines per second, there will be an induced voltage in the coil of 1 volt for every turn of wire.

A circuit in which an appreciable voltage is induced when, or while, the current changes is said to be *inductive,* and the circuit is said to possess the property of *self-inductance.* Such circuits are generally constructed by winding a great many turns of wire upon a continuous magnetic core of high permeability. The direct-current field circuits of most generators and motors are very highly inductive, for which reason considerable voltages may be self-induced when they are suddenly opened. In fact, if a voltmeter is connected directly across the coil ends of a good direct-current electromagnet, excited from a low-voltage source, and the switch is suddenly opened, the voltmeter will be damaged because of the high self-induced voltage. In this connection it should be thoroughly understood that the voltmeter registers the normally low-source voltage when the switch is closed but indicates the self-induced high voltage at the instant the switch is opened. It is true that the induced voltage is momentary, but it is nevertheless sufficiently large to "kick" the needle very sharply and violently against the stop. In using voltmeters in highly inductive direct-current circuits it is, therefore, good practice to keep them disconnected except when the measurement is being made.

It was previously pointed out that the property of self-inductance manifests itself only while the current in a circuit is changing; *i.e., the voltage of self-induction,* opposing the change in the current that creates it, *depends directly upon how rapidly the current changes.* Now then, if the current changes at the rate of 1 *amp. per second and the voltage of self-induction is* 1 *volt,* the circuit is said to possess an inductance of one unit. The unit of inductance (see Chap. 5) is called the *henry* and depends entirely upon the way in which the electric and magnetic elements of the device are constructed.

It is independent of the value of the current flowing in the coil in exactly the same way as the resistance of a wire is independent of the value of the current flowing in the wire. Since one of the factors that influence the inductance is the permeability of the magnetic material used for the core, it is generally difficult and inaccurate to calculate the inductance of a circuit unless the coil is wound around a nonmagnetic substance. The reason for the difficulty is the fact that the permeability varies considerably with changes in flux density (see Fig. 91), which means that the inductance is *not constant* while the magnetizing force (proportional to the current) is changing. However, if the current changes only slightly so that the permeability of the core material is not affected appreciably, it is possible to calculate the inductance with a good degree of accuracy.[1] For the calculation of the in-

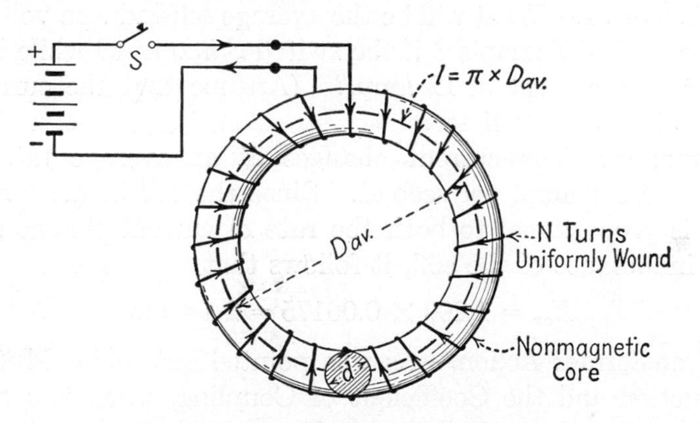

FIG. 125.—Toroid with nonmagnetic core.

ductance in henrys of a single-layer solenoid, closely wound upon a *non*magnetic ring like that illustrated in Fig. 125, the equation is

$$L = \frac{1.257\ N^2A}{l \times 10^8}\ \text{henry} \qquad (45)$$

[1]See Formulas and Tables for the Calculation of Mutual and Self-Inductance, *Bulletin of Bureau of Standards*, Vol. 8, No. 1.

where L = inductance in henrys
N = number of turns in the coil
A = area of the nonmagnetic core in square centimeters
l = average length of the ring in centimeters

Example 3.—Referring to Fig. 125, calculate the inductance of the solenoid, given the following particulars: $N = 1{,}250$ turns; $D_{av} = 4$ in.; diameter of the circular core d around which the coil is wrapped = 0.75 in.

Solution:

$$A = \frac{\pi}{4} \times (0.75)^2 \times 6.45 = 2.85 \text{ sq. cm.} \quad (1 \text{ sq. in.} = 6.45 \text{ sq. cm.})$$

$$l = \pi \times 4 \times 2.54 = 31.9 \text{ cm.} \qquad (1 \text{ in.} = 2.54 \text{ cm.})$$

$$L = \frac{1.257 \times (1{,}250)^2 \times 2.85}{31.9 \times 10^8} = 0.00175 \text{ henry}$$

Example 4.—What will be the average self-induced voltage in the coil of Example 3 if the switch S is opened while it is carrying a current of 12 amp.? (Assume that the current drops to zero in 0.01 sec.)

Solution: The current changes at an average rate of $\frac{12}{0.01} = 1{,}200$ amp. per second. Since the self-induced voltage is proportional to both the rate of current change and the inductance of the coil, it follows that

$$E_{av} = 1{,}200 \times 0.00175 = 2.1 \text{ volts}$$

Transformer Action.—As was pointed out under Mutual Induction and the Coefficient of Coupling, when two coils are coupled magnetically, any change in the current in one of them causes the linking flux to change. Under this condition there will be developed a voltage of mutual induction in the second coil. It should be clear that fundamentally the *secondary induced voltage* results because the flux changes through the coil, although this flux change is occasioned, in the first place, by the current change in the primary coil. The induced voltage of mutual induction in the secondary coil is called a *transformer voltage,* and the action that creates the e.m.f. is known as *transformer action.*

Transformer action takes place in any direct-current system of coupled circuits when a switch is opened or closed, but its more important practical application is in connection with the operation of alternating-current apparatus such as transformers and induction motors. In such electrical equipment one coil, or set of coils, is connected directly to an alternating-current source so that the current and the resulting flux automatically change periodically in both magnitude and direction. And since the linking flux in the coupled coil, or set of coils, changes, a voltage is induced in the latter by transformer action. Furthermore, the frequency of the induced voltage in the second coil is *exactly* the same as the frequency of the primary impressed voltage. If the second coil is now connected to an electrical unit such as an incandescent lamp, a heating device, or electric motor, current will flow. Thus, electrical energy can be transferred from one electric circuit to another electric circuit by transformer action even though there is absolutely no metallic connection between the two. The whole remarkable process of energy transfer takes place by the *principle of electromagnetic induction*, first discovered by Michael Faraday.

The coil that is connected to the primary source of supply is called the *primary* (coil A, Fig. 123), while the coil in which the voltage of mutual induction is induced and which feeds energy to the load is called the *secondary* (coil B, Fig. 123). The primary coil takes electrical energy from the source of supply, while the secondary, receiving this energy by electromagnetic induction, delivers it to the useful electrical unit connected to its terminals.

In order to illustrate the principle of transformer action, with particular emphasis upon the fact that the secondary frequency is exactly the same as the primary frequency, let us consider Fig. 126. The center coil of the E-type electromagnet is excited from a group of dry cells through a reversing switch. The outer coils are connected in series-aiding and to a zero-center milliammeter with a series protecting resistor. Note that the two outer coils are so connected that their polarities are always the same at any instant of time. This arrangement is fundamentally a transformer in which the primary is represented by the center coil and the secondary by the two series-connected outer coils.

If the reversing switch is now suddenly closed to the right, the center pole will try to become a north pole. Under this

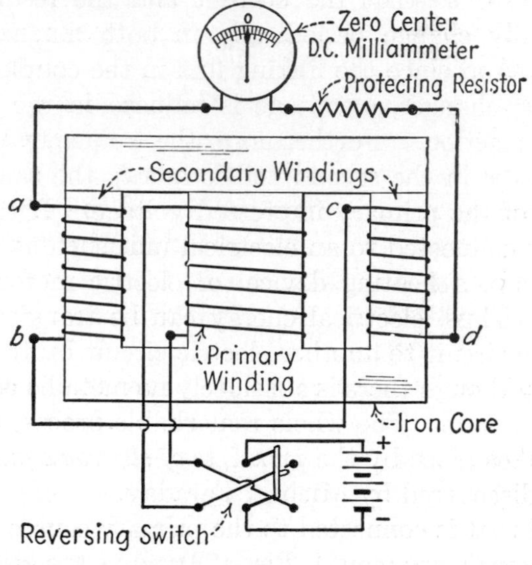

Fig. 126.—Wiring connections to verify the *principle* of transformer action.

condition terminal *d* of the secondary will become plus and terminal *a* will become minus because the secondary, by Lenz's law, will attempt to prevent the flux from establishing itself with a north pole at the center leg. The needle will thus be deflected to the right. If the reversing switch is next opened, the induced voltage in the secondary will be reversed so that terminal *a* will become plus and terminal *d* minus, for the reason that the secondary will attempt to prevent the flux from collapsing. Thus, closing the switch to the right gives a deflection to the right; then opening the switch gives a deflection to the left.

By the same reasoning as given above it should be clear that closing the switch to the left will deflect the needle to the left, whereas opening the switch will deflect the needle to the right.

And now comes the interesting point showing that an alternating current can be established in the secondary if the reversing switch is rapidly closed first to the right, then to the left, again to the right, left, etc. As this is done, the meter will be observed to keep in exact step with switch closings. Thus, closing it to the right deflects the needle right; opening it and quickly closing it to the left will deflect it to the left; again opening it and closing it to the right will deflect it to the right. In other words, the induced voltage in the secondary will be alternating, as evidenced by the left and right deflections of the direct-current instrument, whose frequency will be exactly equal to the frequency of reversals on the primary side. It is concluded, therefore, that *a transformer transfers electrical energy from one circuit to another without a change in frequency.*

Magnitude of Induced Secondary Voltage.—The flux distribution in the E-type core of Fig. 126 is perfectly symmetrical so that one half of the flux created under the primary winding passes through the left leg and the other half passes through the right leg. Obviously then, if the two coils *ab* and *cd* are identical, one half of the voltage registered by the meter is induced in the coil *ab* while the other half is induced in coil *cd*. This can be readily verified by noting the meter deflections when the latter is first connected to terminals *ab*, then to terminals *cd*, and finally to terminals *ad*. If this is done, it will be found, within a good degree of accuracy, that voltage V_{ab} equals the voltage V_{cd} and that $V_{ab} = V_{cd} = \frac{1}{2} V_{ad}$.

Reasoned another way, the voltage induced in every turn of wire in the secondary is exactly the same because the rate of change of flux in the magnetic core is entirely independent of the number of turns in the secondary winding. It follows, therefore, that the voltage induced in coil *ab* is exactly the same as that induced in coil *cd* because both have identically the same numbers of turns.

In the foregoing, coils *ab* and *cd* are connected in series-aiding. If connected in series-bucking so that the induced voltage in *cd* is at all times oppositely directed with respect to *ab*, the resultant voltage across the meter will be zero. This can be easily verified by interchanging the wires connected to coil *ab* or those connected to coil *cd*.

Another possibility is to connect coils *ab* and *cd* in parallel. In this case it is extremely important that points *a* and *c* be joined together and connected to one of the instrument terminals, and that *b* and *d* be joined together and connected to the other instrument terminal. Doing otherwise (*i.e.*, *a* to *d* and *b* to *c*) would result in a *short circuit* so that the two coils, acting additively, would form a closed, low-impedance path for the comparatively high induced voltage. It would be equivalent to a short circuit around the meter. The *proper* parallel connection as indicated above would develop a voltage equal to that induced in a single coil in exactly the same way that the voltage of two dry cells, joined in parallel, is equal to that of a single cell.

Relationship between Voltages and Turns in Transformers.—If the primary coil of a transformer (Fig. 126) is connected to an alternating-current source, the self-induced opposing voltage (counter electromotive force, c.e.m.f.) will be very nearly equal to the impressed voltage. The reason why this is so is that only a comparatively low voltage is necessary to send the small exciting current through the impedance of the primary winding. And since this low voltage is the difference between the impressed e.m.f. and the self-induced c.e.m.f., it follows that the latter two values are nearly equal. In fact, the two are generally considered equal for all practical purposes.

The induced voltage in each turn of the *primary* coil of Fig. 126 is exactly twice the induced voltage in each turn of the secondary, because there is twice as much flux in the center leg as in each of the outer legs. Therefore, the impressed e.m.f. (equal to the induced e.m.f.) on the primary having N turns will be twice as great as the induced e.m.f.

in each of the secondary coils having the same number of turns. Or, if the two secondary coils are connected in series-aiding, the secondary induced voltage will be equal to the primary impressed voltage. It should be thoroughly understood that this special relationship between primary and secondary voltages exists only because the flux passing through the former is double that passing through the latter.

However, when transformers are built for practical service, both primary and secondary coils are so arranged that the same flux passes through all of them. Under this condition the primary and secondary voltages are very simply related to each other by the number of turns of wire on one with respect to those on the other. Thus

$$\frac{\text{Primary impressed voltage}}{\text{Secondary induced voltage}} = \frac{\text{total primary turns}}{\text{total secondary turns}}$$

Or simply

$$\frac{E_p}{E_s} = \frac{N_p}{N_s} \tag{46}$$

There are two general methods used in constructing transformers. In one arrangement, the laminated core is, or is equivalent to, an E with a straight piece across the open ends. Instead of placing the coils on all three legs as in Fig. 126 (this has been done for convenience only), *all* primary and secondary coils are placed over the center leg. The cores are usually made "*pancake*" fashion so that the whole "window" space is completely filled. Figure 127 represents such a transformer, which is designated *shell type*. When a transformer is to be assembled, the various pri-

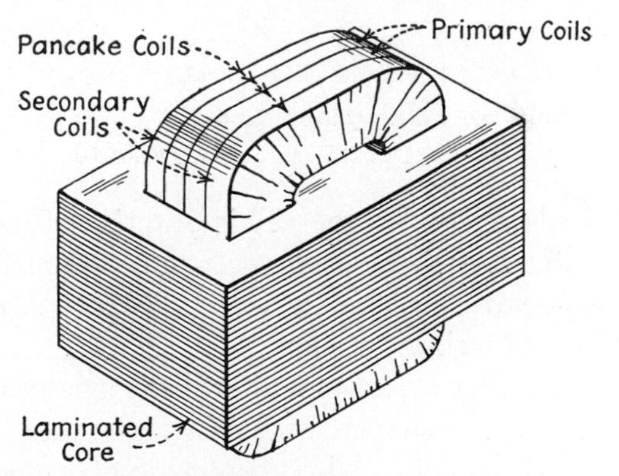

FIG. 127.—Shell-type transformer.

mary and secondary coils are sometimes taped together to form a complete unit, placed on end upon a workbench, after which the sheets of steel are properly stacked around the coils. The assembly procedure is very well illustrated in Fig. 128, in which straight pieces of sheet steel are used for

FIG. 128.—Partially assembled shell-type transformer. (*Wagner Electric Corporation.*)

the laminated core. This practice of using straight sections instead of E, L, or T sections is somewhat cheaper because expensive dies are not needed to cut the steel. Moreover, less material is wasted.

Another arrangement utilizes a laminated core, which, in effect, is U-shaped with a straight piece across its open ends as in Fig. 123. The primary and secondary coils are wound around a circular form to fit over a *cruciform* core section as in Fig. 129 or are wound around a rectangular form to fit over a rectangular core section. As will be noted, one half of both the primary and secondary windings is placed over one core leg while the other half of the primary and secondary windings is placed over the other core leg. Such a transformer is designated *core type*.

Figures 130 and 131 show a core type of transformer with a

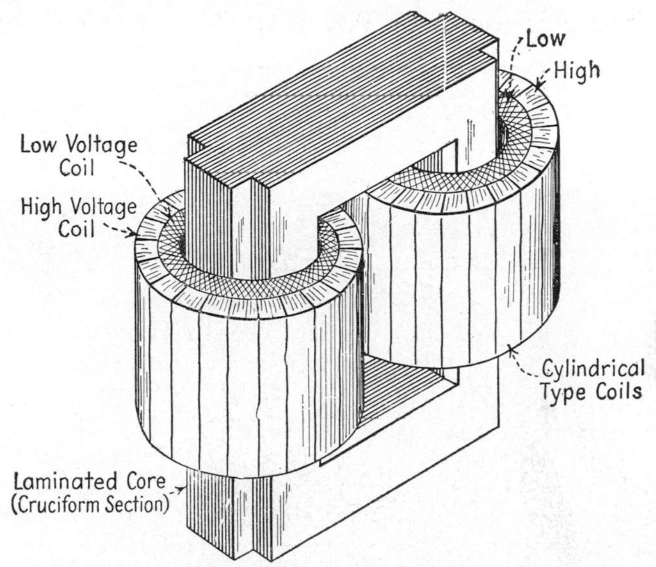

Fig. 129.—Core-type transformer with cruciform core section.

Fig. 130.—Core-type transformer being assembled. Note form-wound, dipped, and baked coils into which sheet-steel laminations are placed. (*Wagner Electric Corporation.*)

laminated core section. The partially assembled core and the manner of placing the straight steel sheets in the coil windows are clearly pictured in Fig. 130, while the assembled transformer is shown in Fig. 131. Note particularly the

FIG. 131.—Completely assembled core-type transformer, shown partially assembled in Fig. 130. (*Wagner Electric Corporation.*)

way in which the dipped and baked windings are carefully insulated from the *grounded* core by the liberal use of insulating papers, tapes, and fiberboard. Also clearly visible are the primary and secondary coil ends, which eventually would be brought out of the transformer case through insulating bushings. The four low-tension wires are the heavy leads shown on top, while the two small high-tension wires may be seen on the bottom resting on the table.

Example 5.—A 60-cycle transformer has 240 primary turns and 96 secondary turns. If the impressed voltage on the primary is 115, what is the secondary induced voltage?

Solution:

$$\frac{E_p}{E_s} = \frac{N_p}{N_s}; \quad \frac{115}{E_s} = \frac{240}{96}$$

Therefore,

$$E_s = 115 \times \frac{96}{240} = 46 \text{ volts}$$

Example 6.—A shell-type transformer is to be constructed with 300 turns on the primary side for connection to a 120-volt, 60-cycle source. (*a*) Calculate the total number of turns to be used for the secondary winding if the latter is to develop 24 volts. (*b*) What provision should be made if it is also desired that the secondary shall provide 12 volts?

Solution:

a. $\frac{E_p}{E_s} = \frac{N_p}{N_s}; \quad \frac{120}{24} = \frac{300}{N_s}$

Therefore, $N_s = 300 \times \frac{24}{120} = 60$ turns

b. Wind the secondary with two coils, each one having 30 turns.

For 24 volts, connect the two coils in series-aiding (see Fig. 132*a*).

For 12 volts, connect the two coils in parallel (see Fig. 132*b*).

Ratio of Transformation.—Transformers are extremely versatile, being used in many kinds of electrical installations for various purposes. Their most important field of application, however, involves those requirements in which electrical energy must be transferred from one circuit to another *with a change of voltage.* Well-known simple examples of this practice are transformers used in connection with bell ringing, welders, toys, radios, street lighting, and distribution systems for domestic and industrial service. In all of these the secondary induced voltage is always less than the impressed primary voltage. This voltage reduction is, of course, accomplished by having fewer secondary turns than primary turns. The *ratio* of the total effective primary turns to the total effective secondary turns is known as the *ratio of transformation.* The word "effective" is used here to designate the number of turns *in series* between primary or secondary terminals. In the case where, for example, two coils are connected in series, the total effective turns

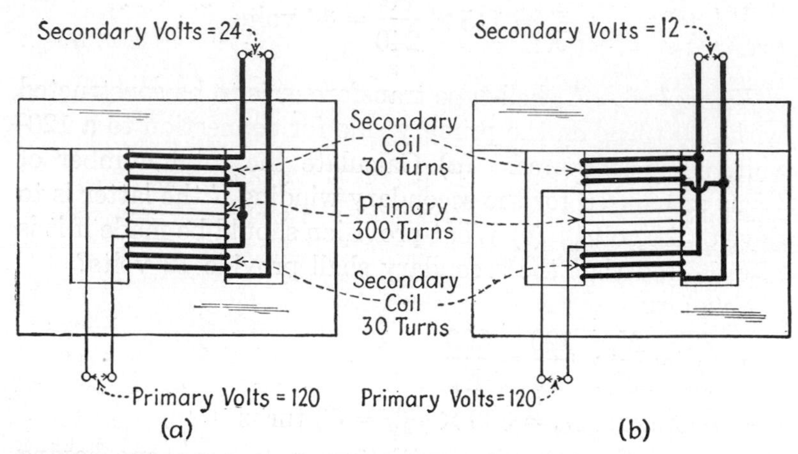

FIG. 132.—Methods of connections on the secondary side of a transformer to obtain two voltages.

would be the sum of the turns on both coils. However, where two coils are connected in parallel, they *must* have equal numbers of turns, in which event the total effective turns would be the same as for a single coil.

There are many installations in which the primary impressed voltage must be raised to a higher secondary voltage. Such transformers would, of course, be constructed with more secondary turns than primary turns. Generally speaking, these are employed only where the domestic or industrial consumer of electrical energy is not likely to come in contact with the distribution systems they serve. When used for this purpose, they are usually called *power transformers* because they are most commonly installed by the power companies to raise the voltage at the beginning of a long transmission line. In this connection it may be pointed out that the transformer generally employed to lower the 2,300-volt transmission voltage to 230 and 115 volts for domestic service is called a *distribution transformer*.

Transformers used to lower or raise the primary voltage are usually referred to as *step-down* or *step-up*. Examples of the step-down type are bell-ringing, welding, toy, and distribution transformers. Power transformers used at the beginning of a long transmission line where the voltage is raised from perhaps 13,800 volts to 230,000 volts are of the step-up variety. Testing transformers used in high-voltage laboratories in connection with the testing of insulators, lightning arresters, circuit breakers, and other high-voltage equipment are also of the step-up type. Although it is practically possible to employ a step-down transformer of the distribution variety for step-up service, this is rarely ever done. However, it is common to make use of power transformers in this dual capacity. The important fact to remember in this connection is that the primary voltage, *i.e.*, the input voltage, must never exceed the rating of the winding to which it is connected. Thus, a 115- to 15-volt step-down bell-ringing transformer can be used as a step-up transformer if the normal 15-volt winding is connected to a 15-volt source; the secondary voltage will then be 115 volts. The same thing is true of a 13,800- to 230,000-volt step-up power transformer. In this case the high-voltage winding becomes the primary, being connected to the 230,000-volt high-tension line, and the low-voltage winding becomes the secondary; used in this way it becomes a step-down transformer.

In designating the ratio of transformation of a transformer it is generally customary to indicate it by saying, for example, 10 to 1 or 20 to 1 step-down or step-up; in writing it the practice is to use the symbols 10 : 1 or 20 : 1. Thus, a bell-ringing transformer having a 115-volt primary and a 15-volt secondary would be referred to as having a ratio of transformation of 7.67 : 1 step-down; a 13,800- to 230,000-volt power transformer would be referred to as having a ratio of transformation of 16.7 : 1 step-up.

Example 7.—A core-type transformer, like that shown in Fig. 129, has two primary coils each with 220 turns, and two secondary coils each with 44 turns. If each of the primary coils is designed for connection to a 115-volt source, what four possible wiring connections can be made and what will be the primary and secondary voltages and the ratio of transformation in each case? Make a simple schematic diagram for each connection.

Solution:

a. Primaries in series, secondaries in series:
$E_p = 115 + 115 = 230$ volts; E_s per coil $= \frac{44}{220} \times 115$ $= 23$ volts
$E_s = 23 + 23 = 46$; $r =$ ratio of transformation $= \frac{440}{88} : 1$ $= 5 : 1$ step-down

b. Primaries in series, secondaries in parallel:
$E_p = 230$ volts; $E_s = 23$ volts; $r = \frac{440}{44} : 1 = 10 : 1$ step-down

c. Primaries in parallel, secondaries in parallel:
$E_p = 115$ volts; $E_s = 23$ volts; $r = \frac{220}{44} : 1 = 5 : 1$ step-down

d. Primaries in parallel, secondaries in series:
$E_p = 115$ volts; $E_s = 46$ volts; $r = \frac{220}{88} : 1 = 2.5 : 1$ step-down

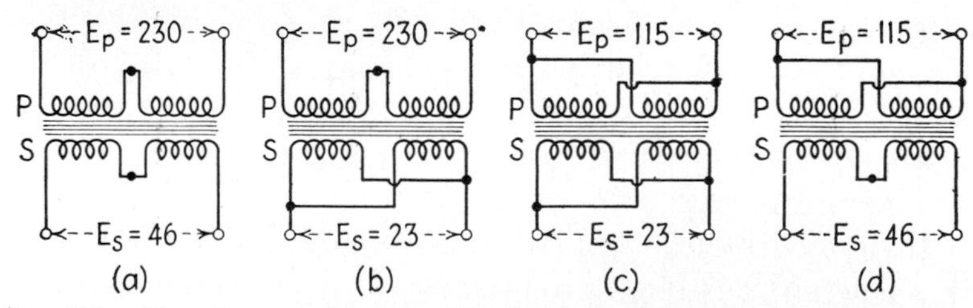

Fig. 133.—Transformer with two primaries and two secondaries connected for two primary and two secondary voltages.

Transformer Loading.—When the secondary of a transformer is connected to a consuming device, called a *load*, such as a lamp, a heater, or a motor, the current that will flow will be determined for the most part by the secondary induced voltage and the impedance of the load. Furthermore, the power factor of the load current will depend upon the relative magnitudes of the resistance and the reactance of the load device (see Chap. 5). The power output of the secondary winding will thus be

$$P_s = E_s \times I_s \times P.F._s \tag{47}$$

where P_s = secondary power output
E_s = secondary voltage
I_s = secondary current
$P.F._s$ = secondary power factor

Since transformers have no moving parts and the copper and iron losses are usually very low, they operate at very high efficiency. If 100 per cent efficiency is assumed (output = input), it must be true that the power delivered by the secondary must be matched by an equivalent power input to the primary, which is equal to

$$P_p = E_p \times I_p \times P.F._p \tag{48}$$

where the subscript p designates the primary side.

Putting Eqs. (47) and (48) equal to each other and assuming that the primary and secondary power factors are equal (for practical purposes they usually are), it follows that

$$E_p \times I_p = E_s \times I_s$$

or

$$\frac{E_p}{E_s} = \frac{I_s}{I_p} \tag{49}$$

Equation (49) is extremely important since it indicates that the primary and secondary currents are *inversely proportional* to their respective voltages. Thus, when the voltage is lowered by a step-down transformer by a given ratio of transformation, the current is raised proportionately by the same ratio of transformation. To illustrate, consider industrial-duty transformer-type welders. These are usually built for 220-, 440-, or 550-volt primary rating and stepped down to approximately 75 volts. The usual welding currents in such welding operations are 200, 300, 400, and 500 amp. When the above formula is applied, it is found that the primary currents on 220 volts are approximately 70, 105, 140, and 175 amp., respectively. When used on higher voltage primary circuits, the currents would be still less. When the voltage is stepped up, as it is at the beginning of a long high-voltage transmission line, the current is, of course, automatically lowered. Since this lowered current must flow through many miles of wire, it is obvious that two important economies result, namely, lower cost of transmission-line copper and lower copper losses (I^2R losses) in the line wires.

Example 8.—A distribution transformer has its high side connected to a 4,600-volt transmission line and delivers 5 kw. at unity power factor to a load. If the ratio of transformation is 20 : 1, calculate (*a*) the low-side voltage and current, (*b*) the high-side current.

Solution:

$$a.\ E_s = \frac{1}{20} \times 4{,}600 = 230 \text{ volts};\ I_s = \frac{5{,}000}{230} = 21.7 \text{ amp.}$$

$$b.\ \frac{I_s}{I_p} = \frac{E_p}{E_s};\ \frac{21.7}{I_p} = \frac{4{,}600}{230};\ I_p = \frac{1}{20} \times 21.7 = 1.085 \text{ amp.}$$

Autotransformers.—In principle and general construction the autotransformer does not differ from the ordinary two-winding transformer, but it does differ from it in the way in which the primary and secondary are interrelated. In the ordinary transformer the primary and secondary windings are completely insulated from each other but are magnetically linked by a common laminated core. In the autotransformer the two windings, primary and secondary, are both electrically and magnetically interconnected. The autotransformer may be constructed in either of two ways; in one arrangement there is a single continuous winding with taps brought out at convenient points determined by the desired secondary voltages; in the other arrangement there are two or more distinct coils that are electrically connected to form a continuous winding. In any case the same laws governing ordinary transformers apply to autotransformers.

Referring to Fig. 134*a*, consider the schematic diagram of an autotransformer. The input voltage E_1 is connected to

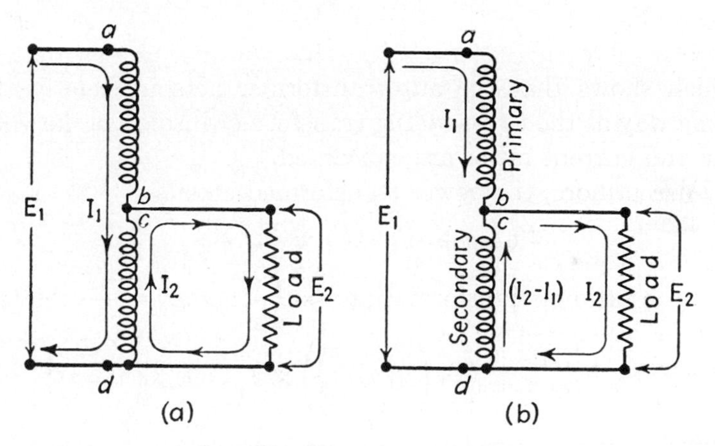

Fig. 134.—The autotransformer.

the complete winding *ad*, and the load is connected across a portion of the winding, *cd*. The voltage E_2 will bear the same relation to E_1 as in the conventional two-winding transformer; *i.e.*, E_2 will equal E_1 multiplied by the ratio of the number of turns between *c* and *d* to the total number of turns between *a* and *d*. Thus

$$E_2 = E_1 \times \frac{N_{cd}}{N_{ad}}$$

Assuming a resistance load ($P.F. = 1$), the load current I_2 will be E_2 divided by the load resistance R_L. If the transformer efficiency is considered to be 100 per cent, the power input $E_1 \times I_1$ must equal the load power $E_2 \times I_2$.

Note that I_1 flows only in the portion of the winding *ab*, whereas the current $(I_2 - I_1)$ flows in the portion of the winding *cd*; this is shown in Fig. 134*b*. If winding *ab* is considered as the primary and winding *cd* is considered as the secondary, it follows that

$$I_1 \times (E_1 - E_2) = (I_2 - I_1) \times E_2$$

or $$\frac{E_1 - E_2}{E_2} = \frac{I_2 - I_1}{I_1}, \quad \text{and} \quad \frac{E_1}{E_2} - 1 = \frac{I_2}{I_1} - 1$$

Therefore, $$\frac{E_1}{E_2} = \frac{I_2}{I_1} \tag{50}$$

which shows that the autotransformer acts in exactly the same way as the two-winding transformer insofar as the voltage and current ratios are concerned.

Furthermore, the power transformed equals

$$P_{\text{(transformed)}} = (E_1 - E_2) \times I_1$$

But the ratio of transformation $r = \dfrac{E_1}{E_2}$; or $E_2 = \dfrac{E_1}{r}$.

Therefore, $P_{\text{(transformed)}} = \left(E_1 - \dfrac{E_1}{r}\right) \times I_1 = E_1 I_1 \left(1 - \dfrac{1}{r}\right)$

Hence

$$\text{Power transformed} = \text{power input} \times \left(1 - \frac{1}{r}\right) \tag{51}$$

Example 9.—An autotransformer having a primary voltage of 120 and a secondary voltage of 90 delivers a load of 5 kw. at unity power factor. What power is *transformed* by the transformer and how much power is conducted directly from the source to the load?

Solution:

$r = \frac{120}{90} = 1.33{:}1$

Power transformed $= 5{,}000 \times (1 - \frac{1}{1.33}) = 1{,}250$ watts

Power conducted $= 5{,}000 - 1{,}250 = 3{,}750$ watts

The solution of the above example should make it especially clear that *an autotransformer of given physical dimensions can handle much more load power than an equivalent two-winding transformer.* In the above case 5 kw. are handled with a transformer of one-fourth that capacity, or 1.25 kw. The difference, 3,750 watts, is *conducted directly* to the load *without transformer action.*

Autotransformers are cheaper in first cost than conventional two-winding transformers for the same loading. They also have better regulation, *i.e.*, the voltage does not drop so much with load, and they have better efficiency. However, they are unsafe for use on ordinary distribution circuits because the high-voltage primary circuit is directly connected to the low-voltage secondary circuit. For connecting one high-

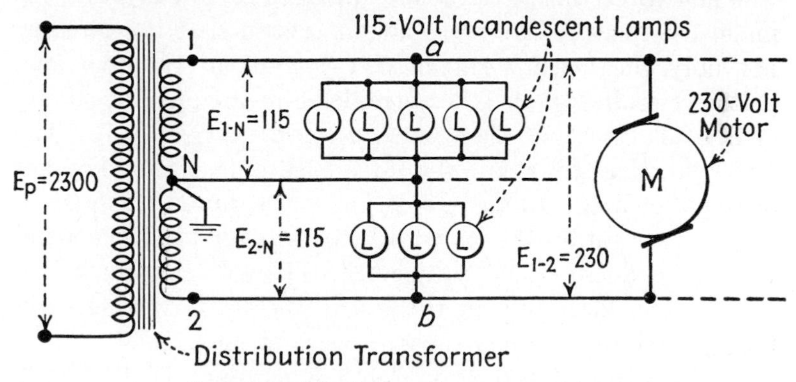

FIG. 135.—The Edison three-wire system.

voltage system, say 22,000 volts, to another, say 13,800 volts, they are especially suitable, for the reasons given above. They are also used to supply lower than line voltage to certain types of alternating-current motors during the starting period.

Three-wire Edison Distribution Systems.—One of the important advantages of a transformer is its ability to provide a three-wire circuit from the low-voltage side. This service is particularly advantageous in general-distribution systems for two reasons: (1) it reduces the cost of copper feeders, and (2) it provides a method whereby the normal lighting circuits are supplied with 115-volt service, and the 230-volt service can be provided for the motor loads. In such a system (see Fig. 135), used extensively and known as the *Edison three-wire system,* the transformer secondary has two sets of coils of equal numbers of turns connected in series. The junction between the two coils, N, is usually grounded in order to ensure some measure of protection to persons who might accidentally come into contact with a transformer whose insulation has failed. The line wire carried from this point to the several loads is known as the *neutral.* The neutral wire generally carries less current than the outside wires 1 and 2, except where the load is on one side only, *i.e.*, 1 to N or 2 to N. The 230-volt motor load does not affect the current flowing in the neutral wire.

When three-wire systems are installed, it is customary to make the neutral wire of sufficient size so that it can carry not only the normal unbalanced current in the two low-voltage circuits but also the entire load on any one side should all the load on the other side be completely cut off. The latter could easily occur should a fuse or a circuit breaker open either line. In any event, no protection in the form of a fuse or circuit breaker must ever be provided in the neutral wire. To do so would subject the 115-volt circuits to approximately 230 volts in the event the loads were greatly unbalanced and the neutral wire were opened.

Example 10.—Referring to Fig. 135, assume that the upper 115-volt load is 25 amp., the lower 115-volt load is 15 amp., and the motor load is 30 amp. If the power factor in all cases is considered unity, calculate the current (*a*) in line $1-a$, (*b*) in line $2-b$, (*c*) in the neutral line N. Determine the power delivered (*d*) by transformer coil $1-N$, (*e*) by transformer coil $N-2$, (*f*) by the primary coil. (*g*) Calculate the current in the primary coil.

Solution:

a. $I_{1-a} = 25 + 30 = 55$ amp.

b. $I_{2-b} = 15 + 30 = 45$ amp.

c. $I_N = 25 - 15 = 10$ amp.

d. $P_{1-N} = 55 \times 115 = 6{,}325$ watts

e. $P_{N-2} = 45 \times 115 = 5{,}175$ watts

f. $P_{\text{prim}} = 6{,}325 + 5{,}175 = 11{,}500$ watts

g. $I_{\text{prim}} = \dfrac{11{,}500}{2{,}300} = 5$ amp.

Instrument Transformers.—When it becomes necessary to measure high currents or high voltages, it is found particularly desirable to use standard low-range instruments in conjunction with specially constructed, accurate-ratio transformers. The latter are called *instrument transformers* and are of two kinds, namely, *current transformers* and *potential transformers*. In use they are required to transform relatively small amounts of energy because their only loads, called *burdens*, constitute the delicate moving elements of ammeters and voltmeters.

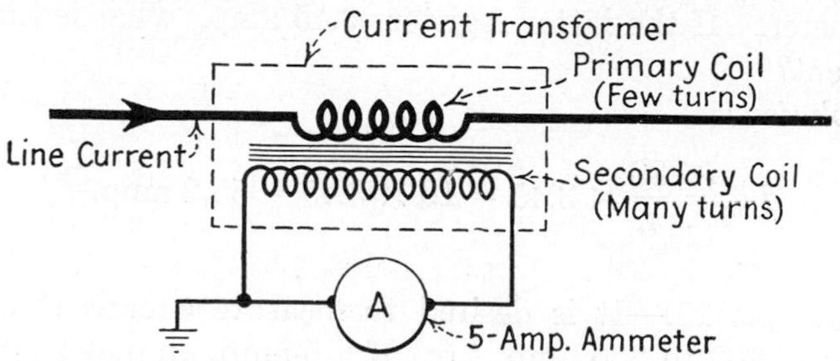

FIG. 136.—Wiring diagram of a current transformer.

Current transformers, as the name implies, are used with ammeters to measure currents in alternating-current circuits. Potential transformers, on the other hand, are used with voltmeters to measure potential differences, or voltages, in alternating-current circuits. In practice, the current transformers are always coupled to common 5-amp. ammeters, while potential transformers are usually coupled to common 150-volt voltmeters.

A current transformer has a primary coil of one or more turns of *heavy* wire which is always connected in *series* in the circuit in which the current is to be measured. The secondary has a great many turns of *fine* wire which is always connected across the ammeter terminals (5-amp. range usually); the latter indicates *indirectly* the current flowing in the primary. In Fig. 136 it should be obvious that, insofar as voltages are concerned, the transformer is of the step-up variety because the secondary has more turns than the primary. It follows, therefore, that *the current will be stepped down* in the same ratio as the voltage is stepped up. Thus, if the current transformer has a ratio of 100:5, it means that the voltage is stepped up in the ratio of 20:1, but more particularly that the current is stepped down by the same ratio. A designation like the above (100:5) is commonly used for current transformers because it indicates both the maximum allowable primary current and the proper ammeter range for the connected instrument.

Example 11.—An 80:5 transformer is connected to a 5-amp. ammeter. If the latter registers 3.45 amp., what is the line current?

Solution:

$$I_{\text{line}} = \frac{80}{5} \times 3.45 = 16 \times 3.45 = 55.2 \text{ amp.}$$

Example 12.—It is desired to measure a current of the order of 200 to 250 amp. (*a*) If a 5-amp. ammeter is to be used in conjunction with a current transformer, what should be the ratio of the latter? (*b*) With this transformer what should the instrument deflection be multiplied by to give the true line current?

Solution:

a. Use a 300:5 or 400:5 standard current transformer.

b. For 300:5, multiply instrument deflection by 60.
For 400:5, multiply instrument deflection by 80.

One of the most practical types of current transformer is the *clamp-on* or *clip-on* type. This ingenious instrument has a laminated core so arranged that it may be opened out at a hinged section by pressing a triggerlike projection. When the core is opened, it permits admission of the current-carrying conductor whereupon the trigger is released and the core is closed tight by a spring. The current-carrying conductor thus acts as a single-turn primary while the accurately wound secondary is permanently connected to the ammeter conveniently mounted in the handle. Figure 138 shows such a clamp-on type of current transformer having six current scales. By moving a pointer over a dial, full-scale current deflections of 10, 25, 50, 100, 250, and 500 amp. will be registered. The wiring connections for this multirange instrument are shown in Fig. 137.

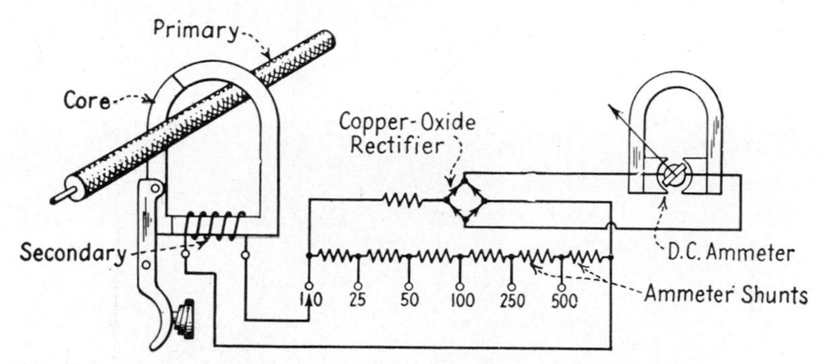

FIG. 137.—Internal wiring connections of a clamp-on-type alternating-current ammeter. Note that the current-transformer secondary is connected to a direct-current ammeter through a copper-oxide rectifier and a properly designed multiple shunt. (*Weston Electrical Instrument Corporation.*)

Potential transformers are carefully designed, extremely accurate-ratio step-down transformers. They are used in conjunction with standard low-range voltmeters, whose deflection, when multiplied by the ratio of transformation, gives the true voltage on the high side. In general, they differ very little from the ordinary two-winding transformers already discussed, except that they handle an extremely small amount of power. Since their secondaries are required to operate instruments and sometimes relays and pilot lights in electric circuits, they ordinarily have ratings of 40 to 100 watts. Common ratios of transformation are 10:1, 20:1, 40:1, 80:1, 100:1, 120:1, etc. As a rule, transformers for this service are of the shell type because this construction develops a higher degree of accuracy. Ordinary 150-volt voltmeters are generally used with such transformers to indicate *indirectly* the primary voltage. Figure 139 shows a potential transformer connected for the measurement of a high voltage with a common 150-volt voltmeter. Note particularly that the secondary circuit, for safety, is completely isolated from the high-voltage circuit and, in addition, is *grounded*. Such grounding serves

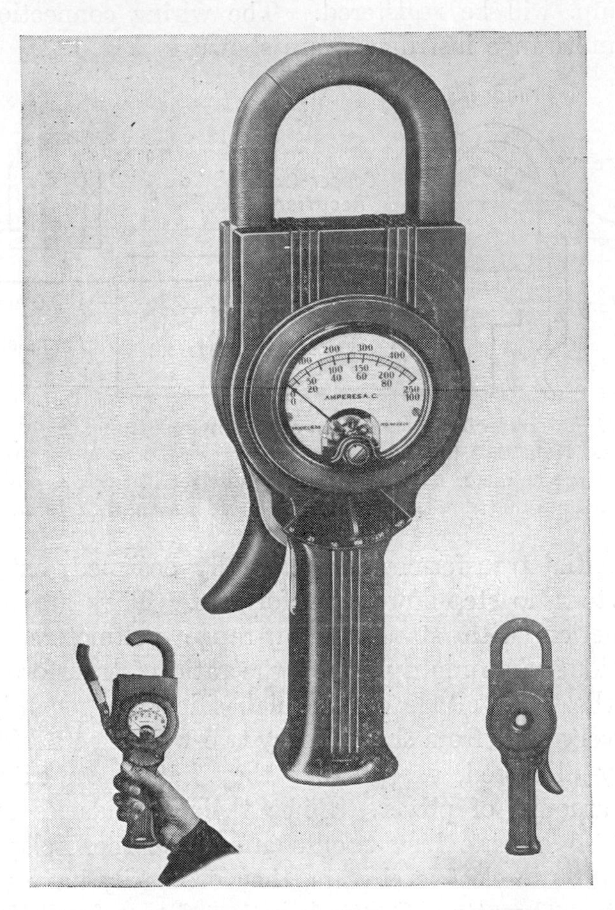

Fig. 138.—Photograph of a clamp-on ammeter. Note open position in the lower left, ready for clamping over a current-carrying conductor. (*Weston Electrical Instrument Corporation.*)

to protect the operator from the high-voltage hazard should he accidentally come in contact with the wiring.

Example 13.—An 80:1 potential transformer and a 150-volt voltmeter are connected as in Fig. 139 for the measurement of the high-line voltage. If the voltmeter deflection is 142, what is the transmission-line voltage?

Solution:

$$E_{\text{line}} = 80 \times 142 = 11{,}360 \text{ volts}$$

General Transformer Considerations.—The ideal transformer is one that (*a*) would change the primary voltage to a secondary voltage by a *constant ratio*, known as the *ratio of transformation*, (*b*) would transfer electrical energy from one circuit to another without loss (efficiency equals 100 per

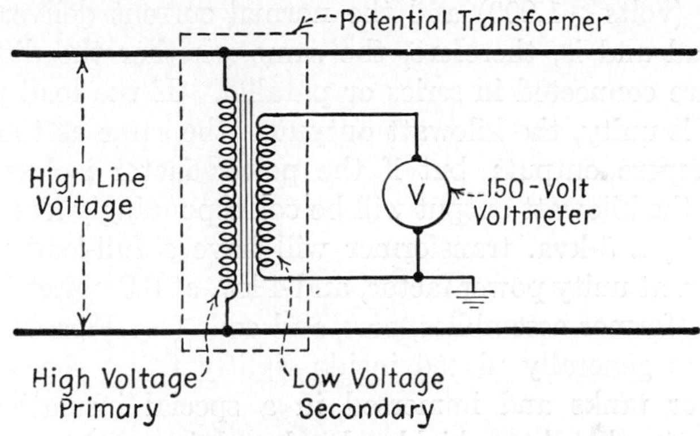

FIG. 139.—Wiring diagrams of a potential transformer.

cent), and (*c*) would maintain a constant secondary terminal voltage at all loads. In the actual transformer, however, there are losses that reduce the efficiency somewhat, although these losses, which occur in the copper windings and the laminated steel core, are comparatively small. When a constant alternating voltage is impressed across the primary terminals, the exciting current that flows sets up a definite magnetic flux, corresponding to this voltage. This flux is, for all practical purposes, approximately constant at all loads. However, the exciting current increases very rapidly when the voltage is increased or the frequency is decreased.

When the transformer is loaded, the secondary voltage decreases very slightly because of the internal *voltage drop* in the windings. If this change in voltage between the unloaded condition and the loaded condition is divided by the voltage of the transformer under load, the ratio is known as the *regulation.* Or, represented as a percentage, the ratio may be multiplied by 100. For example, if the voltage at no load is 230 and the voltage at full load is 225, the difference of 5 volts divided by 225 and then multiplied by 100 gives $\frac{5}{225} \times 100 = 2.22$ per cent.

A transformer is always rated by its kilovolt-ampere *output* (except in the case of those used for small-power purposes). This is simply the product of the kilovolt-output rating (volts ÷ 1,000) and the normal current delivered to the load and is, therefore, the same whether the different coils are connected in series or parallel. If the load power factor is unity, the kilowatt output is the same as the kilovolt-ampere output; but if the power factor is less than unity, the kilowatt output will be correspondingly less. For example, a 5-kva. transformer will have a full-load rating of 5 kw. at unity power factor, and 4 kw. at 0.8 power factor.

Transformer assemblies, core and coils (see Figs. 127 and 129) are generally placed inside tightly fitted sheet-metal cases or tanks and immersed in a special insulating oil. The latter has been highly developed in recent years so that it acts to insulate the windings from one another and ground and serves also as a circulating medium to carry the heat from the transformer elements to the case. While modern transformer oils have, in general, excellent properties, they do nevertheless have the disadvantage that they have a tendency to absorb moisture. The importance of tightly sealing a transformer case against this tendency to absorb moisture should be emphasized because the addition of only 8 parts of water in 1,000,000 reduces the insulating quality of the oil to a value that is generally recognized as below standard. Another thing to watch in oil is sludging, which is simply the decomposition of the oil with continued use. It is due principally to the exposure to oxygen during heating and results in the formation of heavy deposits of dark, heavy matter that will eventually clog the cooling ducts in the transformer. When carried too far, sludging will cause transformers to overheat.

No feature in the construction of a transformer should be given more attention and care than the insulating materials, because the life of the unit will depend to a very large extent upon the quality, durability, and handling of these materials. All insulating materials such as paper, pressboard, cloth, mica, asbestos, and impregnating compounds should be selected on the basis of their high quality and their ability to preserve this quality after many years of normal service. The coils should generally be wound on forms, and must afterwards be dipped in a good insulating varnish and baked in an oven. The insulating compound should be capable of providing a solid moisture-resisting surface after proper treatment.

Experiment 24. Generated Voltages

Objectives: (*a*) To show that a voltage will be *generated* in a rectangular coil of wire if one side is moved across a magnetic field. (*b*) To show that the direction of the generated e.m.f. depends upon the direction of the magnetic field and the direction of motion. (*c*) To show that *no* voltage will be generated in a coil if the latter is bent in such a manner that the voltage in one half of the inductors is oppositely directed with respect to the other half.

Procedure: To perform this experiment it will be necessary to make two simple coils like that shown in Fig. 140*a* and *b*. Both coils should have about 50 turns of No. 25 enameled wire. One of them (Fig. 140*a*) is simply rectangular in shape and is fastened to a pencil or stick with tape. The other (Fig. 140*b*) is likewise wound over a rectangular form but is a little wider than the first; it is then bent over a pencil or stick at the middle of its two longer sides. Additional equipment needed will be an electromagnet of some sort, a battery, a reversing switch, and a direct-current, zero-center, sensitive voltmeter. These are connected as shown in Fig. 141, in which the E-type electromagnet, previously described, is used.

Part 1. Using the straight coil first (Fig. 140*a*), close the reversing switch on one side. Holding the pencil at

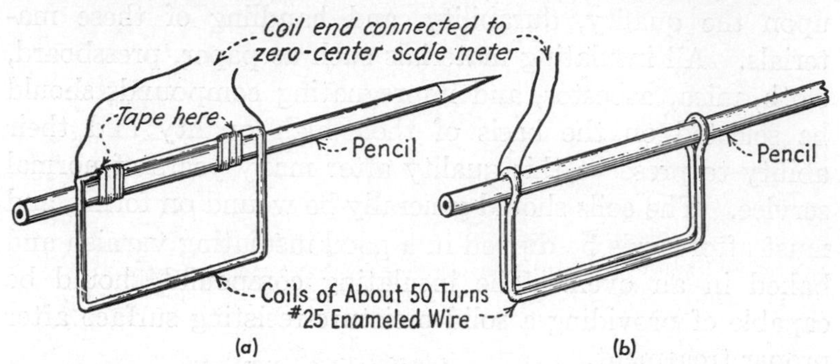

FIG. 140.—Construction arrangements of coils to verify the *principle* of generation of voltage.

its end, roll it back and forth so that the lower side of the coil moves over the pole face of the electromagnet in such a way that lines of force are cut. Note that the deflections reverse as the motion changes direction. Observe particularly which way the needle deflects as the coil is moved to the right and then to the left.

Now close the reversing switch on the other side. This will change the direction of the current through the exciting coil. Repeat the operations described above, noting especially that the needle deflections will be opposite those observed in the previous test.

To prove that the generated voltage depends upon the rate of flux cutting it will be necessary to change the value of the current in the exciting coil, which in turn will change the value of the flux. This may be done readily by using more or fewer dry cells in series or by inserting a rheostat in the battery circuit.

Part 2. Replace the straight coil with the bent one (Fig. 140*b*). Repeat tests performed in Part 1. In all cases it will be observed that instrument deflections will be practically zero, regardless of the direction of motion, the polarity of the electromagnet, or the magnitude of the flux.

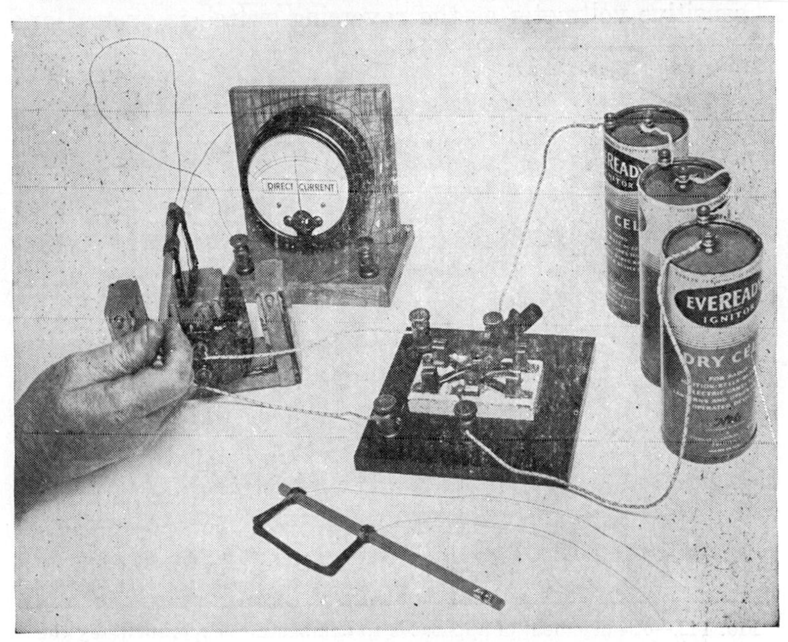

FIG. 141.—Arrangement of apparatus to demonstrate experimentally the *principle* of voltage generation.

Carefully explain why no voltage is generated in the complete coil, although the e.m.f. in all the wires is in the same direction at any given instant of time.

EXPERIMENT 25. INDUCED VOLTAGES

Objectives: (*a*) To show that a voltage will be *induced* in a coil of wire if the flux passing *through* it is changed. (*b*) To show that the magnitude of the induced voltage will depend upon the relative position of a coil of wire with respect to a pole.

Procedure: Without disturbing the arrangement of parts and connections illustrated in Fig. 141, be prepared to place the straight rectangular coil over the center pole, or either of the outside poles, in any of four positions. In each position it will be our purpose to observe the *direction* and magnitude of the deflections on the zero-center-scale sensitive voltmeter as the reversing switch is opened and

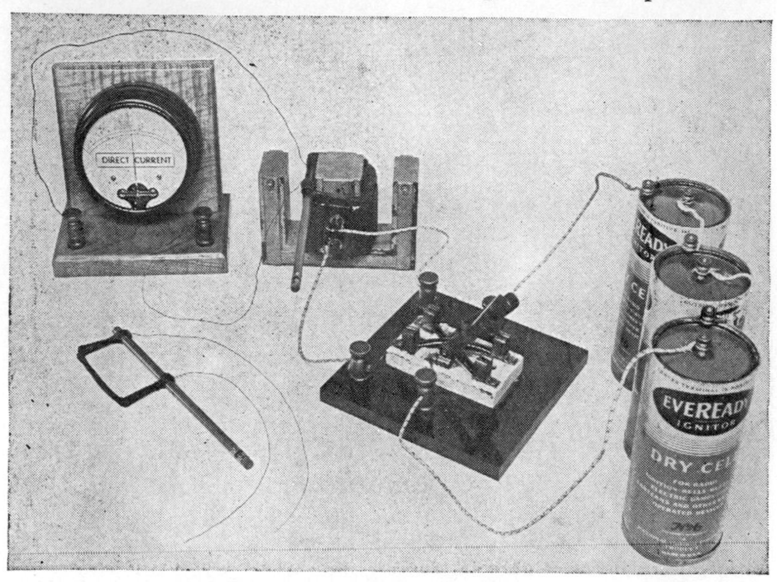

FIG. 142.—Arrangement of apparatus to demonstrate experimentally the *principle* of electromagnetic induction.

closed. Several combinations are possible for each one of the poles. For example,

1. Pencil extension forward and left—switch opened, then closed
2. Pencil extension forward and right—switch opened, then closed
3. Pencil extension rear and right—switch opened, then closed
4. Pencil extension rear and left—switch opened, then closed

Figure 142 shows the arrangement for position 1 with the pencil extension forward and left, facing the equipment.

It will be well to note particularly that every time *one* position change is made, the needle deflection will be reversed. When two position changes are made, the same deflection direction will be observed. Thus, deflection is reversed when the coil is changed from pencil extension rear right to rear left, or from rear right to front right, or from front-left-center leg to front-left-outer leg; there is no deflection when the coil is changed from pencil extension rear right to front left.

As each of the above tests is made, the student should try to explain exactly why the needle either reverses or does not reverse.

Next hold the coil over the center pole face in various positions. For example, (1) hold the coil in a vertical plane resting the bottom side on the center pole face; (2) tilt the coil at various angles. In each position close and open the switch and note the direction and *magnitude* of the deflections. Of particular interest is the fact that no deflection will be observed when the coil is held in a vertical plane with the bottom side resting directly on the middle of the center pole face. As the vertically held coil is moved to the right or left of the middle of the pole face, the magnitude of the deflection will increase. In all cases observations should be made both for closing and opening the switch.

Experiment 26. Lenz's Law Demonstration

Objective: To demonstrate *Lenz's law,* and to show that the *induced voltage* and the resulting current flow *depend upon the rate of change of flux.*

Procedure: For the purposes of this experiment it will be necessary to obtain or make an *aluminum* cup-shaped piece like that shown in Fig. 143. The one used by the author was an aluminum die casting, before machining, originally made to act as one of the end bells of a small motor. A $\frac{1}{2}$-in. hole was drilled in the center of the bottom of the cup, whose thickness was $\frac{1}{8}$ in., outside diameter $2\frac{3}{4}$ in., and depth $\frac{3}{4}$ in. A steel rod about 4 in. long and slightly less than $\frac{1}{2}$ in. in diameter was then made so that it could easily slide in the hole of the cup.

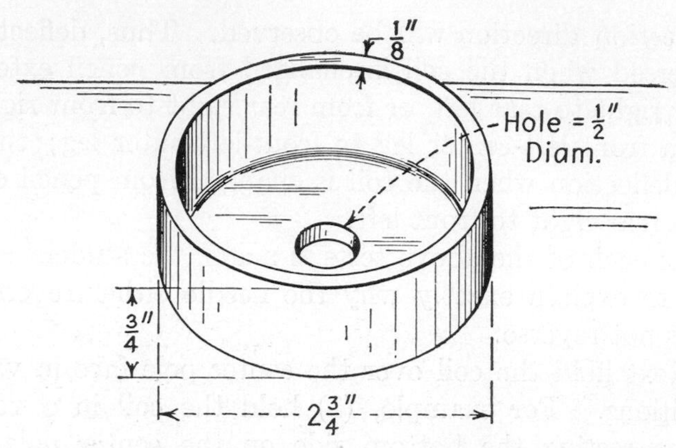

FIG. 143.—Construction details of aluminum cup.

With the same E-type electromagnet as in Experiment 24, the steel rod is first placed on end on the center pole face. The aluminum cup is then slipped over the rod so that it rests flat on the pole face. Finally, the ex-

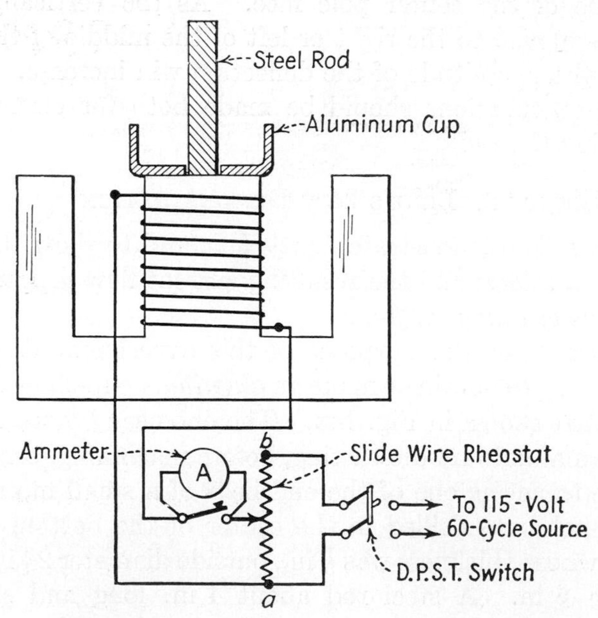

FIG. 144.—Wiring diagram showing method of testing an electromagnet to determine the force exerted upon an aluminum cup.

citing coil is connected to a 115-volt, 60-cycle source of supply through an alternating-current ammeter of the proper range and a slide-wire rheostat. Figure 144 shows how the parts are arranged and wired, and Fig. 145 is a photograph illustrating the assembly of the apparatus when the electromagnet is excited. Note particularly

Fig. 145.—Arrangement of apparatus to demonstrate experimentally the force action exerted by an electromagnet upon a weighted aluminum cup. (See Fig. 144 for wiring diagram.)

how the aluminum cup hangs suspended in space with no apparent support.

Part 1. Starting with the slider of the slide-wire rheostat at *a*, progressively increase the current through the exciting coil in steps until the maximum value is reached at *b*. At each current setting accurately measure the height of the aluminum cup above the pole face, recording the results in a neat table.

Part 2. Starting again, as in Part 1, with the slider at *a*, progressively increase the current in steps, but this time pour sand into the cup for each current setting until the bottom of the cup drops down and just rests on the pole face. A record should be kept in a neat table of the total weight of the cup and the sand for each value of current.

Using the data thus obtained, plot a curve showing the relation between the force exerted upon the cup (ordinate) and the current (abscissa).

Discussion: Lenz's law provides an explanation for the action of repulsion that exists between the electromagnet and the aluminum cup. The alternating flux created by the primary circuit magnetizes the steel rod placed over the center pole face. Since this alternating flux must pass up through the cup, voltages are induced in successively increasing circular sections, each of which acts like a short-circuited transformer secondary. Thus, alternating currents flow in the cup in circular paths around the steel rod. Since these currents are, at every instant, in such a direction as to create flux tending to oppose any change in the existing primary flux, it follows that the primary and secondary currents are always oppositely directed. Thus, when the primary current is clockwise and increasing, the secondary (cup) current is counterclockwise and increasing. And since the cup is *in effect* a single turn coil of wire carrying a very large current, a force of repulsion will exist between the primary and the secondary because they are collinear and carry currents in opposite directions. Furthermore, the force of repulsion will depend upon the original primary alternating flux, which in turn is determined by the current setting.

Experiment 27. Transformer-action Demonstration

Objective: To demonstrate transformer action by mutually coupling one primary coil and two series-connected coils, using an E-type core for the magnetic circuit.

Procedure: Using an E-type core and three coils as illustrated in Fig. 102 (any other equivalent arrangement will be satisfactory), connect the latter as shown in Fig. 126. Note that the outer two coils are in series-aiding and that they represent the secondary; they are connected to a zero-center-scale direct-current instrument. The latter should be properly protected by sufficient series resistance if the instrument is very sensitive. The primary coil is connected to a battery of dry cells through a reversing switch.

With everything in readiness, try opening and closing the reversing switch, first on one side and then on the other. Always note the deflection directions and their magnitudes. Try to predict the deflection direction *before* the switch is operated.

Next, very quickly "flip" the reversing switch from one side to the other, noting the magnitude of the deflection and comparing its value with those obtained by merely closing or opening the switch. Try to explain any differences that are observed.

Firmly holding the base of the switch down on the table with one hand, quickly operate the switch blades with the other hand from one side to the other. Do this as rapidly as possible, observing how accurately the needle deflections keep pace with motions of the switch. It is extremely important that the student recognize the fact that the secondary frequency is exactly equal to the primary frequency, and this simple experiment demonstrates its truth.

Experiment 28. Transformer Voltage and Turns Ratios

Objective: To prove experimentally that the ratio of the primary to the secondary turns is equal to the ratio of the primary to the secondary voltages.

Procedure: Using an E-type core, place one coil having *a known number of turns* over the center leg. (In the case of the coil of Figs. 141 and 142, the author used 344 turns of No. 17 wire.) Next, wind several rectangular coils of different numbers of turns so that they will loosely fit on top of the form-wound primary. The wire size may be any convenient B & S gauge number, say No. 24 or No. 25. The numbers of turns for the various secondary coils should preferably be less than the number of primary turns; in the example cited above, these might be 86, 115, and 172.

Connect the primary coil (344 turns) to a 60-cycle alternating-current source through a simple double-pole single-throw (d.p.s.t.) switch. Placing one of the secondary coils on top of the primary, bridge the pole faces with the crosspiece. Be sure the secondary coil ends do not come in contact. Figure 146 shows the arrangement described.

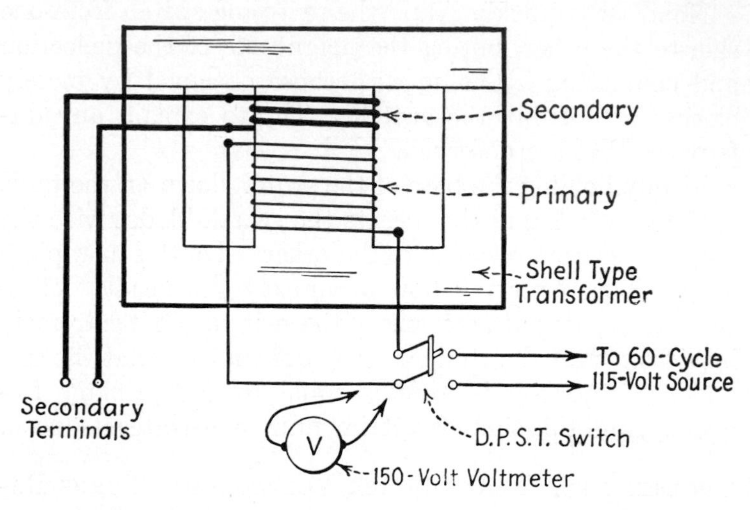

Fig. 146.—Arrangement of coils in a simple shell-type transformer.

Close the primary switch and measure both the primary and secondary voltages. Repeat the test, using each of the other two coils. Use one voltmeter, moving the leads from primary to secondary terminals. Next, connect two coils in series-aiding, then in series-bucking. Do this for the three possible combinations of two coils in series. Finally, connect the three coils in series-aiding. All data should be arranged neatly in a table similar to that indicated on the following page, and the ratio of turns and voltages calculated.

After the ratio columns have been properly calculated, the results should be checked and compared. Any discrepancies from expected values should be verified or explained.

Coil	Voltages		Ratios	
	Primary	Secondary	Turns	Voltages
A^*				
B^*				
C^*				
$B + A$				
$B - A$				
$C + A$				
$C - A$				
$C + B$				
$C - B$				
$A + B + C$				

$^*A =$ .... turns $B =$ .... turns $C =$ .... turns

EXPERIMENT 29. SECONDARY CURRENT IN STEP-DOWN TRANSFORMER

Objective: To show that, in a step-down transformer, the current on the secondary side is greater than the current on the primary side.

Procedure: In order to perform this extremely interesting experiment it will be necessary to make a simple figure 8 copper coil using as large a gauge number of wire as may be available. The author constructed one as shown in Fig. 147, using No. 4 annealed copper. Note that one half of the loop of the figure 8 is carefully shaped to fit around the primary coil of the transformer, while the other half of the loop is approximately circular, about 5 in. in diameter.

The apparatus should then be set up like that shown in Fig. 148. An asbestos sheet should be wrapped around the primary coil before the secondary is fitted over it. Note that the primary winding is connected to a 60-cycle,

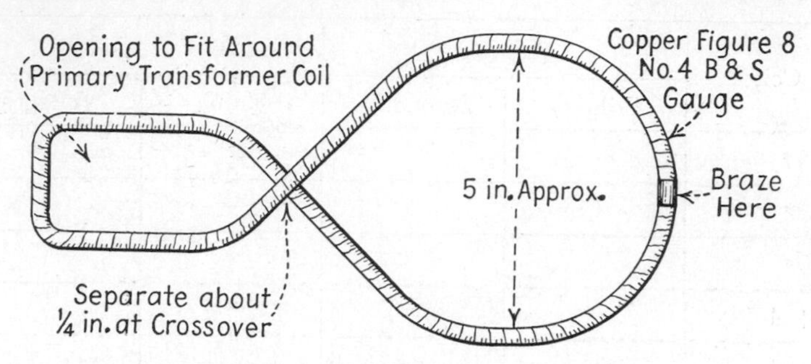

FIG. 147.—Sketch showing construction details of a figure 8 conductor.

115-volt source through an alternating-current ammeter. The figure 8 secondary circuit should be supported in some convenient manner so that it occupies a rigid horizontal position. If a clamp-on ammeter is available, it should certainly be used to measure the secondary current, as shown.

With everything in readiness, close the primary switch. Observe and record the primary and secondary currents. Even if a clamp-on ammeter is not used, it will be noticed that the figure 8 coil will become very hot in a short time, a condition indicating that the current is very high.

Since the secondary winding has only one turn, the turn ratio will be equal to the number of primary turns, *i.e.*, N_p:1. Therefore, the secondary current, if measured, should be found to be approximately this number of times as much as the measured primary current. Check this.

After these preliminaries, it will be interesting to observe the action of the powerful magnetic field intensity at the surface of the large loop. Bring nails, filings, blocks of iron, and any other magnetic substances near the loop. Observe how iron filings cling to the wire; how an unmagnetized block of iron becomes strongly magnetized when placed within the loop; how small bits of iron may be thrown at the wire and are found to remain there. Notice

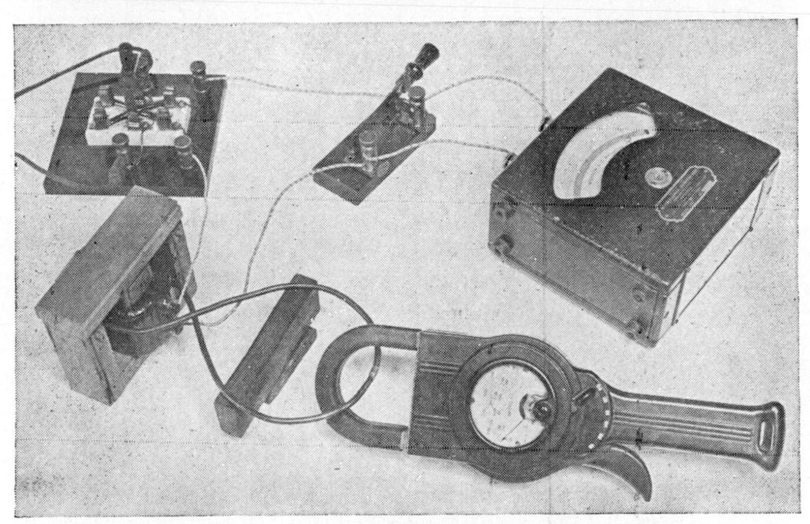

FIG. 148.—Arrangement of apparatus to demonstrate experimentally the action of a transformer. Note that in this shell-type transformer with a single-turn secondary the current in the latter is very much larger than the current in the primary.

many other simple procedures that may suggest themselves. It will also be apparent that *the greatest field intensity exists at the surface of the wire on the inside.*

EXPERIMENT 30. HEATING DEMONSTRATION OF CURRENT IN SHORT-CIRCUITED SECONDARY OF STEP-DOWN TRANSFORMER

Objective: To demonstrate that the high value of the current in the secondary of a single-turn short-circuited transformer will develop a considerable amount of heat.

Procedure: For the performance of this experiment it will be necessary to construct two simple pieces of equipment as shown in Fig. 149. The copper trough may be made from 0.035-in.-thickness sheet copper about $1\frac{1}{2}$ in. wide. Four pieces should be cut having the shape indicated in Fig. 150*a*. The dimension *cd* for two of the pieces should be about $\frac{1}{4}$ in. longer than one side of the center pole of the E-type electromagnet (if this is used), while the other two pieces should have this dimension

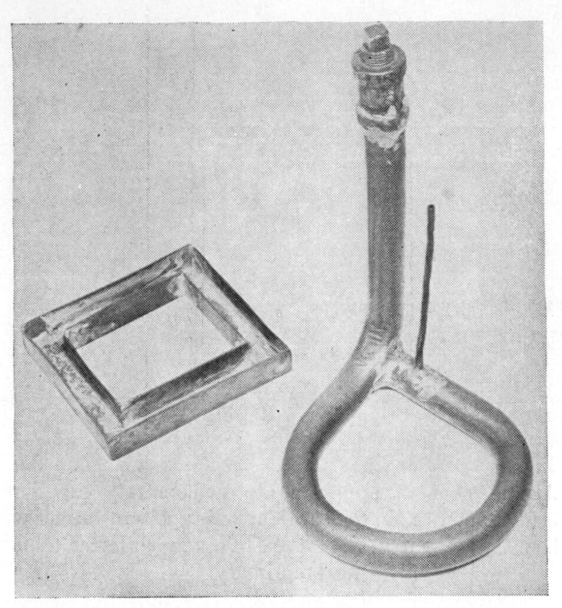

FIG. 149.—Copper trough and copper water "geyser." Both may be used to demonstrate that a very large current flows when the secondary of a transformer is short-circuited.

about $\frac{1}{4}$ in. longer than the other side of the same pole face. When bent along lines *ab* and *cd* so that sides *aa′bb′* and *cc′dd* are parallel and perpendicular to *abcd*, each piece will look like Fig. 150*b*. They can then be butted against each other properly and brazed or silver-soldered at the seams. The resulting trough should then fit neatly around the pole on top of the exciting coil. The second piece (Fig. 149) is constructed from $\frac{1}{2}$-in. copper pipe having a wall thickness of about $\frac{1}{16}$ in. One end of a 14-in. length is first closed by hammering and brazing. Beginning with the closed end it is then bent into a loop about $2\frac{1}{2}$ in. in diameter. The remaining section is next turned up so that it is perpendicular to the flat loop. Where the closed end butts against the lower part of the vertical section, a good brazing job must be done. This is important because the hollow copper loop represents a very low-resistance single-turn short-circuited secondary. The final step is to braze a water plug at the open end and to insert and braze a fine copper tube, about 3 in.

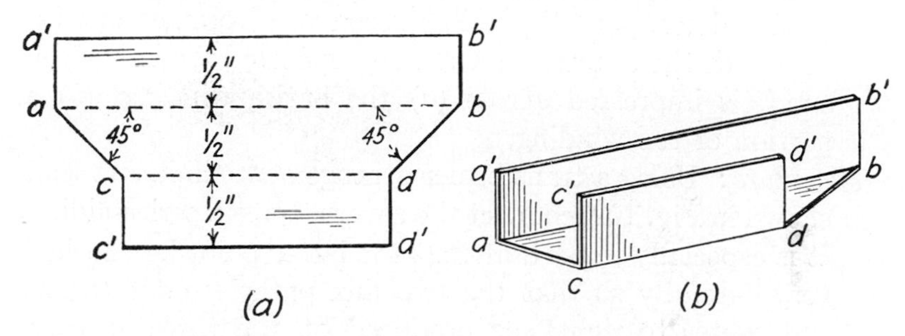

FIG. 150.—Sketch showing construction details of copper trough.

long, in any part of the loop. When completed it should look like Fig. 149 (right-hand figure).

The first test will be performed with the copper trough. Using the E-type core and the center exciting coil, place a sheet of asbestos over the latter and then set the trough, half full of water, on top of the combination. Connect a 115-volt, 60-cycle source to the coil through a d.p.s.t. switch. Firmly holding the trough down with a block of wood, close the switch. After a few minutes the water will begin to boil vigorously and in a short time will evaporate completely. The copper trough, obviously acting like a short-circuited secondary, develops a considerable amount of heat.

The second test will be performed with the bent copper tube. Pour in enough water to fill the flat-loop section, after which the plug should be screwed in tightly. Holding the upright part with a pair of pliers, place the loop over the exciting coil as in the previous test. With the primary coil excited permit the short-circuited secondary copper pipe to become heated. In a short time bursts of hot water and steam will shoot irregularly out of the small copper tube as though it were a "geyser."

Experiment 31. The Autotransformer

Objectives: (1) To connect the several coils of a transformer in such a way that it will operate as an autotransformer. (2) To determine all possible secondary voltages obtainable with the autotransformer so connected when a given e.m.f. is impressed across (*a*) the entire winding, (*b*) a portion of the winding.

Procedure: Using a transformer arrangement similar to that shown in Fig. 102, connect the several coils in series-aiding. It is especially important that the latter point be checked very carefully so that the two flux paths (center to left and center to right), as produced by the three exciting coils simultaneously, will be in the proper direction. Figure 151 shows how this must be done for the coils of

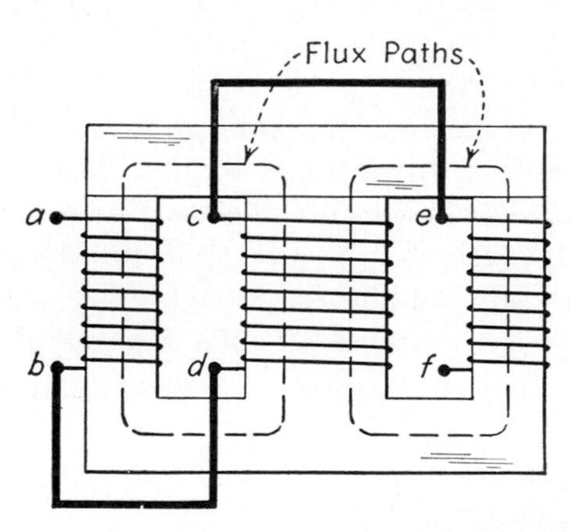

Fig. 151.—Transformer coils connected series-aiding.

Fig. 102, all of which were wound in exactly the same way. (Note connection *b* to *d* and connection *c* to *e*.)

Part 1. *Step-down Autotransformer.*—Connect the 120-volt, 60-cycle source to terminals *af*, measuring this voltage carefully. Call this E_{af}. Next, measure voltages

E_{ab}, E_{cd}, and E_{ef}. If all coils have been wound with the same number of turns, E_{cd} will be twice E_{ab} or E_{ef}. This should make $E_{ab} = E_{ef} = \frac{1}{4} E_{af}$ and $E_{cd} = \frac{1}{2} E_{af}$.

Next, measure E_{ac} and E_{df}. These should be equal to each other and $\frac{3}{4} E_{af}$.

Obviously, any pair of secondary terminals may be used to supply current to a load, the ones selected depending upon the voltage desired. In all cases the autotransformer acts in a step-down capacity.

Part 2. *Step-up Autotransformer.*—Connect the 120-volt, 60-cycle source to terminals *cd*, measuring this voltage carefully. Call this E_{cd}. Again, measure voltages E_{ab} and E_{ef}. These should be approximately equal to each other and $\frac{1}{2} E_{cd}$ if all coils have the same number of turns.

Next, measure E_{ac} and E_{df}. These should be equal to each other and $1\frac{1}{2} E_{cd}$. Finally, measure E_{af}, which should be found to be $2 E_{cd}$. Obviously, these higher secondary voltages indicate that the autotransformer acts in a step-up capacity.

Experiment 32. The Edison Three-wire System

Objective: To study the operation of an Edison three-wire system under balanced and unbalanced loading conditions.

Procedure: For this experiment it will be necessary to have a transformer with two *identical* secondary coils. The primary may be designed to operate on any convenient voltage and may have one coil or many coils properly connected. If a transformer like that of Fig. 102 (or Fig. 151) is used, it should be connected as shown in Fig. 152. Note that the primary winding is coil *cd* and that the two secondary coils are *ab* and *ef*.

Provision should be made to vary the loads across each of the secondary coils, and for the measurement of the two outside line currents and the neutral current. This can be readily done by using ordinary incandescent lamps with individual switches (or by merely screwing the lamps *in* or *out* as desired) and by connecting an ammeter across line switches S_1, S_2, and S_N in turn after each load adjustment is made.

Starting with a load of three lamps between L_1 and N progressively increase the load between N and L_2 one

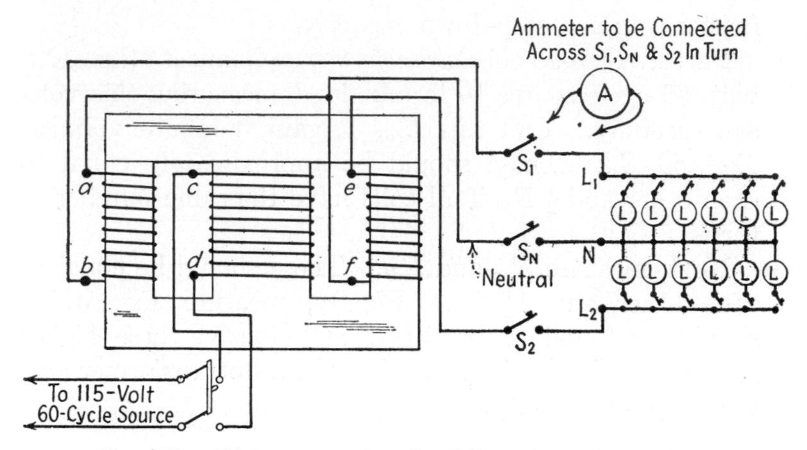

FIG. 152.—Wiring connections for Edison three-wire system.

lamp at a time until six lamps are connected across the *ef* transformer coil. For each adjustment measure the currents in the three wires at switches S_1, S_N, and S_2 and the voltages across the two loads L_1N and NL_2. Record the data in a neat table similar to that given below, noting particularly that

a. The current I_N is equal to $(I_1 - I_2)$ or $(I_2 - I_1)$.

b. The neutral current will be *zero* when both loads are equal (three lamps across each circuit).

c. The greater voltage will exist across the side of the line that has the smaller load, and vice versa.

d. The two line-to-neutral voltages, E_{1N} and E_{2N} will be equal when the two loads are balanced (three lamps across each circuit).

After the above test has been performed, connect a constant load of three lamps across line L_2N and vary, as before, the load across line L_1N one lamp at a time. The results of this test should be identical with those of the first tests except that the values will be reversed with respect to the two sides of the line.

Lamps connected to		Currents			Voltages	
L_1N	L_2N	I_1	I_2	I_N	E_{1N}	E_{2N}
3	0					
3	1					
3	2					
3	3					
3	4					
3	5					
3	6					

SUMMARY

1. An e.m.f. may be established (*a*) by chemical action, (*b*) by heating the junction of two dissimilar metals, (*c*) by permitting light to fall upon a photosensitive substance, (*d*) by moving a conductor across a magnetic field, (*e*) by electromagnetic induction.
2. The principle of electromagnetic induction, discovered by Faraday in 1831, is responsible for the operation of induction motors, transformers, automatic control equipment, and other devices and machines.
3. The principle of electromagnetic induction requires that the flux passing through a coil, or across a conductor, change if a voltage is to be induced in the coil or conductor.

4. Faraday's law states that the magnitude of the generated voltage is directly proportional to the rate at which a conductor cuts lines of force.
5. When 100,000,000 lines of force are cut per second by a moving conductor, 1 volt will be *generated* in it.
6. When the flux passing through one turn of wire changes at the rate of 100,000,000 lines per second, 1 volt will be *induced* in it.
7. The direction of the voltage generated in a moving conductor depends upon the direction of the magnetic field *and* the direction of motion of the conductor.
8. Lenz's law, relating to electromagnetic induction, states that the induced voltage always tends to send a current in such a direction as to create flux opposing any change in the existing flux.
9. The primary coil of a transformer is always connected to the source of supply; the secondary is the load-delivering coil.
10. When two coils are linked by mutual flux and the current through one of them changes, a voltage is induced in the other by mutual induction.
11. The degree to which magnetic coupling between two coils exists determines the coefficient of coupling. The coefficient of coupling can have values from zero to unity.
12. General terms applied to magnetic coupling are tight, loose, close, etc. Tight coupling exists when the coils are linked by a good grade of magnetic steel. Loose coupling exists when the coils are linked by air.
13. Self-induction refers to the action in a single coil, wherein a voltage is induced in a coil if the current through it is changed.
14. The voltage of self-induction depends upon the inductance of the coil and the rate of change of current through it.
15. Transformer action refers to the voltage of mutual induction, wherein a voltage is induced in one coil that is

magnetically linked to another through which the current is changed.

16. Transformer action can take place in any direct- or alternating-current system in which there is a current change. Its usual application is, however, to alternating-current systems.
17. The ratio of the primary to the secondary voltage in a transformer is equal to the ratio of the primary to the secondary turns.
18. There are two general types of transformer, namely, *core* and *shell*. In the *core type* the coils surround the core; in the *shell type* the core surrounds the coils.
19. The "ratio of transformation" of a transformer is a term used to designate the change of the secondary voltage with respect to the primary voltage. It is usually stated as 10:1, 20:1, etc., step-down or step-up.
20. With regard to their general fields of application transformers are generally divided into two classifications, namely, power transformers and distribution transformers. Power transformers are used by public-service companies in connection with their own needs on transmission systems; the ultimate consumer of energy is never connected directly to such transformers. Distribution transformers are used in distribution systems that run directly into the ultimate consumers' premises.
21. The current is lowered in the same ratio as the voltage is raised in a step-up transformer. The current is raised in the same ratio as the voltage is lowered in a step-down transformer.
22. An autotransformer has a single continuous winding that is used for both the primary and secondary circuits.
23. In a conventional two-winding transformer, all the power passing through it is transformed. In an autotransformer only a part of the power delivered to the load is transformed; that portion of the total power which is not transformed is conducted directly from the source to the load.

24. Autotransformers are generally unsafe for ordinary distribution service and must be used only where operators are not likely to come in contact with the circuits they supply.
25. Three-wire Edison systems are generally supplied by properly designed transformers. Such systems (*a*) are less costly than two-wire circuits, and (*b*) supply 115-volt service for ordinary lighting and domestic appliances and 230-volt service for the heavier power requirements such as motors, heaters, stoves, etc.
26. The neutral wire in an Edison system carries the difference of the two 115-volt loads.
27. Two types of instrument transformer are in common use, namely, potential transformers and current transformers. The former are used in connection with the measurement of high voltages while the latter are employed where large currents are to be measured.
28. Transformers are highly efficient because they have no moving parts. The only losses occurring in transformers are copper losses in the windings and hysteresis and eddy-current losses in the iron core.
29. Transformers are commonly rated by their kilovolt-ampere (kva.) output.

QUESTIONS

1. Give five methods for establishing an e.m.f. Describe the device or machine used in each method.
2. What is meant by the principle of electromagnetic induction?
3. How is a voltage generated in a direct-current generator? an alternating-current generator? Explain carefully.
4. Describe Faraday's discovery of the *principle of electromagnetic induction.*
5. State *Faraday's law.*
6. How many lines of force must be cut per second by a conductor if 1 volt is to be generated?

7. What must be the change in flux through one turn of wire if 1 volt is to be induced in it?
8. What determines the direction of the generated voltage? Use a sketch to illustrate your explanation.
9. State Lenz's law.
10. Explain how the direction of the induced e.m.f. may be determined.
11. What is meant by mutual induction? Under what conditions are two coils mutually inductive?
12. To what does the term "coefficient of coupling" refer?
13. Distinguish between *tight* and *loose* coupling. Explain how each type of coupling may be attained practically.
14. Discuss the action of self-induction. Under what conditions is a voltage of self-induction created?
15. Explain how a high voltage of self-induction can be created in a coil of wire to which a direct-current source of supply is connected.
16. Name and define the unit of inductance.
17. What is meant by transformer action?
18. Is transformer action possible in a direct-current system? Explain.
19. What is a transformer? Define it accurately.
20. Referring to transformers, define the following terms: primary, secondary, ratio of transformation, step-up, step-down.
21. Describe an experiment that shows that the secondary frequency is exactly the same as the primary frequency.
22. Describe the principle of operation of the ignition coil in an automobile, showing that the high spark-plug voltage results from transformer action.
23. In a transformer what determines the magnitude of the induced voltage in the secondary?
24. When two similar secondary coils are used, in what two practical ways may they be connected? What will be the voltage for one of the connections with respect to the other?

25. How are the primary and secondary voltages and turns related to each other in a transformer?
26. How are the primary and secondary currents and turns related to each other in a transformer?
27. How are the primary and secondary voltages and currents related to each other in a transformer?
28. Distinguish between *core-* and *shell-type* transformers. Make simple sketches of each type.
29. Is it possible to construct a transformer using an E-type core by placing the primary on one of the outside legs and the secondary on the other outside leg?
30. Distinguish between distribution and power transformers.
31. What are the usual primary and secondary voltages in standard distribution transformers?
32. How are transformers loaded? Under what conditions is a transformer loaded 100 per cent?
33. What is the power factor on the primary side with respect to that on the secondary side of a transformer?
34. What is an autotransformer?
35. Why is an autotransformer more efficient and less costly than a conventional two-winding type of the same capacity?
36. Where are autotransformers used? Where must they not be used? Explain.
37. What is meant by *transformed* power and *conducted* power when referring to an autotransformer?
38. Using a sketch, explain how a transformer may be used to supply a three-wire Edison system.
39. What advantages does an Edison system have when compared with conventional two-wire systems?
40. What current does the neutral wire carry in an Edison system?
41. Is any of the 230-volt load current carried by the neutral wire in a 115/230-volt Edison system? Why?
42. Name the two types of instrument transformer, giving their general fields of application.

43. Why are instrument transformers desirable when used in connection with the measurement of electrical quantities?
44. What are the common instrument ranges when these are used with instrument transformers?
45. Name all of the common materials used in the construction of a transformer.
46. Why are transformers highly efficient? What losses occur in transformers? What effect do such losses have upon transformer operation?
47. Why is oil used in a transformer? What important properties must it possess?
48. How are transformers rated?
49. How are transformers cooled? What would happen if they were not cooled?
50. What attention must be paid to the insulating materials in a transformer?
51. Why does a transformer "hum"? Explain carefully.

PROBLEMS

1. Make a sketch showing the approximate arrangement of the apparatus used by Faraday when he discovered the principle of electromagnetic induction.
2. The armature of a four-pole direct-current generator has 500 conductors. (*a*) What is the average voltage generated in each one of the conductors if it cuts 1.5×10^6 lines of force under each pole as the armature rotates at a speed of 900 r.p.m.? (*b*) If the conductors are connected in two parallel paths (250 per path), what is the total generated voltage?
3. Two 350-turn coils are inductively coupled. One of them is connected to a direct-current source and produces 600,000 lines of force. If the coefficient of coupling between the two coils is 0.6, what voltage will be induced in the second coil if the first coil is disconnected from the source and the flux drops to zero in 0.1 sec.?

4. What is the coefficient of coupling between two coils if their axes are placed perpendicular to each other?
5. The flux produced by a given coil is 250,000 lines when it is excited from a direct-current source. If 120,000 of these lines link with all the turns of a similar coil, what is the coefficient of coupling?
6. A ring (see Fig. 125) of nonmagnetic material has an average diameter, D_{av}, of 3 in. It has a circular section whose diameter d is 0.75 in. If a coil of 1,450 turns is wrapped uniformly around the ring, calculate the inductance.
7. Using the data of Prob. 6, calculate the voltage of self-induction if an exciting current of 8 amp. drops to zero in 0.005 sec. when the switch is opened.
8. What will be the inductance of the coil of Prob. 6 if the core material is a magnetic substance whose permeability is 1,200 when the current is a certain value?
9. The high side of a 2,300-230/115-volt distribution transformer has 800 turns. How many turns are there in each of the secondary coils?
10. Make a sketch showing how the two secondary coils should be connected (*a*) for 230-volt operation; (*b*) for 115-volt operation; (*c*) for 230/115-volt, three-wire operation.
11. Calculate the full-load primary and secondary currents of a 5-kva., 2,300/115-volt distribution transformer.
12. A transformer has 180 primary turns. The secondary has 120 turns and is tapped at the 30th turn and the 105th turn from one end. If the primary voltage is 120, determine the values of all of the secondary voltages obtainable with this transformer, and make a sketch showing the wiring connections and the various voltages.
13. The secondary winding of a 10-kva., 4,800/240-volt transformer delivers a load of 8 kw. at 0.75 power factor. Calculate the secondary and primary currents. (Assume 100 per cent efficiency.)

14. An autotransformer is connected to a 117-volt source and delivers a unity power factor load of 4.8 kw. at 78 volts. Calculate the power transformed and the power conducted to the load.
15. In Prob. 14, determine the primary and secondary transformer currents.
16. An Edison three-wire system delivers one 115-volt load of 40 amp. between one line and neutral, and another 115-volt load of 50 amp. between the other line and neutral. It also delivers a 230-volt load of 20 amp. All loads may be assumed to operate at unity power factor. Determine the two line currents and the neutral current.
17. In Prob. 16, calculate (*a*) the total power delivered by the transformer, and (*b*) the primary current if the primary line voltage is 1,150.
18. A 20:1 potential transformer is used in connection with a 150-volt voltmeter to measure the high voltage. If the voltmeter registers 116 volts, what is the primary line voltage? Make a sketch showing all wiring connections.
19. A 120:5 current transformer is used in connection with a 5-amp. ammeter to measure a large line current. If the ammeter registers 4.3 amp., determine the line current.
20. A 10-kva. distribution transformer has two 1,150-volt primary coils and two 115-volt secondary coils (see Fig. 133). Make sketches showing the four possible connections that can be made with the transformer, and for each connection calculate (*a*) the ratio of transformation, (*b*) the full-load line currents on the primary and secondary sides.
21. If it is possible to overload a given 5-kva. transformer by 20 per cent, what kilowatt load can be delivered when the power factor is 0.85?
22. A 3-kva. 2,200/110-volt two-winding transformer is to be connected as an autotransformer to step the voltage down from 2,310 to 2,200 volts. Draw a diagram showing how the connections should be made, and calculate

the full-load transformed and conducted kilovolt-amperes.

23. The winding of a 115-volt autotransformer is to have a total of 216 turns. At what *turns* should the winding be tapped for secondary voltages of 32, 40, 48, and 72?

24. Make a wiring diagram showing how a 230-volt center-tapped autotransformer may be used to provide Edison three-wire service. If the load between one outside line and neutral is 3 kva., between the other outside line and neutral is 2 kva., and between the two outside lines is 5 kva., all at unity power factor, calculate the neutral-wire current and the *transformed* kilovolt-amperes.

CHAPTER 9

GENERATORS—DIRECT AND ALTERNATING CURRENT

The Principle of Generator Action.—The electric generator is, for all practical purposes, the most important *source* of electrical energy, although, as was pointed out at the beginning of the last chapter, other methods may be used for this function. It is always a rotating type of machine because this kind of motion is the simplest and most efficient. Consisting essentially of a set of field magnets, always an even number of them, and an armature, either the magnets *or* the armature remains stationary while the other part is rotated mechanically by a prime mover. In practice it is customary to rotate the armature, keeping the field magnets stationary if direct current is to be generated; the field magnets are rotated inside a stationary armature when alternating current is generated. In either case, direct current or alternating current, *the electric generator converts mechanical energy into electrical energy.*

The fundamental principle of generator action requires that lines of force be cut by wires (called *conductors*). This flux cutting may be accomplished by moving the conductors across the magnetic lines of force (as in the direct-current generator) or by moving the magnetic poles (and the lines of force they create) across the conductors (as in the alternating-current generator). For every 100,000,000 lines of force cut per second by a conductor 1 volt is generated [see Eq. (43), Chap. 8].

Consider Fig. 153, which represents an elementary *alternating-current generator.* For simplicity a single-turn coil, *abdc*, is shown mounted on a rotating drum placed between the two poles of a stationary field. This arrangement of rotating the conductor instead of the field is illustrated here for two reasons: (1) it is easier to analyze, and (2) it will help the student visualize how an alternating-current generator may be readily changed into a direct-current generator by replacing the collector rings with a single split ring.

As the drum is rotated in a clockwise direction, a voltage

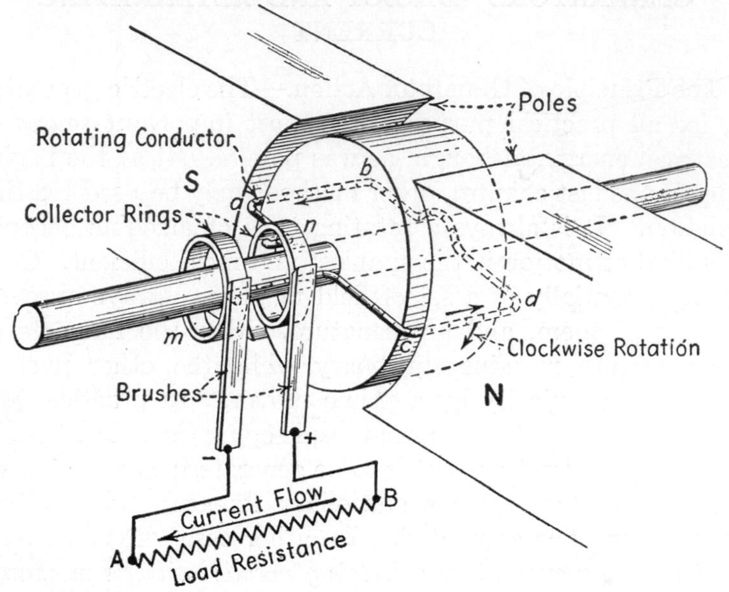

FIG. 153.—Elementary two-pole alternating-current generator.

is generated in conductor *ab* from *b* to *a*, and in conductor *cd* from *c* to *d*. This will make collector ring *n* positive and collector ring *m* negative so that current will flow in the load resistance from *B* to *A*. When conductors *ab* and *cd* change places under respective poles, the polarities of the collector rings will reverse so that *m* will be positive and *n* will be negative. This will result in a reversal of the current flow in the load resistance from *A* to *B*. It should be clear, therefore, that, *with slip rings and brushes* for the current-collecting mechanism, *the load current will be alternating*.

Nothing can possibly be done to change the alternating current to direct current in the conductors *ab* and *cd*. But, by replacing the two rings *m* and *n* with a single split ring, it is quite possible to maintain the current flow *through the load resistor always in the same direction.* Thus, the *alternating current* that *always flows in the generating conductors* can be rectified into an externally flowing direct current by using a split ring and two brushes. Figure 154 shows how the alternating-current generator is modified to deliver a

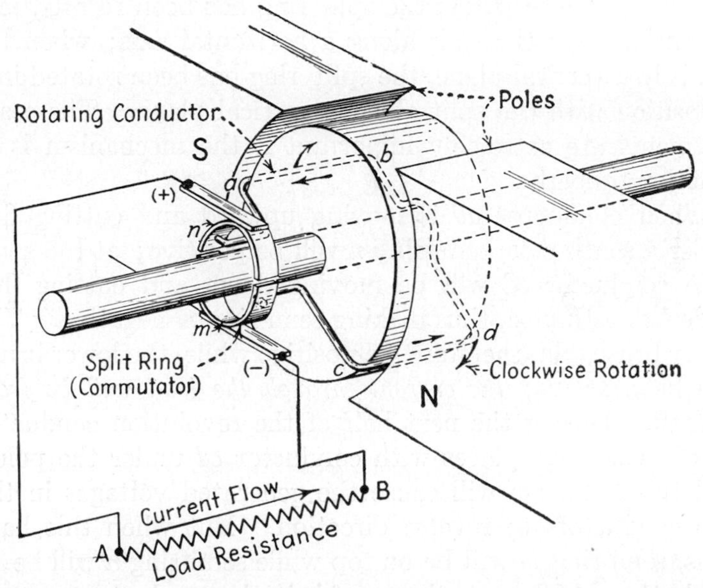

Fig. 154.—Elementary two-pole direct-current generator with two-segment commutator.

pulsating direct current to the load resistance. The important fact to remember in this connection is that no change takes place in the generating conductors; alternating current flows in wires *ab* and *cd* regardless of whether the collector mechanism is a pair of rings and brushes or a split ring and brushes. But, when a split ring and brushes are used, a direct current will flow in that portion of the electric circuit consisting of the two brushes, the load resistance, and the connecting wires.

The Commutation Process.—Referring again to Fig. 154, let us analyze the action of the split ring and the brushes as a rectifier of alternating current. Note particularly that conductor *ab* is permanently connected to semi-ring *n* and that conductor *cd* is permanently connected to semi-ring *m*; also, the split ring turns with the rotating coil *abdc*. The top and bottom brushes and the two horizontally mounted poles are stationary. Furthermore, observe that, when the coil is in a horizontal plane, the split ring has been rotated into a position with the split along a horizontal axis; when the coil is in a vertical plane, the split ring has been rotated into a position with the split along a vertical plane. These adjustments are extremely important if the mechanism is to function properly.

When conductor *ab* is moving upward and cutting flux under a south pole, semi-ring *n* will be positive; at the same time conductor *cd* will be moving down and cutting flux under a north pole, thus making semi-ring *m* negative. The upper brush will, therefore, be positive while the lower brush will be negative; *the current through the load will be from A to B*. During the next half of the revolution conductor *ab* will exchange places with conductor *cd* under the poles, and this exchange will cause the generated voltages in the two conductors to reverse direction. But when this happens, semi-ring *m* will be on top while semi-ring *n* will be on the bottom. Thus, as the e.m.f.'s in the conductors reverse direction, the semi-rings to which they are connected automatically change places under the stationary brushes. It follows, therefore, that *the polarity of the brushes does not change* so that the load current will always be in the same direction, *i.e.*, from *A* to *B*. It is true, of course, that the magnitude of the current will change as the conductors occupy different positions under the poles, but *there will be no reversal of current through the load.*

In the actual generator many coils of wire are used, and this necessitates the use of a ring divided into many segments. Such a segmented ring is called a *commutator*, which, together with brushes properly mounted thereon, constitutes the rectifying mechanism of the generator.

Frequency of Alternating-current Generator.—As the coil *abdc* of Fig. 153 rotates between the two magnet poles, the rings and the brushes alternately change polarity every half revolution. Since one complete positive and negative pulse of current, one cycle, occurs in one revolution, it follows that the frequency in cycles per second will depend directly upon the number of revolutions per second (revolutions per minute ÷ 60) made by the rotating coil. Moreover, if the generator is multipolar, *i.e.*, if it has four, six, eight, or more poles, then the frequency per revolution will be, respectively, 2, 3, 4, or more. Or, to put it more generally, the frequency per revolution is equal to the number of *pairs* of poles. It follows, therefore, that the frequency of the alternating current in an alternating-current generator is proportional to (1) the speed in revolutions per second (revolutions per minute ÷ 60), and (2) the number of pairs of poles, $P/2$. This relationship may be written in the form of the equation

$$f = \frac{P}{2} \times \frac{\text{r.p.m.}}{60} = \frac{P \times \text{r.p.m.}}{120} \qquad (52)$$

where f = frequency in cycles per second
P = number of poles in the machine
r.p.m. = speed of the rotating element in revolutions per minute

Example 1.—A generator has eight poles and operates at 900 r.p.m. (*a*) What frequency does it generate? (*b*) At what speed must the machine be operated if it is to have a frequency of 25 cycles? 50 cycles?

Solution:

$$a.\ f = \frac{8 \times 900}{120} = 60 \text{ cycles}$$

$$b.\ \text{R.p.m.}_{25} = \frac{120 \times 25}{8} = 375$$

$$\text{R.p.m.}_{50} = \frac{120 \times 50}{8} = 750$$

Example 2.—What is the maximum speed at which a 60-cycle alternating-current generator can be operated to develop 60 cycles? 25 cycles? 50 cycles?

Solution: Since the maximum speed at which a generator must be operated for a given frequency occurs when the

TABLE XII

Poles	Revolutions per minute		
	$f = 60$ cycles	$f = 25$ cycles	$f = 50$ cycles
2	3,600	1,500	3,000
4	1,800	750	1,500
6	1,200	500	1,000
8	900	375	750
10	720	300	600
12	600	250	500
14	514	214	429
16	450	187	375
18	400	167	333
20	360	150	300
22	327	136	273
24	300	125	250
26	277	115	231
28	257	107	214
30	240	100	200
32	225	94	187

machine has the fewest number of poles, it follows that there must be *two* poles in the machine. Therefore,

$$\text{R.p.m.} = \frac{120 \times 60}{2} = 3{,}600 \qquad \text{for 60 cycles}$$

$$\text{R.p.m.} = \frac{120 \times 25}{2} = 1{,}500 \qquad \text{for 25 cycles}$$

$$\text{R.p.m.} = \frac{120 \times 50}{2} = 3{,}000 \qquad \text{for 50 cycles}$$

The three most common frequencies used in this country are 60, 25, and 50 cycles per second. Table XII gives the pole-speed combinations that must be used for a wide range of alternating-current generators operating to provide 60, 25, and 50 cycles.

Field Excitation.—Before an e.m.f. can be generated, two factors must exist, namely, flux and motion. In direct-current generators it is customary to rotate an armature winding, mounted upon a laminated iron core, through a strong magnetic field. In alternating-current generators

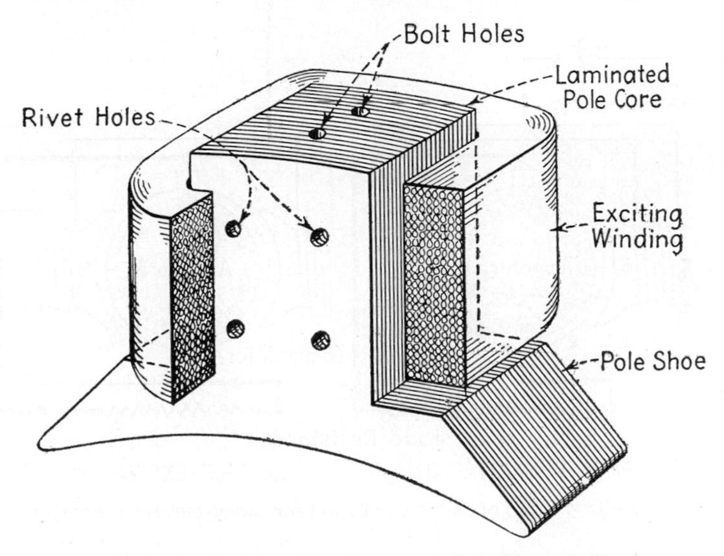

Fig. 155.—Laminated pole core and exciting winding.

it is the practice to rotate a set of strongly magnetized poles inside a hollow, slotted, laminated, cylindrical structure upon which has been placed an armature winding. In either case the pole cores are excited by simple windings similar to those studied in Chap. 6.

In direct-current machines the laminated pole cores and their windings are bolted to a steel ring called a *yoke*. Figure 155 shows one such pole assembly with a sectional view of a field coil. The windings of all the coils are generally connected in series (although a parallel or parallel-series connection is sometimes used), after which they are excited from an external source of supply or from their own armature. When excited from a separate outside direct-current source such as a battery or another generator called an *exciter*, the generator is said to be *separately excited* (see Fig. 156*a*). If its own armature serves as a source of excitation, the generator is said to be self-excited (see Fig. 156*b*).

*In alternating-current generators it is customary to bolt the laminated pole assemblies to a hub mounted on the

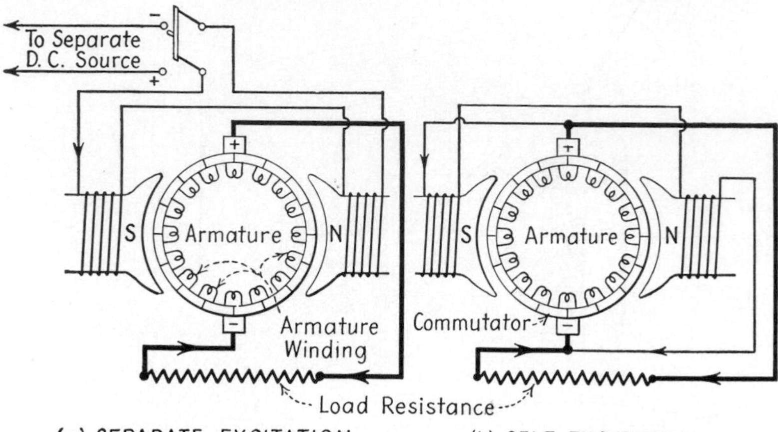

Fig. 156.—Two types of shunt excitation for direct-current generators.

shaft of the generator. The poles, therefore, radiate out like the spokes of a wheel and have their pole faces properly shaped so that they are concentric with the inside surface of the hollow laminated cylindrical structure called the *stator*. The latter, as stated before, carries the armature winding. Since the field winding must be supplied with direct current, it is always necessary to excite alternating-current generators separately from some external source such as an exciter or a battery. Obviously, this must be done through stationary brushes and rotating slip rings, the latter being permanently connected to the field-winding ends. Figures 157 and 158 represent the arrangements commonly used for direct-current and alternating-current generators. These drawings should be studied carefully *together* because they represent, in simplified form, modern constructional practices. Note particularly the essential differences between the two types of generator with regard to stationary and rotating elements, brushes, commutator

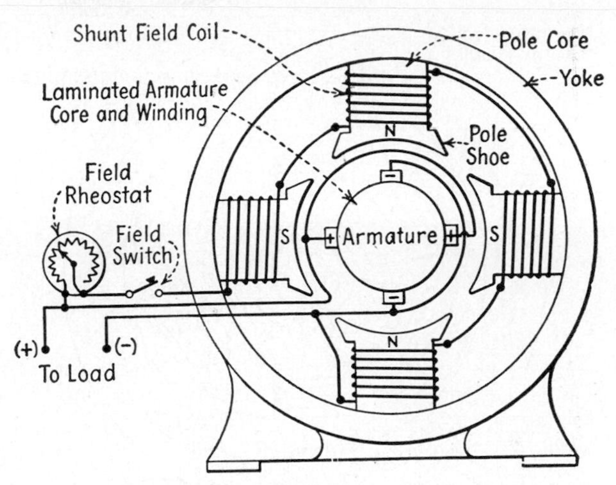

FIG. 157.—Self-excited four-pole shunt generator.

and slip rings, methods of excitation, pole constructions, and methods of mounting.

Voltage of Generator Operating without Load.—When a given generator is driven by a prime mover (steam engine, gasoline engine, diesel engine, turbine, electric motor, etc.) at its normal or rated speed, it will develop a voltage whose magnitude will depend upon the field excitation, which in turn produces the flux per pole. If the field winding is open —not excited—the voltage may be very small, say 5 volts, because the conductors cut a weak *residual* field. This residual flux is generally present after the machine has had its first operating experience, although it is possible for this residual field to disappear after an extended period of idleness. When the field winding carries current, however, the generated voltage will generally be much higher than the residual value. In practice it is customary to provide some sort of rheostatic control in the field circuit so that adjustments can be made for any desired voltage within the operating limits of the given machine. Obviously, the generated voltage may be increased by decreasing the rheostat resistance, and vice versa. Rheostats used for this purpose are called

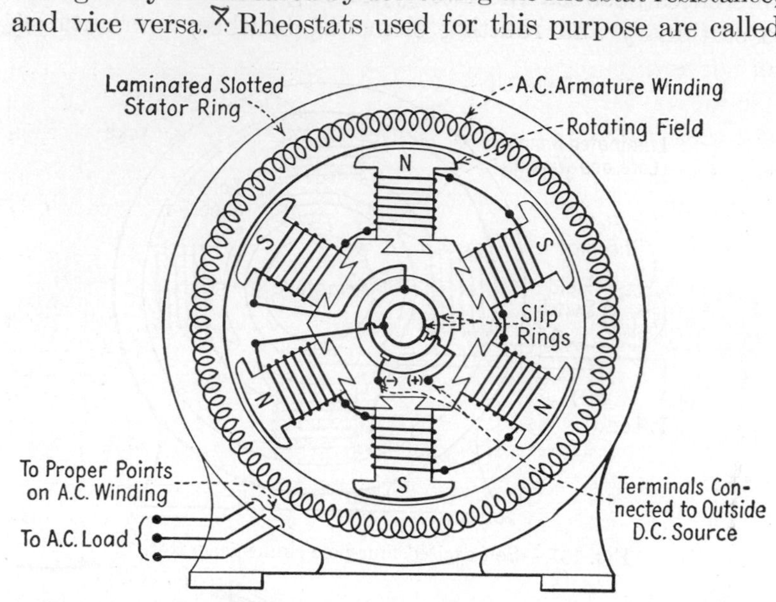

FIG. 158.—Alternating-current generator with a six-pole rotating field.

field rheostats and are always included in generator installations to provide a method for adjusting the terminal voltage.

If the speed of a separately excited generator is kept constant, which is usually the case, and the field current is varied from zero upward, the flux will likewise increase. For a time the two, field current and flux, will be directly proportional to each other; but after the iron begins to saturate, the flux increases much more slowly than the current. In fact, after the iron is very highly saturated, any increase in field current will produce very little change in flux. And since the voltage is directly proportional to the rate at which flux is cut, it should be clear that a voltage versus field-current relationship should resemble very closely the saturation curve, studied in Chap. 6 (see Fig. 90).

In order to obtain data for plotting such a curve as indicated above, it is merely necessary to drive the rotating part of the generator at its rated speed and provide some method of varying the field current. Figure 159*a* shows how this may be done conveniently, and Fig. 159*b* represents the type of curve obtainable from the data of such a test. The field (shunt type) is separately excited through a slide-wire resistor. Provision is made to measure the field current and the armature voltage while the armature is rotated at constant speed. When the slider is at *a,* the field current is

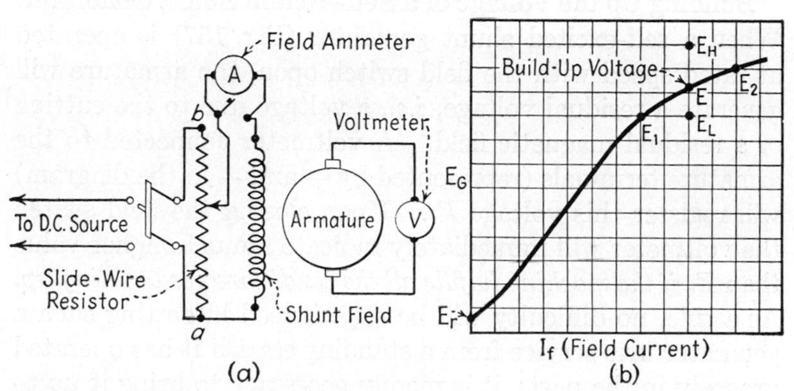

FIG. 159.—Wiring diagram showing connections for testing a separately excited shunt generator at no load, and the resulting saturation curve.

zero; the voltage will, therefore, be the residual value E_r. As the slider is moved *progressively* toward *b,* readings of field amperes and armature voltage are taken at uniform intervals.

Such a curve emphasizes an extremely important fact, namely, that the generated voltage is directly proportional to the flux *and not the field current.* Since it is also true that the generated voltage is directly proportional to the speed of rotation, it is easily possible to calculate the voltage at *any* speed after the saturation curve (Fig. 159*b*) has been plotted. Thus, if E is 120 volts at 1,200 r.p.m., E_H will be $\frac{1,500}{1,200} \times 120 = 150$ volts at 1,500 r.p.m. Also, E_L will be $\frac{1,000}{1,200} \times 120 = 100$ volts at 1,000 r.p.m. In fact, if a saturation curve is determined by experiment for one speed, it is quite possible to *calculate* values for another such curve at any other speed by the method of proportionality.

What has been said above about direct-current generators applies equally well to alternating-current generators. In the latter case, however, the field is separately excited through slip rings and brushes (since the field is usually the rotating element of the machine). The field ammeter is, as before, a direct-current instrument while the voltmeter must be of the alternating-current type.

Building Up the Voltage of a Self-excited Shunt Generator. When a self-excited shunt generator (Fig. 157) is operated at rated speed with the field switch open, the armature will generate a residual voltage, *i.e.*, a voltage due to the cutting of a residual magnetic field. A voltmeter connected to the armature terminals (represented by + and − in the diagram) will register this voltage E_r. Upon closing the field switch the voltmeter will immediately indicate a much higher value than E_r *if the machine fulfills all the conditions for building up.* As a rule, no difficulty will be experienced in getting such a generator into service from a standing start if it has operated properly in the past; it is merely necessary to bring it up to speed, close the field switch, and make a minor field-rheostat adjustment to obtain the desired voltage. After that, the generator can deliver power to any number of loads up to its rated output.

The fact that a self-excited shunt generator *will* build up, *i.e.*, rise from its residual value to its normal operating value, means that several important conditions have been fulfilled. Moreover, the *value of the voltage* to which a given generator will build up will be determined by other factors.

The first requirement necessary for the build-up process *is a small voltage due to residual* magnetism. A generator will *not* build up if the residual flux is insufficient; in 110- and 220-volt generators this flux should be of such magnitude that about 4 to 10 volts is developed. The residual voltage, represented by E_r in Fig. 159*b*, causes a small current to flow through the exciting coils of the field winding. The M.M.F. thus produced acts upon the residual field either to strengthen or to weaken it. If the excitation is in such a direction that the residual field is weakened, the generator will not build up. However, if the field is strengthened because the field winding is properly connected to the + and − brushes, the generated voltage rises; this in turn causes an increase in field current, a further increase in flux, and a still larger generated voltage. This cumulative process continues until a point of equilibrium is reached. *Equilibrium implies that the generated voltage causes a field current to flow which is just sufficient to develop the required excitation for the generated voltage.* Thus, at a point on the saturation curve below the build-up value (say E_1 in Fig. 159*b*) the excitation is greater than that necessary for this particular voltage; the result is that build-up continues. On the other hand, if the available excitation is less than that required for a particular voltage (say E_2 in Fig. 159*b*), build-up cannot proceed to this value.

Since a self-excited shunt generator cannot build up unless it is given an initial "boost" or "push" by a residual voltage, it should be clear that a new machine, or one that has lost its residual flux because of a long period of idleness, must be separately excited to create the necessary magnetism. This is usually done while the armature is at rest by connecting the field winding to an outside direct-current source, such as a battery or another generator, for a few seconds. This practice is generally referred to as *flashing* the field.

A second requirement for build-up is a field circuit resistance that is less than the so-called "critical value" for the speed used in operating the generator. Since the field circuit resistance consists of the field winding, the field rheostat, and all the connecting wires, it is important that there be no breaks or loose connections. Furthermore, the brushes must make good contact and ride freely on a clean commutator because the field current is fed through the brush contacts. The critical resistance, mentioned above, is merely the total field resistance below which the generator will build up and above which it will refuse to do so. By gradually cutting out resistance in the field rheostat from its "all-in" position it is readily possible to pass through the critical value to a desired build-up voltage.

A third requirement is that the speed be high enough for the field resistance used. In this connection it should be said that a generator is usually operated at some definite speed, originally fixed by the manufacturer. However, should it be desirable to operate at some higher or lower speed, because pulley diameters or gear ratios do not permit operation at the rated speed, the field resistance must be adjusted for the new speed. In general, it will be found that for a given field resistance a critical speed exists below which the generator will not build up and above which it will.

Finally, there must be a proper relation between the direction of rotation and the field connections to the armature. If a generator will not build up when operated clockwise, for example, it will build up when the direction of rotation is counterclockwise. Furthermore, the polarity of the brushes will be reversed when the direction of rotation is reversed. In this connection it should be stated that the polarity of the residual magnetism, *north and south*, has absolutely no effect upon whether or not a generator builds up; it merely determines the polarity of the brushes, *plus and minus*.

Concerning alternating-current generators, it should be stated that no build-up problem ever exists. This is obviously true because such machines are always *separately excited*. To put this type of generator "on the line" it is merely necessary to bring it up to that speed required for the proper frequency, after which the direct-current field is energized by an independent direct-current source. Separately excited direct-current generators are likewise free from build-up problems for the same reason as mentioned above. The speed can, however, be any reasonable value because the frequency is not a condition of operation as it is in alternating-current generators.

Shunt-generator Operation under Load.—As previously mentioned, after a self-excited shunt generator builds up, it may be used to supply power to any number of loads up to its rated capacity. Figure 160 illustrates the connections for such a simple system. Note particularly that *the armature supplies both the field current I_f and the load current I_L*; *i.e.*, $I_A = I_f + I_L$. In this type of generator the terminal voltage, as indicated by the voltmeter, is a maximum before the main switch is closed or before the individual load switches are closed. As load is applied, however, the terminal voltage

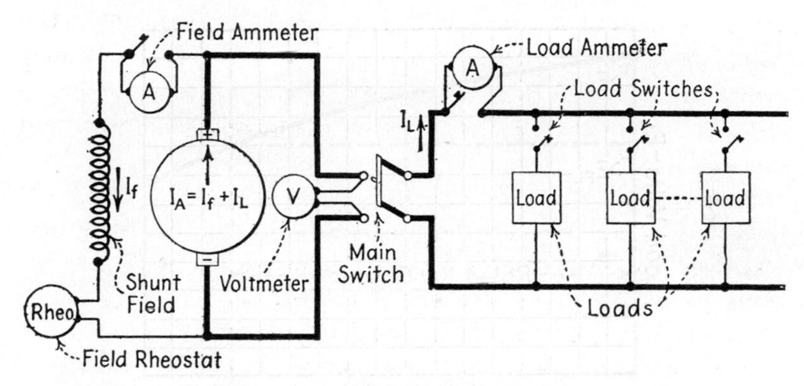

FIG. 160.—Self-excited shunt generator supplying several loads.

drops. If the loads are incandescent lamps or heating devices such as toasters, percolators, and the like, they do not function efficiently unless operated at rated voltage; the light output and life of incandescent lamps are very sensitive to applied voltage, while the thermal output of heating devices varies as the *square* of the applied voltage. If the loads are motors operating mechanical devices, the speed and the temperature rise are greatly affected by voltage changes. In any event, it should be clear that an inherent voltage drop in the generator due to loading is very undesirable.

In order to understand how a self-excited shunt generator operates under load it is necessary to perform a load test. This standard procedure involves running the generator at rated speed as the load is varied from zero to somewhat above rated output. Measurements are taken of speed, which must be kept constant, load current I_L, and load voltage E_L. The field current I_f is measured and recorded if desired, though this is not essential. For each load the power output is calculated by multiplying E_L by I_L. A graph similar to that indicated in Fig. 161 should then be plotted from the data thus obtained.

Note particularly that the load voltage drops from its no-load value E_{NL} to its full-load value E_{FL}. If E_{FL} represents the normal operating voltage of the generator, say

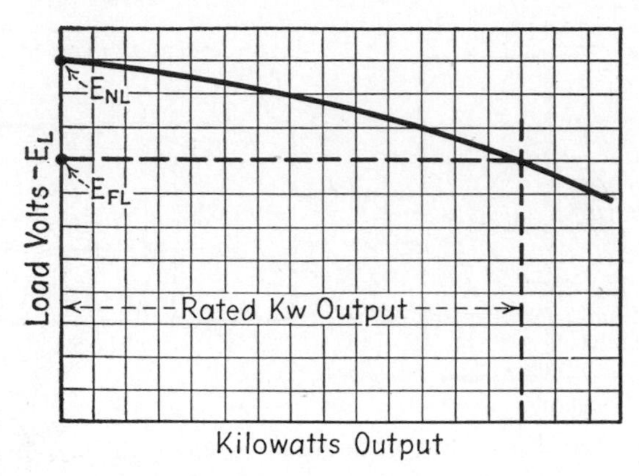

Fig. 161.—Characteristic *load volts versus kilowatt output* of self-excited shunt generator.

110 volts, it is seen that *the voltage rises as load is removed.* The total rise in voltage from full load to no load is especially important because it is a measure of how poorly or how well a generator performs. The ideal would, of course, be zero change in voltage; under this condition the voltage would remain essentially constant. A poor generator, on the other hand, would be one whose voltage changes considerably between full load and no load.

In order to have a standard of reference, it is convenient to measure performance *by referring the change in voltage between full load and no load to the full-load value.* This is represented as a percentage and is called the *per cent regulation.* In equation form

$$\text{Per cent regulation} = \frac{E_{NL} - E_{FL}}{E_{FL}} \times 100 \qquad (53)$$

Example 3.—The voltage of a 10-kw., 110-volt, shunt direct-current generator rises to 120 volts when the load is removed. What full-load current does it deliver, and what is the per cent regulation of the generator?

Solution:

$$I_{FL} = \frac{10{,}000}{110} = 91 \text{ amp.}$$

$$\text{Per cent regulation} = \frac{125 - 110}{110} \times 100 = 13.6 \text{ per cent}$$

Example 4.—A 50-kw., 230-volt, shunt generator has a regulation of 8.7 per cent. To what voltage will the machine rise when the load is removed?

Solution:

$$8.7 = \frac{E_{NL} - 230}{230} \times 100$$

$$E_{NL} = \frac{8.7 \times 230}{100} + 230 = 250 \text{ volts}$$

Example 5.—Referring to Example 4, assume that the change in voltage is uniform, *i.e.*, that the voltage-load curve is a straight line. Under this condition what will be the kilowatt output of the generator when the voltage is 240 volts? 235 volts?

Solution:

$$P_{240} = \frac{250 - 240}{250 - 230} \times 50 = \frac{10}{20} \times 50 = 25 \text{ kw.}$$

$$P_{235} = \frac{250 - 235}{250 - 230} \times 50 = \frac{15}{20} \times 50 = 37.5 \text{ kw.}$$

Controlling the Terminal Voltage of Shunt Generators.—It is possible to prevent thc terminal voltage of a shunt generator from changing as the load changes. This may be accomplished quite simply by merely adjusting the field rheostat (Fig. 160) as the voltage changes in accordance with the load. If the load changes gradually, or if the expense of automatic regulating equipment is not warranted, the field rheostat may be adjusted by hand with each change in load voltage; field-rheostat resistance is cut out as the voltage drops and cut in as the voltage rises. Automatic control is, of course, much more desirable and satisfactory since it not only eliminates the need for watching the generator as it operates but performs its regulating function quickly and accurately without attention. Such automatic regulators, called *Tirrill regulators,* operate on a simple principle using electromagnets for this purpose. A pair of short-circuiting contacts are connected across the field rheostat, which are made to open or close by the electromagnetic action of a so-called "relay." If the voltage drops, the relay causes the contacts to close and thus raise the voltage, because field resistance is cut out; if the voltage rises, the relay causes the contacts to open and thus lower the voltage, because field resistance is cut in. In practice the field rheostat is usually adjusted so that the generator voltage is about 25 to 35 per cent below rated value when the machine is delivering full load with the relay contacts held open. Other types of automatic regulators, beyond the scope of this book, make use of specially designed electronic and electromagnetic devices and circuits.

Still another method that may be used to maintain constant load voltage with changes in load is to *compound* the generator. This involves adding a series field winding directly over the shunt field winding, the former being connected either in series with the armature circuit or in series in the line circuit. The operation of compound generators is entirely automatic and, being cheaper than a shunt machine with a regulator, is much more satisfactory.

Compound-generator Operation under Load.—The addition of a second field winding, connected in series in the armature circuit or in the line circuit, provides a generator with two sources of excitation, namely, the shunt field and the series field. The shunt field winding consists of many turns of relatively fine wire, whereas the series field is wound with comparatively few turns of conductor of large cross section. The resistance of the shunt field is very much greater than that of the series field; for example, for a 5-kw., 230-volt generator these values might be of the order of 100 ohms and 0.03 ohm, respectively.

Figure 162 shows the two ways in which the series field may be connected for compound-generator operation. Note

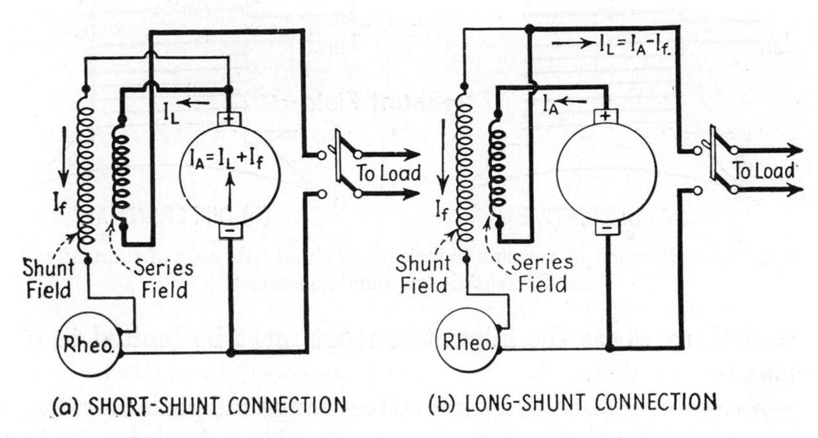

FIG. 162.—Cumulative-compound-generator connections.

that in Fig. 162*b* the shunt field is connected across a combination of armature and series field in series; this is known as the *long-shunt* connection. In Fig. 162*a* the shunt field is connected directly across the armature alone, with the series field in the line wire leading to the load; this is known as the *short-shunt* connection. Since there is very little difference in operating characteristics between the two connections, the short-shunt generator is generally preferred because less complication is caused in the switchboard circuits.

Compound generators may be classified on the basis of *relative direction* of the current in the series field with respect to the shunt field. When the two fields act to aid each other, as in Fig. 163*a*, the machine is said to be *cumulative-compound.*

When the two fields act to oppose each other, as in Fig. 163*b*, the generator is said to be *differential-compound.* Since differentially compounded generators are rarely used, they will not be discussed beyond the mention of the fact that they are sometimes employed in special applications where, for example, the speed changes over wide limits or in in-

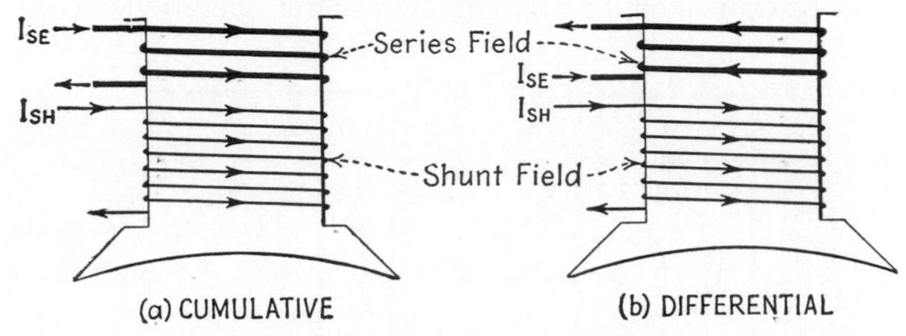

Fig. 163.—Direction of currents in series- and shunt-field coils of cumulative- and differential-compound generators.

stallations where the kilowatt output must be limited to a maximum value.

As load is applied to a cumulative-compound generator, the series-field excitation aids the shunt-field excitation. This action results in the creation of more flux *in proportion to the increase in load.* The armature conductors, therefore, cut more lines of force as the load increases, which in turn causes the generated voltage to rise. And *if this increase in generated voltage is exactly equal to the inherent voltage drop in the armature circuit, the terminal voltage remains constant.* Under this condition the machine is said to be *flat-compound.* However, if the rise in the generated voltage is either more than or less than that necessary to compensate for the inherent drop in the armature circuit, the generator is said to be *over-compound* or *under-compound,* respectively.

The *degree of compounding, i.e.,* whether it is flat-, over-, or under-compound, is determined primarily by the number of series-field turns. Many series-field turns will produce over-compounding, whereas few series-field turns will give the generator an under-compound characteristic. In practice it is customary to use flat-compound generators where the transmission distance between the generator and the load is short. Over-compound generators are employed where the load is a considerable distance from the generator. A generator supplying power in a small building would be flat-compounded, while a machine used for traction service would be over-compounded. In the latter case the voltage drop in the line wires must be considered as being an integral part of the electric system. Under these conditions

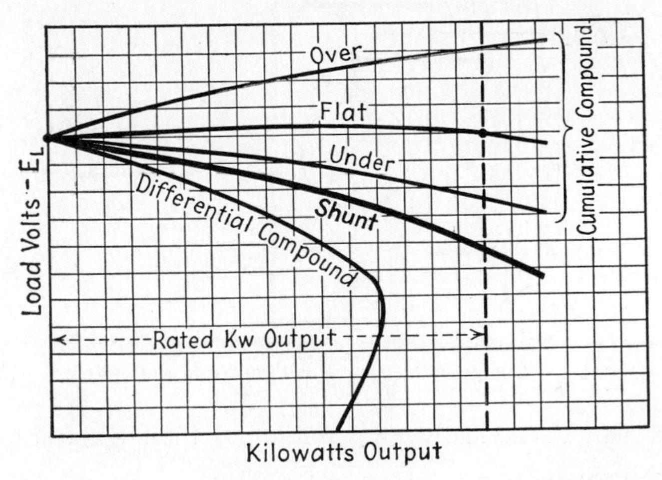

Fig. 164.—Characteristic *voltage-load* curves for shunt and compound generators.

the voltage at the generator must rise with increasing load if the voltage at the end of the transmission line is to remain substantially constant.

In order to compare the operating characteristics of the various types of generator discussed, Fig. 164 has been drawn. Assuming that the no-load voltages for all types of generator are the same, it should be noted that

1. The full-load voltages of the cumulative-type generators, *i.e.*, under, flat, and over, are *higher* than the full-load voltage of the shunt machine.

2. The differential-type generator has a limited output, less than full load, and a decidedly drooping *voltage-load* curve.

3. The full-load voltage of the over-compound generator rises to the highest value above the shunt machine.

4. The full-load voltage of the flat-compound generator is the same as its no-load value; it is generally a little higher between no load and full load.

5. The full-load voltage of the under-compound generator

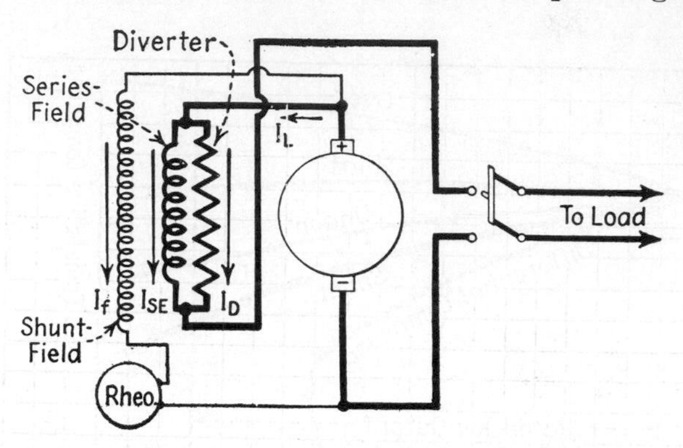

Fig. 165.—Compound generator with series-field diverter.

is less than its no-load value but more than the full-load shunt value.

Adjusting the Degree of Compounding.—Manufacturers of generators usually construct their machines so as to be somewhat over-compounded. Then, by connecting a *low-resistance shunt directly across the series field*, the full-load voltage may be brought down to almost any desired value to meet individual demands. This low-resistance series-field shunt is called a *diverter* because it *diverts* or by-passes some of the load current through a section of wire that creates no flux. Thus, the effectiveness of the series field is reduced to an extent determined by the diverted current. Referring to Fig. 165, which represents the connections of a compound generator with a *series-field diverter*, it should be noted that the line current divides into two parts, namely, the flux-producing series-field current I_{SE} and the non-flux-producing current I_D. Since the two resistors R_{SE} and R_D are in parallel, the two currents I_{SE} and I_D are related to each other by an inverse ratio of the respective resistances. It follows, therefore, that

$$\frac{I_{SE}}{I_D} = \frac{R_D}{R_{SE}} \tag{54}$$

where I_{SE} = series-field current
I_D = diverter current
R_D = diverter resistance
R_{SE} = series-field resistance

In practice it is customary to adjust the diverter resistance by experiment. The no-load voltage of the generator is first set for the proper speed by manipulating the shunt-field rheostat. The machine is then loaded to rated value and the load voltage is observed. If this is higher than desired, a diverter is connected across the series field and the full-load test is repeated. If the full-load voltage is still too high, the diverter resistance is reduced; if the full-load voltage is less than desired, the diverter resistance is increased. After several trials the experimenter will be able to find the proper diverter wire length, following which all joints must be properly prepared for permanent use.

It is sometimes possible to make calculations in advance to determine the approximate diverter resistance. Without going into a discussion of how the data are obtained, the following example is given to illustrate how Eq. (54) is used to determine its value:

Example 6.—The series field of a compound generator has a resistance of 0.025 ohm. If the full-load current is 80 amp. and it is necessary to divert 22 amp. in order to bring the full-load voltage down to a desired value, (*a*) what should be the diverter resistance? (*b*) If No. 10 gauge, Manganin wire is used, what should be its length in inches?

Solution:

a. $$\frac{80 - 22}{22} = \frac{R_D}{0.025}$$

$$R_D = \frac{58}{22} \times 0.025 = 0.066 \text{ ohm}$$

b. No. 10 wire has 10,380 *C.M.* (Table II).

ρ for Manganin = 265 (Table I)

$$0.066 = \frac{265 \times l \text{ (feet)}}{10{,}380}$$

$$l = \frac{0.066 \times 10{,}380}{265} \times 12 = 31 \text{ in.}$$

Commutation and Commutating Poles.—The commutator and its accompanying brushes are very important parts of the direct-current generator. It is here that two essential actions take place, namely, *the commutation process and the passage of current from a moving armature to a stationary load.* The commutation process involves the change from a generated *alternating e.m.f.* to an externally applied *direct-current voltage.* The transfer of current from the rotating armature to the stationary brush (and thence to the load) involves a continuously sliding contact. Both of these actions must be carefully controlled by the use of suitable materials and proper adjustments, for otherwise there would be serious arcing and possible breakdown of the machine.

As one of the armature coils rotates between a positive brush and the succeeding negative brush, current flows through it in one direction. Then, this coil is short-circuited by a brush for an extremely short fraction of a second, after which it passes into the next section between a negative brush and the succeeding positive brush where the current reverses.

Figure 166 should make this clear. In Fig. 166*a* the commutator and one of the armature coils are shown rotating clockwise. As the coil moves from position 1 to position 2, the current in the coil is to the left to the positive brush.

Then suddenly the coil is short-circuited by the negative brush as indicated by Fig. 166*b*. Finally, the coil is relieved of the short circuit as it passes into the region between the negative and positive brushes where the current reverses to flow to the right (Fig. 166*c*). Note that there are three stages in this commutation process: (1) before short circuit, when the current is in one direction, (2) the short circuit, which is the most severe period, and (3) after short circuit, when the current begins to flow in the opposite direction.

During the short-circuit period the voltage generated in the coil must be zero. If it is not zero, the commutation process will be accompanied by severe arcing at the brush

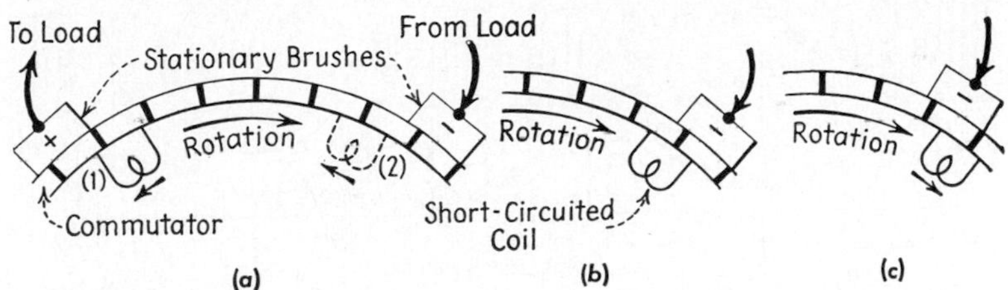

FIG. 166.—Commutation process, showing coil *before, during,* and *after* short circuit.

and much heating. To avoid this the brushes must be very carefully adjusted so that they occupy positions at the magnetic neutrals with respect to the sides of the coils as the latter pass from the influence of a pole of one polarity to the next pole of opposite polarity. Moreover, there must be a good, clean contact between every brush and the commutator, and the spring pressure on the brushes must be uniform and neither too much nor too little. It is also necessary that the brushes be of the proper grade, and this means generally following the recommendations of the manufacturer. Under good operating conditions the commutator should have a smooth chocolate-brown color, not bright and shiny, while the brushes should be carefully fitted so that a glazed surface makes complete contact with the commutator.

Assuming that all conditions for good commutation are present for one load, it does not necessarily follow that this will be true for all other load conditions. The fact is that the magnetic neutral *tends* to shift as the armature current changes. When the load is zero, the armature current is extremely small, being equal to the low excitation current for the shunt field; under this condition the magnetic neutral and the mechanical neutral coincide. This is shown in Fig. 167*a* for a two-pole generator. When the armature delivers a load

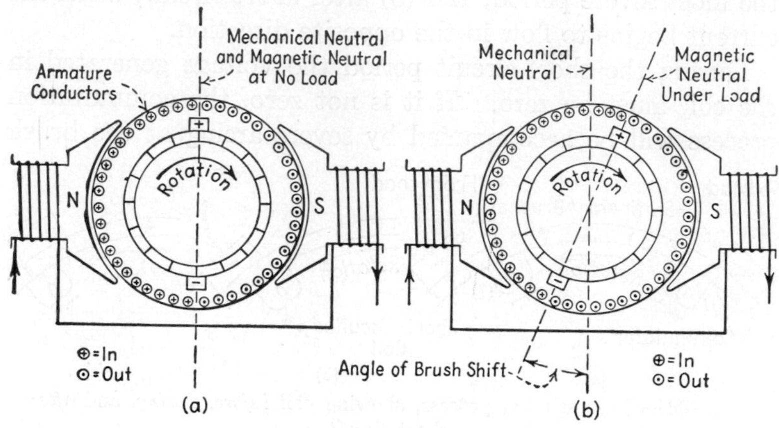

FIG. 167.—Brush positions of shunt generator—at no load and under load.

current, *the magnetic neutral shifts to a new position in the direction of rotation,* as indicated in Fig. 167*b*. Therefore, if good commutation is to result, the brushes must be shifted to the new magnetic neutral. Obviously, this requires continual back-and-forth shifting of the brushes with every load change or setting the brushes in some compromise position on the basis of the average load. Where the load is comparatively steady as in generators that supply field currents to alternators (alternating-current generators), good commutation is possible with a permanent brush setting. But in the usual generator where the load is changing frequently, either of these practices (brush shifting or compromise setting) would be quite unsatisfactory. To overcome these difficulties it is the general practice to provide the generator with commutating poles, sometimes called *interpoles*.

Commutating poles are narrow poles placed exactly halfway between the main poles and directly on the mechanical neutral. The *exciting windings of these poles are always permanently connected in series with the armature* because they must produce fluxes *in proportion to the armature current.* It

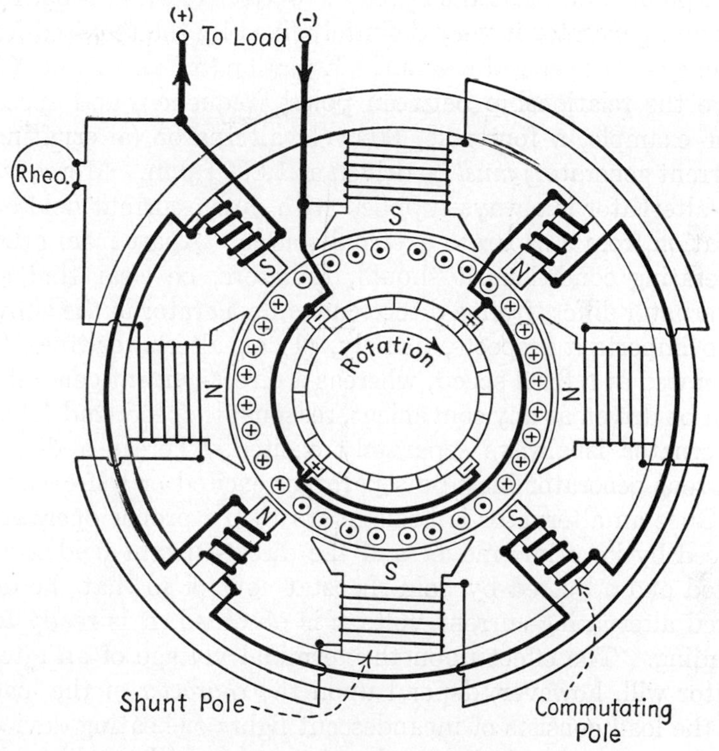

FIG. 168.—Shunt generator with commutating poles.

is the latter current passing through the armature winding around the laminated iron core that tends to create a flux of its own, apart from the shunt-field flux, to shift the magnetic neutral plane. And it is by neutralizing this armature flux that the commutating poles perform their mission of keeping the neutral plane fixed in position regardless of the load. Their use is so widespread that noninterpole machines are rarely employed, and then only when the load is known to be constant at all times. Figure 168 shows the connections for a four-pole interpole shunt generator. Note particularly that for generators *the polarity of the interpoles is the same as the succeeding main poles in the direction of rotation.*

Alternating-current Generator Operation under Load.—It was pointed out that the speed of rotation of an alternating-current generator is very definitely fixed by the required frequency of the generated e.m.f. Equation (52) and Table XII give the relationship between poles, frequency, and speed. For example, a four-pole, 60-cycle alternator (alternating-current generator) *must* be driven at 1,800 r.p.m. Moreover, an alternator is always supplied with direct-current field excitation from a separate external source. Apart from other operating conditions it should, therefore, be clear that an alternator differs from a direct-current generator in the above two important respects, namely, (1) an alternator must be operated at a fixed speed, whereas a direct-current generator can be driven at any convenient, reasonable speed, and (2) an alternator is always separately excited, whereas a direct-current generator may be separately excited or self-excited.

Once an alternator is brought up to the proper operating speed by its prime mover and the direct-current field is excited and adjusted by field-rheostat control so that the desired alternating-current voltage is obtained, it is ready for loading. The effect upon the terminal voltage of an alternator will, however, depend upon the *character* of the load. If the load consists of incandescent lights or heating devices such as toasters, flatirons, electric stoves, and the like, the power factor will be unity; this type of load will cause the terminal voltage of the alternator to drop about 8 to 15 per cent below its no-load value. A lagging power-factor load, such as induction motors (to be discussed in Chap. 10), electric welders, fluorescent lighting, and electromagnetic devices, will cause the terminal voltage of the alternator to drop as much as 25 to 40 per cent below the no-load value. Leading power-factor loads, however, such as capacitor devices or special types of synchronous motor, will tend to raise the terminal voltage of the alternator above the no-load value. Just how much the terminal voltage will drop or rise will depend upon (1) the magnitude of the load, and (2) the actual value of the power factor. In general, it can be said that (1) the greater the load, the greater the drop or rise, (2) the lower the lagging power factor, the greater will be the voltage drop, and (3) the lower the leading power factor, the greater will be the voltage rise.

Figure 169 shows the general relation between the *percentage of terminal voltage* and the *percentage of full-load amperes*

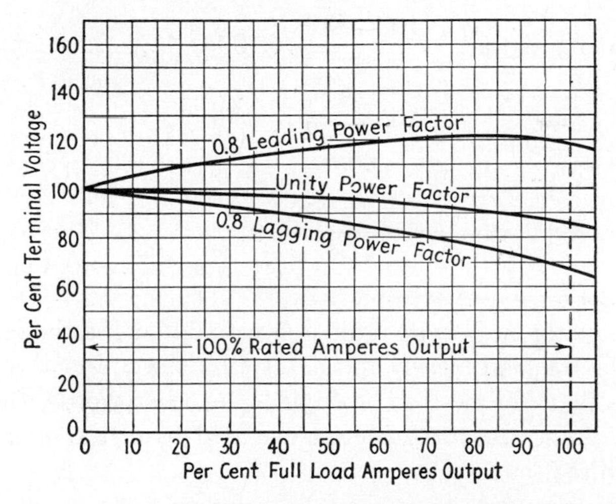

FIG. 169.—*Voltage-versus-load* characteristics of an alternator at different power factors.

output for three types of loading. The curves were plotted in terms of percentage because typical operating conditions can be illustrated better in this way. Note that when 100 per cent of rated current is delivered by the alternator, the voltages are about 85, 68, and 118 per cent of the starting or no-load values for unity, 0.8 lagging, and 0.8 leading power factors, respectively. It should be understood that the data for such curves as are represented in Fig. 169 are obtained by starting at exactly the same voltage for all three types of loading and maintaining the direct-current field-excitation current absolutely constant at all times as the alternator progressively delivers more current to the load.

Since the per cent regulation formula [Eq. (53)] applies equally well for alternators, it may be calculated as before. This is done in the following example:

Example 7.—Referring to Fig. 169, calculate the per cent regulation for the three types of loading indicated by the unity power factor, 0.8 lagging power factor, and 0.8 leading power factor curves.

Solution:

$$\text{Per cent regulation} = \frac{100 - 85}{85} \times 100 = 17.6 \text{ per cent} \quad (\text{for } P.F. = 1.0)$$

$$\text{Per cent regulation} = \frac{100 - 68}{68} \times 100 = 47.1 \text{ per cent} \quad (\text{for } P.F. = 0.8 \text{ lagging})$$

$$\text{Per cent regulation} = \frac{100 - 118}{118} \times 100 = -15.3 \text{ per cent} \quad (\text{for } P.F. = 0.8 \text{ leading})$$

The minus or negative regulation calculated for the leading power factor load merely indicates that the full-load voltage is more than the no-load voltage. In other words, the terminal voltage rises with increasing load as in the over-compound direct-current generator.

It is much more essential that automatic voltage regulators be used in connection with the operation of alternators than with direct-current generators. There are several reasons for this. In the first place, an alternator cannot readily be compounded to make its voltage-load characteristics correspond to that of the direct-current compound generator. Thus, the inherent voltage drop in the alternator, especially with lagging power factor loads, cannot be compensated. Secondly, the voltage variations due to load changes and power factor changes are considerably greater than those found in direct-current systems. And, thirdly, the alternator generally must feed a comparatively long transmission system consisting of wires and transformers whose resistance and reactance introduce additional voltage drops. The combined result of all these elements acting simultaneously is to cause the load voltage to change very greatly with load changes. And since large voltage fluctuations cannot be tolerated in otherwise satisfactory transmission systems, it is necessary that Tirrill regulators or equivalent types of equipment, designed for alternating-current generators, be used.

The principle of operation of the Tirrill regulator is essentially the same whether used with direct-current or alternating-current generators. As explained before, the voltage is controlled by causing a pair of short-circuiting contacts, connected across the field rheostat, to open or close in accordance with the normal alternating-current line-voltage changes. If the alternating-current voltage drops, the contacts are made to close by the action of a relay; this in turn raises the direct-current excitation, increasing the flux and then the alternating-current voltage. Conversely, if the alternating-current voltage rises, the contacts are made to open by the action of the same relay; this in turn inserts resistance in the field circuit, lowering the excitation and the flux, with a resulting drop in voltage. Actually, the contacts of a Tirrill regulator open and close many times per second in practice and thus tend to hold the load voltage at some average preset value.

Operation of Generators in Parallel.—Power plants will generally be found to have several small generators rather than large single units capable of taking care of the maximum peak loads. This is true of both direct-current and alternating-current stations. The several units can then be operated singly or in various parallel combinations on the basis of the actual load demand. Such practice is considered extremely desirable from the standpoint of efficiency, continuity of service, maintenance and repair problems, and additions to the plant capacity as the power-plant load increases.

As a rule, the load on an electrical power plant fluctuates, usually having its peak sometime during the day and reaching a minimum during the night hours. And since generators operate most efficiently when delivering full load, it is logical to use a single small unit delivering near rated capacity when the load is light. Then, as the load increases, a larger generator is substituted for the smaller one or another unit is connected to operate in parallel with the one already in operation. Further generator additions or changes can be made as the need arises. Exactly how a generator is "put on" or "taken off" a line without interruption to service will be discussed subsequently.

One of the most important operating requirements of electrical systems is that there should be *continuity of service.* This would obviously be impossible if a power plant contained a single unit because a breakdown of the prime mover or the generator would require complete shutdown of the entire station. This matter of uninterrupted service has become so important in recent years, especially in factories or in the operation of such domestic appliances as electric refrigerators, that it is now recognized as an *economic necessity.*

It is considered good practice to inspect a machine carefully and periodically to forestall the possibility of failure. This can, of course, be done only when the unit is at rest, which means that other machines must be in operation to take care of the load. Furthermore, when a generator does break down, it can be repaired with care, not in a rush, provided that other machines are available to maintain service.

Finally, additions are frequently made to power plants as the latter are called upon to deliver increasingly greater loads. In fact, engineers usually make plans for future extensions when they design power plants. Such extensions are made only when the existing equipment begins to prove inadequate and when the installation of new machines has been proved economically advisable.

A circuit diagram illustrating how the connections should be made for operating two *shunt generators* in parallel is given in Fig. 170. Assume that generator G_A is connected to the bus bars through switch S_A and carries a load. As the load increases, it will ultimately become necessary to use a larger generator than G_A or to connect a second generator G_B in parallel with it. The procedure for accomplishing this is as follows: Generator G_B is first brought up to speed

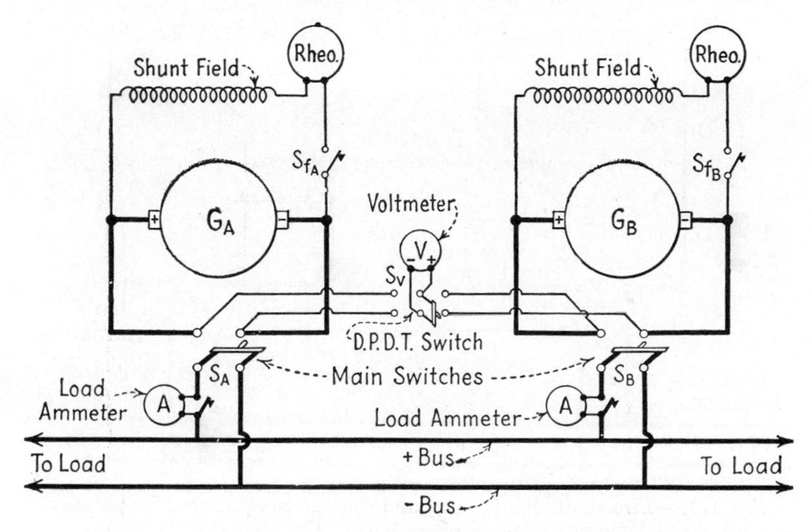

FIG. 170.—Two shunt generators connected for parallel operation.

by its prime mover. As soon as the field switch S_{f_B} is closed, the voltage will build up, whereupon its value is adjusted with the field rheostat until it is equal to or slightly higher than the bus-bar voltage. This is readily done by observing the voltmeter as the d.p.d.t. switch is closed first to the left and then to the right. It is, of course, important that the generator polarities be correct, which means that plus must be connected to plus and minus to minus. If this is not the case, a serious short circuit will occur when switch S_B is closed. Assuming that all the conditions for paralleling have been fulfilled, switch S_B is quickly closed. At this point G_A still carries the entire load and G_B runs idly. To shift the load G_A to G_B it is necessary merely to manipulate both field rheostats at the same time. This is done by gradually cutting in resistance in the field of G_A and, *at the same time*, cutting out resistance in the field of G_B. Any amount of load shifting can be readily accomplished in this way; in fact, the entire load can be shifted to G_B whence the main switch S_A may be opened if desired. While the load is shifted from

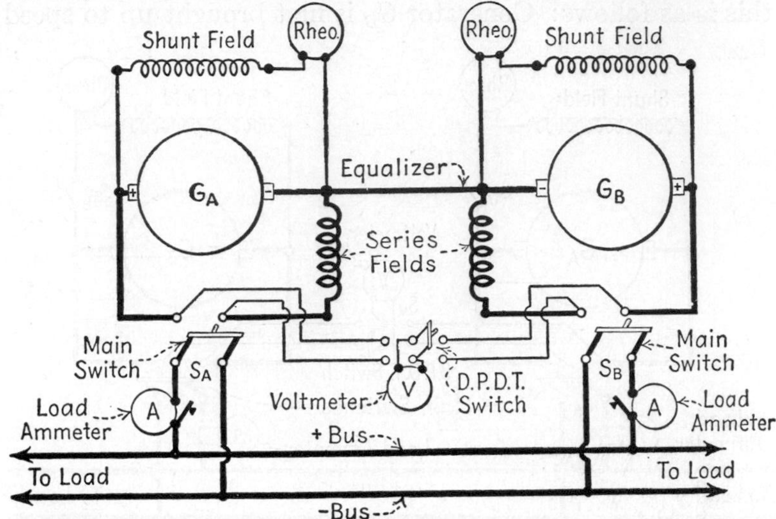

Fig. 171.—Two short-shunt compound generators connected for parallel operation.

one generator to the other, load ammeters A_A and A_B should be carefully watched to make sure that overloading does not occur.

When two *compound generators* are to be operated in parallel, it is necessary to use essentially the same wiring as shown in Fig. 170, *with the addition of an equalizer connection.* If the latter connection, which is a very low-resistance copper wire, is not used, the two machines will not operate satisfactorily in parallel. Instability will result because any tendency on the part of one generator to assume more than its proper share of the total load will cause it to take on still more load. In the meantime the second generator continues to drop its load until it is running without load. It is, in fact, even possible for one of the machines to carry the entire load and, in addition, drive the other generator as a motor. Figure 171 shows the wiring connections that should be used when compound generators are to be operated in parallel. Connecting one compound machine in parallel with another and shifting the load from one to the other are accomplished in exactly the same way as described for shunt generators.

When *two alternators* are to be connected in parallel, it is essential that the same two conditions be fulfilled as those described above for shunt and compound generators. The

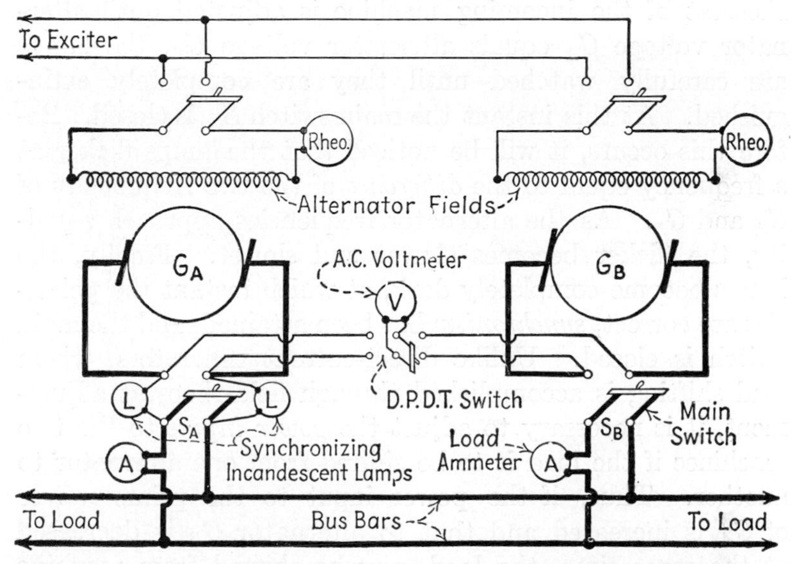

FIG. 172.—Two single-phase alternators connected for parallel operation.

voltage of the incoming machine must be adjusted to equal that of the one already in operation and carrying a load. As before, a voltmeter can be switched from the terminals of one machine to the other until, by field-rheostat adjustment, the voltages are equal. The correct polarity is, however, quite another matter since, with alternating current, this has a tendency to change from instant to instant. It must be understood that the alternating-current voltmeter does not indicate polarity but registers only the effective e.m.f. Several methods for observing the polarities of alternators are in use, but the simplest of these is the incandescent-lamp method. Referring to Fig. 172, which represents two single-phase alternators, assume that alternator G_B is in operation and carrying a load. Machine G_A is first brought up to the proper speed

$$\text{Revolutions per minute} = \frac{120 \times f}{P}$$

after which the field switch is closed. After the field rheostat of the incoming machine is adjusted until alternator voltage G_A equals alternator voltage G_B, the lamps are carefully watched until they are completely extinguished. At this instant the main switch S_A is closed. Before this occurs, it will be noticed that the lamps flicker at a frequency equal to the *difference* of the two frequencies of G_A and G_B. As the alternator frequencies approach equality, the flicker becomes slower and slower. Finally, the lamps become completely dark, at which instant the polarities are correct, *synchronism* has been attained, and the main switch is closed. Unlike direct-current generators, where load shifting is accomplished through field-rheostat adjustment, it is necessary to adjust the *power inputs* to the two machines if the load is to be shifted from one alternator to another. Thus, if the power input to the prime mover of G_A is increased and that to alternator G_B is decreased at the same time, the load may be shifted from machine B to A.

Experimental Laboratory Equipment for Testing Generators. *The Motor-generator Set.*—To test a generator it is necessary that it be driven by some type of prime mover. The most convenient laboratory arrangement is to use a direct-current motor to drive the generator, because it simplifies the installation and provides, in addition, an excellent means of varying the speed of the motor-generator set. Such a direct-current to direct-current motor-generator set can be readily mounted on a substantial platform and properly coupled together with a standard coupling. All the armature and field wires should be brought out to a convenient terminal board where the necessary connections can be easily made for the many kinds of test. Figure 173 shows a photograph of such a direct-current to direct-current motor-generator set, which can be purchased completely mounted and ready for operation. Note how all the internal wiring connections are shown connected to terminal boards fastened to the sides of the machines.

The Rectifier Set.—Since a direct-current source of power is not always available for the direct-current driving motor

FIG. 173.—Direct-current motor-generator set used for the performance of direct-current machinery experiments. (*Westinghouse Electric Corporation.*)

in some of the smaller schools, the author has designed a 115-volt, 60-cycle rectifier unit that can be used to drive direct-current motors up to about $\frac{3}{4}$ hp. capacity. The wiring diagram for such a rectifier set is given in Fig. 174. Included are the winding specifications for the main transformer, the filament transformer, and the choke. The dimensions of the laminations of these three units are given in Fig. 175.

Note that the same size lamination is used for both the main transformer and the choke. The over-all stack length of the main transformer is $3\frac{1}{4}$ in. while that of the choke is $1\frac{3}{8}$ in. For the filament transformer the stack length should be $1\frac{1}{2}$ in. A good grade of transformer (silicon) sheet steel, 0.014 in. thick, should be used for all laminations.

In assembling the main transformer, the center leg of each lamination is opened out at the diagonal cuts and pushed through the coil window. The laminations should

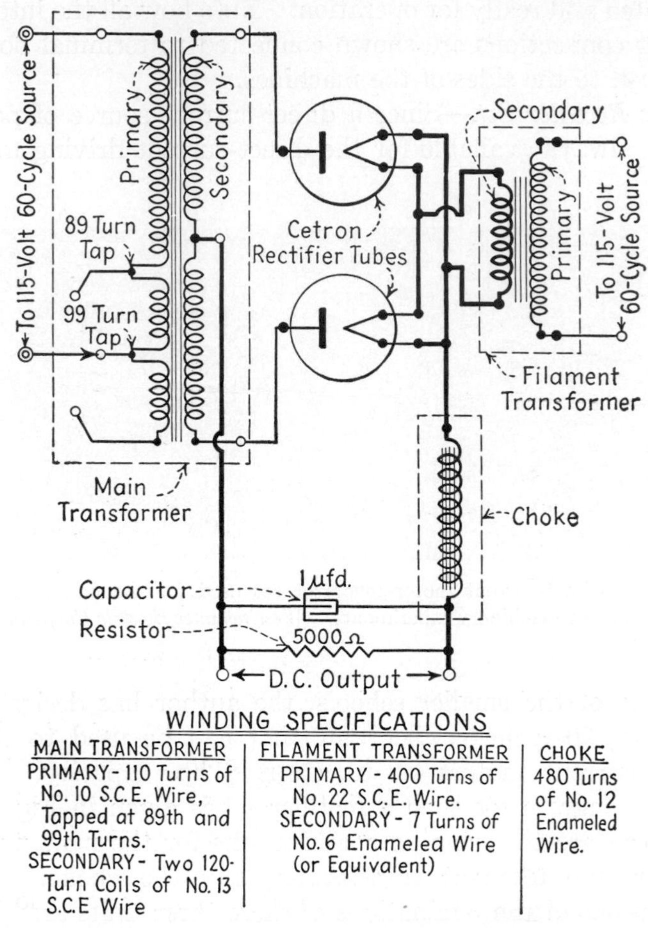

FIG. 174.—Wiring diagram and winding specifications for transformers and choke for a rectifier set. Equipment to be used to supply direct-current power to a direct-current motor of a motor-generator set.

be alternated from one side of the coil to the other so that the cuts are overlapped. This practice not only provides a good mechanical transformer construction but permits the transformer to operate efficiently and without overheating.

The assembly of the choke is, however, quite another matter. In the first place, all the laminations must be filed along both cuts so that there are two diagonal air gaps, each one 0.03 in. long, between the edges. Then, when the laminations are pushed through the window of the coil, the air gaps must match *on one side.* Do not alternate the laminations as in the main transformer.

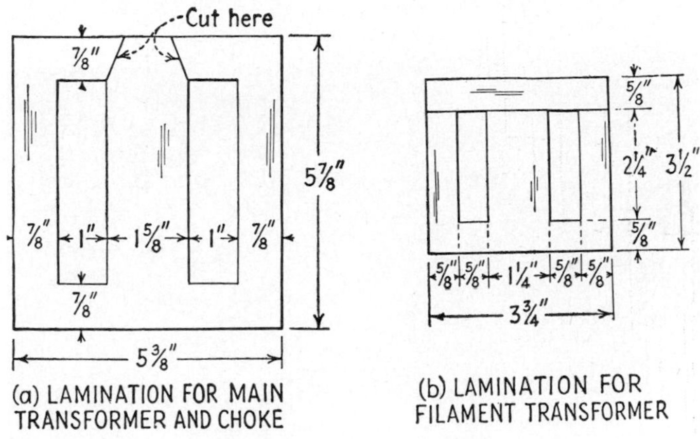

FIG. 175.—Dimensions of laminations for transformers and choke for units used in rectifier set. (See Fig. 126.)

The filament transformer should be assembled in the usual manner, pushing the center leg of the E section through the window of the coil first from one side and then from the other. This procedure will provide each set of air gaps with an overlapping lamination and thereby improve the mechanical construction and the operating characteristics of the transformer.

A photograph of the completed rectifier set is shown in Fig. 176. When in use the 60-cycle source is first connected to the primary input terminals of the filament transformer. After the filaments of the *Cetron* tubes have been heated for a period of about 5 min., the entire main transformer primary winding (110 turns) should be connected to the same 60-cycle, 115-volt source of supply. The voltage should then be measured at the direct-current output terminals with a suitable direct-current voltmeter. If this is found to be too low, say 110 volts or less, the 99-turn tap or the 89-turn tap should be used. This shifting from one tap to another can be conveniently arranged by using a pivoted arm or several jacks and a movable plug.

Fig. 176.—Completely assembled rectifier set, with protecting grille removed. (See Fig. 126 for wiring connections.)

The Load Rheostat.—When a generator is tested in the laboratory to determine its operating characteristics under load, some sort of *variable load rheostat* must be used as a substitute for the customary types of electrical device employed in practice. It is obviously inconvenient to use such things as flatirons, electric motors, incandescent lamps, and the like as loads; moreover, the use of such devices would not permit the application of uniformly increasing loads, a very important requirement when generators are tested. Load rheostats of many types are available, although to be satisfactory they must be compact, rugged, portable, and safe to handle; in any case they must not be permitted to overheat and thereby introduce a fire hazard. Figure 177 shows a good type of load rheostat in which seven single-pole double-throw (s.p.d.t.) switches are used to permit changing the load resistance. The resistor units consist of ceramic tubes upon each of which has been wound the proper length and size of resistance wire. Six equal resistances are connected to the pivot points of the switches. Since there are 21 possible resistance combinations with

Fig. 177.—Load rheostat employing six groups of vitreous enameled resistors and seven s.p.d.t. switches. (*Westinghouse Electric Corporation.*)

this type of rheostat, from a maximum when all units are in series to a minimum when all units are in parallel, the loading can be increased in sufficiently small steps. A wiring diagram showing the internal connections of the rheostat is given in Fig. 178.

In loading generators or in performing any test in which the current in the circuit must be raised from zero to some maximum value, it is desirable to vary the rheostat resistance from its maximum value to its minimum value in *uniform* steps. This can be readily done with the type of rheostat illustrated in Fig. 178 if the switches are closed and opened in a very definite sequence. The following procedure is recommended:

1. Close switch S_7 *up* and permit it to remain closed in this position at all times. Open all other switches S_1 to S_6.

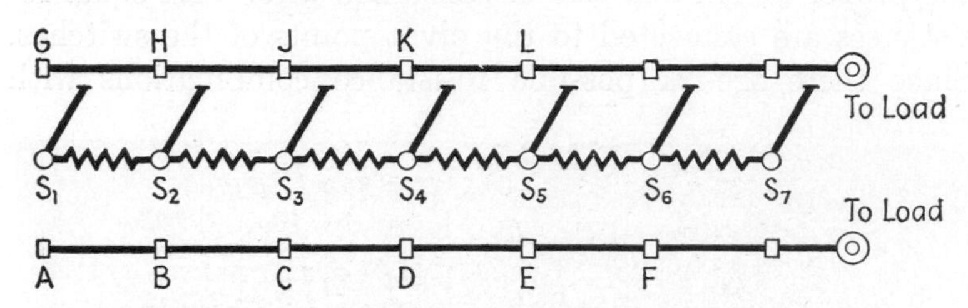

FIG. 178.—Internal wiring connections of load rheostat. (See Fig. 177 for photograph of rheostat.)

This should always be the first step in operating the rheostat because the latter will be open-circuited.

2. In changing the rheostat resistance from one value to a lower one, always close the proper switch, *then* open another. Never do this in reverse because an arc will be caused.

3. Assuming switch S_7 closed *up*, switches S_1 to S_6 should then be operated in this sequence:

First group[1]—*A*; *B*; *C*; *D*; *E*; *F* (two switches closed)
Second group—*FG*; *FH*; *FJ*; *FK*; *FL* (three switches closed)
Third group—*FLA*; *FLB*; *FLC*; *FLD* (four switches closed)
Fourth group—*FLDG*; *FLDH*; *FLDJ* (five switches closed)
Fifth group—*FLDJA*; *FLDJB* (six switches closed)
Final step—*FLDJBG* (seven switches closed)

With all resistor units having *equal* values of R ohms, which is usually the case, this rheostat will permit changing the total resistance from $6R$ ohms to $R/6$ ohms. If additional control is desired, more switches and resistor units can be added.

[1]Close *A*; close *B*, open *A*; close *C*, open *B*; close *D*, open *C*; close *E*, open *D*; close *F*, open *E*.

Electrical Measuring Instruments.—An extremely important aspect of laboratory testing involves the use of electrical instruments that not only are accurate but have appropriate ranges. This implies, of course, that measuring equipment, in reasonably good calibration, should be selected with due regard to the magnitudes it is expected to register. A 50-amp. ammeter in a circuit whose maximum current is less

FIG. 179.—Portable alternating-current ammeter. Note heavy metal terminals. (*Weston Electrical Instrument Corp.*)

than 5 amp. would, for example, yield unreliable data; moreover, a 150-volt voltmeter would probably be damaged if used in a 220- to 250-volt circuit.

As pointed out in Chap. 7, ammeters and voltmeters are generally employed in direct-current circuits and, when provided with one or more shunts and multipliers, may be made to serve in many kinds of tests as well as the several circuits of a given experiment. Wattmeters are seldom used for the measurement of power in direct-current systems, since this quantity is readily calculated from the product of volts and amperes ($P = E \times I$).

In addition to ammeters and voltmeters it is nearly always necessary to include wattmeters in alternating-current experiments. This is true because, except for unity-power-factor circuits, power is *not* equal to the product of volts and amperes. Furthermore, it is usually desirable to know the power-factor conditions in circuits, and this information is obtained by the measurement of watts in addition to volts and amperes (P.F. $= P/E \times I$).

The ranges of alternating-current instruments are not readily changed by the use of shunts and multipliers. Such measuring devices are generally used in circuits for which they are designed, although, as discussed in Chap. 8, their ranges may be extended if properly coupled to current transformers (Fig. 136) and potential transformers (Fig. 139). Figure 179 shows a 5-amp alternating-current ammeter, and Fig. 180 a 150/300-volt alternating-current voltmeter. Note especially that the scales are not uniformly divided as in the case of direct-current instruments.

Experiment 33. Constructional Details of a Dynamo

Objectives: To study the constructional details of a dynamo (direct-current generator or motor) (*a*) observing the general shape and the kind of material of each part, (*b*) observing how the various parts are assembled to form a completed machine, and (*c*) learning the function of each part.

Procedure: A comparatively small direct-current generator or motor should be disassembled with care. Every step in the dismantling process should be noted, with particular reference to the way in which the various parts fit together. Furthermore, it will be well to remember the exact order followed in removing each part because this will facilitate the reassembly of the machine, in the reverse order, later.

A compound dynamo, with interpoles, will be most satisfactory. Such a machine consists of the following parts: yoke ring; end bells and bearing supports; shunt field winding; series field winding; interpole winding; main pole cores; interpole cores; armature core; armature winding; shaft; commutator; brush holders; brushes; mounting base; miscellaneous screws, nuts, etc.

As each part is very carefully examined, a sketch should be made showing its shape and the important dimensions. A note should also be added indicating the kind of material used and the function of the part. For convenience this

Fig. 180.—Portable alternating-current voltmeter. Note two voltage ranges (150 and 300 volts) and light plastic terminals. (*Weston Electrical Instrument Corp.*)

might be done in a properly ruled table with suitable headings at the top and the parts of the machine along the side.

Of particular importance are the following: relative resistances of the several field windings; arrangement of shunt windings with respect to series-field winding; number of armature slots and commutator bars; whether or not the commutator is undercut; current carried by each brush under load; possibility of shifting the brushes circumferentially and axially; type of bearings; lubrication facilities.

Experiment 34. No-load Characteristics of a Separately Excited Shunt Generator

Objectives: To study the no-load characteristics of a separately excited shunt generator, determining experimentally (*a*) the saturation curve, and (*b*) the voltage-speed relationship.

Procedure:

Part 1. *Saturation Curve.*—Using a direct-current motor to drive the armature of a direct-current generator (Fig. 173), make the wiring connections as shown in Fig. 181. The shunt field of the driving motor should be in series with a field rheostat, the purpose of the latter being to provide a method for controlling the speed of the motor-generator set. As will be explained in Chap. 10, the motor speed will increase as the field-rheostat resistance is increased. (It should be stated, in this connection, that motors must always be started with the field-rheostat resistance *cut out.*)

With the generator field switch S_G open, start the direct-current motor by closing the motor switch S_M. [If the direct-current motor is larger than $\frac{3}{4}$ hp., it will be necessary to use a starting box (see Chap. 10).] Adjust the speed of the generator armature to its rated (name-plate) value, using the field rheostat in the motor circuit for this purpose. Thereafter, the speed of the generator must be maintained at this value throughout the test. After moving the slider of the slide-wire resistor to *a*, close the generator-field switch S_G.

Now take a series of readings of generated voltage E_g versus field current I_f for *progressively increasing* values of I_f from slider position *a* to slider position *b*. With the slider at *a* the voltage will be the residual value E_r as in Fig. 159*b*; when the slider reaches *b*, the generator voltage will be a maximum for the given speed.

After completing the test, a magnetization (saturation) curve should be plotted on a good grade of graph paper.

All points should fall on a smooth curve, which should resemble that given in Fig. 159*b*. If the data have been properly taken, the curve should be a straight line for the lower values of field current and bend gently toward the *X* axis for the larger field currents.

Part 2. *Voltage-speed Characteristic.*—The purpose of this part of the experiment will be to determine the relation between the speed of the armature and the generated voltage *for a constant value of field current.*

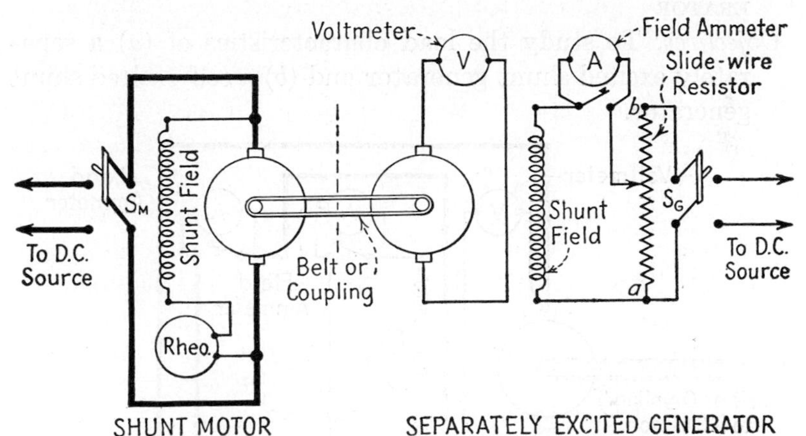

FIG. 181.—Wiring diagram for testing a separately excited shunt generator at no load.

In order to determine the value of the field current to be used, make the following preliminary test: Operating the generator armature at its highest safe speed, adjust the field current until the voltmeter registers a value very near the upper end of the scale. This value of field current should then be used in performing the test.

Starting with the highest speed setting, take readings of speed and voltage for every 100-r.p.m. interval until the field-rheostat resistance in the motor circuit is cut out completely. At each step make sure the generator field current is adjusted to its original value. Data should be recorded in a table whose columns are headed

Revolutions per minute, E_g, and I_f, the latter marked constant.

Finally, plot a curve of E_g as ordinate versus revolutions per minute as abscissa. If an upward-sloping *straight line* is obtained, it is to be assumed that the test results are satisfactory. Try to explain why the generated voltage is directly proportional to the speed, for a constant field current.

EXPERIMENT 35. LOAD CHARACTERISTICS OF A SHUNT GENERATOR

Objectives: To study the load characteristics of (*a*) a separately excited shunt generator and (*b*) a self-excited shunt generator.

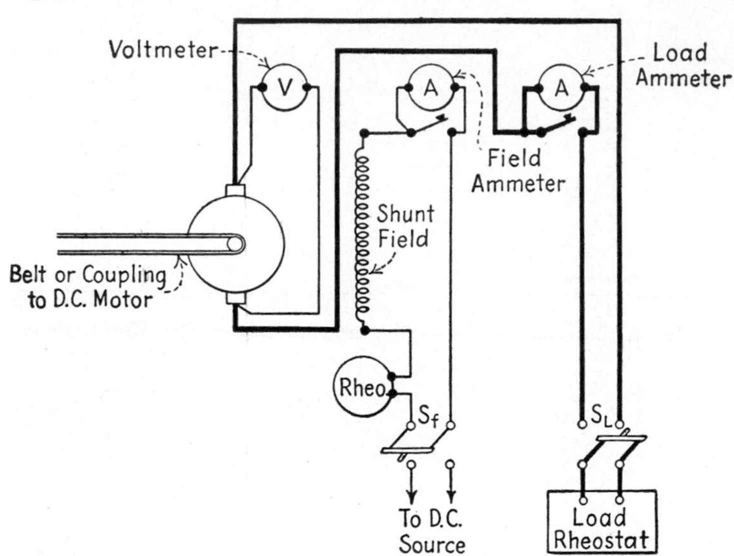

FIG. 182.—Wiring diagram for testing a separately excited shunt generator under load.

Procedure:

Part 1. *Separately Excited Shunt.*—Following the wiring diagram shown in Fig. 182, make provision for separately exciting the generator field through a switch S_f, an ammeter, and a field rheostat. With the load switch S_L open, bring the generator up to rated speed and keep it at this value throughout the test. Next, close the field switch S_f and, using the field rheostat, adjust the armature voltage to name-plate value. Note the field current and also keep it constant throughout the test. Now proceed to load the armature by first closing load switch S_L and then increasing the load current, in steps, to full load by properly manipulating the load rheostat. Take readings of voltage E_L, load current I_L, field current I_f, and speed in revolutions per minute. The latter two quantities should be kept constant, as stated before. Record the data in a table similar to that given below, and calculate the power output for each load.

$$(P_o = E_L \times I_L)$$

E_L	I_L	I_f	R.p.m.	Power output

Finally, plot a curve of E_L as ordinate versus power output as abscissa. Pick off the no-load and full-load voltages from this curve and calculate the per cent regulation of the generator.

Part 2. *Self-excited Shunt.*—Remove the two wires connected to switch S_f in Fig. 182 and connect them directly across the armature terminals. This change will convert the separately excited generator into a self-excited generator. Figure 183 shows the connections to be used.

With the load switch S_L open, *start the generator, as before, bringing it up to exactly the same speed as in Part* 1. After the machine builds up, *adjust the no-load voltage to exactly the same value as in Part* 1. The two conditions, no-load voltage and speed, must be fulfilled if comparative results are to be obtained for separately and self-excited shunt generators.

Now proceed to load the generator, in steps, to full load or as high as possible, taking readings of E_L, I_L, I_f, and revolutions per minute. All data should be recorded in a table similar to that used in Part 1. After calculating the power output for each set of readings, plot a curve, *on the sheet same as in Part* 1, of the same units as there, *i.e.*, E_L versus power output. Pick off the proper voltages from the curve and calculate the per cent regulation of the generator.

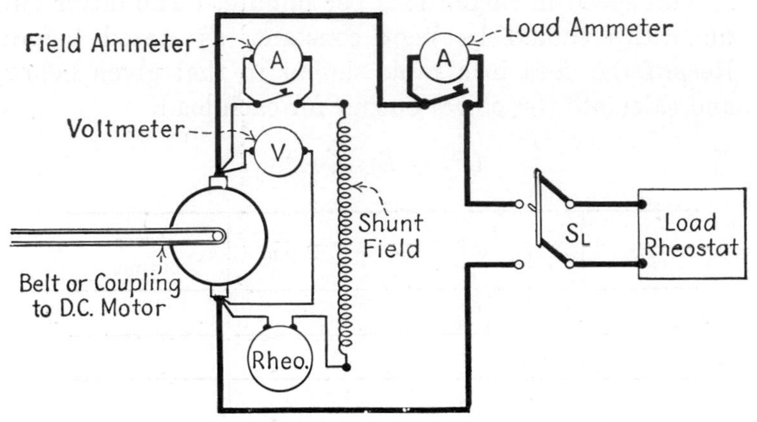

FIG. 183.—Wiring diagram for testing a self-excited shunt generator under load.

The important fact to notice, in comparing the volts-versus-power-output curves for separate and self-excited shunt generators, is that the former (Part 1) maintains its voltage better than the latter (Part 2). Try to explain why this is so.

EXPERIMENT 36. LOAD CHARACTERISTICS OF COMPOUND GENERATORS

Objectives: To study the load characteristics of (*a*) a cumulative-compound generator, and (*b*) a differential-compound generator.

Procedure:

Part 1. *Cumulative-compound.*—To perform this experiment it will be necessary to make one simple change in the wiring of Fig. 183, in order to convert the self-excited shunt generator into a short-shunt compound generator. Proceed in this way: (1) remove either one of the line wire ends from the load switch S_L; (2) connect this wire end to either terminal of the series field; (3) connect one end of another wire to the other series field terminal, and the other wire end to the load switch from which the first end was removed. The wiring will then appear like that given in Fig. 184.

For cumulative operation the series field must produce flux of the same polarity as the shunt field (see Fig. 163). Since the arbitrary insertion of the series field leaves this

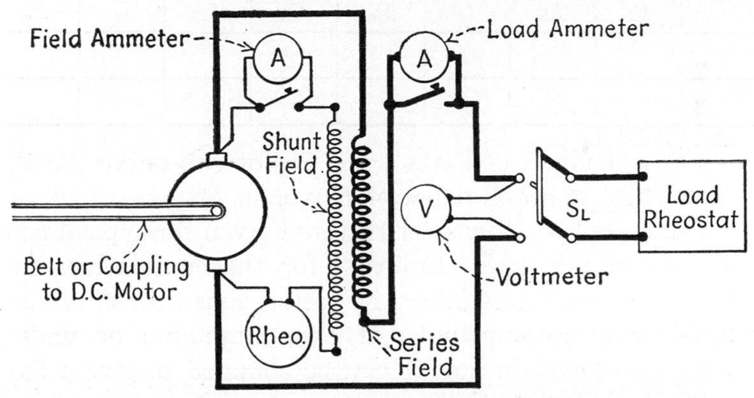

FIG. 184.—Wiring diagram for testing a compound generator under load.

matter to chance, the following preliminary test is recommended: (1) operate the generator at exactly the same speed and no-load voltage as in Experiment 35; (2) deliver a load current of about 25 per cent of rated value; (3) if the voltage at this load is higher than that obtained for the self-excited shunt operation, the generator is connected cumulative-compound; (4) if the voltage at this load is lower than for the self-excited shunt operation, the generator is connected differential-compound. To change from a differential connection to a cumulative connection, merely interchange the two series-field wires.

Assuming that the cumulative-compound connection has been made, proceed to load the generator as in Experiment 35. Be sure to maintain the speed absolutely constant, recording, as before, E_L, I_L, I_f, and revolutions per minute. All data should be recorded in a table similar to that given under Part 2.

Part 2. *Differential-compound.*—Convert the cumulative-compound generator into a differential-compound generator by interchanging the series-field wires. Again load the generator, recording the same values as before in a table similar to that given below.

R.p.m.	Cumulative-compound				Differential-compound			
	E_L	I_L	I_f	P_o	E_L	I_L	I_f	P_o

From the data of Parts 1 and 2 plot two curves on the same sheet of graph paper of E_L versus P_o.

Compare these curves with those given for typical generators in Fig. 164. Indicate, for the cumulative-compound generator, whether the tested generator is under-, flat-, or over-compound. If over-compound or under-compound, explain how it can be changed to give a flat-compound characteristic.

Alternator Experiments.—No detailed instructions will be given for the performance of alternator tests because these would be essentially the same as those outlined for the direct-current generator. If an alternator is available, it is recommended that the following experiments be performed:

1. Detailed examination of the constructional features of an alternator. Follow the same procedure as outlined in Experiment 33. Make comparisons between the constructional details of an alternator and a direct-current generator.

2. No-load characteristics of the alternator. (*a*) Obtain data for plotting the saturation curve. The field should, of course, be separately excited with direct current, while the output voltage should be measured with an alternating-current voltmeter. (*b*) Data for plotting the voltage-speed

characteristic should be obtained as in Experiment 34. For each value of speed, the frequency should be calculated by Eq. (52).

3. Load characteristics of the alternator. This should be done in essentially the same way as outlined in Experiment 35, Part 1. Use a unity-power-factor load, and if possible one whose power factor is less than unity lagging.

SUMMARY

1. An electric generator is a rotating type of machine that converts mechanical energy to electrical energy.
2. A generator consists essentially of a set of magnet poles and an armature winding. In the direct-current generator the armature winding is rotated with respect to the stationary magnetic field; in the alternating-current generator (alternator) the field poles are generally rotated with respect to the stationary armature winding.
3. The fundamental principle of generator action requires that flux be cut by conductors; *i.e.*, there must be *relative* motion between flux and conductors.
4. The generated voltage in the armature winding of either the direct-current generator or the alternator is alternating.
5. The commutator and its brushes in a direct-current generator function to rectify the alternating-current generated voltage so that the voltage at the brushes is always direct current.
6. The frequency of the alternating-current e.m.f. developed in an alternator is equal to ($P \times$ r.p.m./120).
7. Direct-current generators may be classified first as separately excited or self-excited machines. Alternators are always separately excited.
8. When a given generator is operated without load, the voltage that it develops depends upon the speed of rotation and the flux. When operated without a field, the voltage generated is due to the residual flux.

9. The saturation curve of a generator represents the relationship between the generated voltage and the exciting field current. For low values of field current the voltage is practically proportional to the field current; for high values of field current the voltage increases very little with increases in field current.
10. A self-excited shunt generator will build up only if all the conditions for build-up are fulfilled. These conditions are as follows: residual magnetism must be present; the field resistance must be below the critical value; the speed must be above the critical value; the field must act to aid the residual flux; the brushes must be properly located on the commutator.
11. Modern generators can also be classified as shunt or compound. If the latter, the generator may be under-, over-, or flat-compound.
12. The number of series-field turns in proportion to the number of shunt-field turns will determine whether the generator is under-, over-, or flat-compound.
13. The per cent voltage regulation of a shunt generator is defined as the per cent rise in voltage when full load is removed, based on the full-load voltage.
14. The voltage of a generator may be controlled by the use of a rheostat in the shunt-field circuit. This rheostat may be operated manually or by an automatic regulating device.
15. The degree of compounding of a compound generator may be permanently adjusted by connecting a diverter resistance of the proper value across the series field.
16. In a differential-compound generator the series field opposes the action of the shunt field. Such generators are rarely used.
17. Commutating poles are narrow poles placed exactly midway between the main poles and directly on the mechanical neutral. They eliminate the necessity for shifting the brushes as the load changes. Most modern machines have commutating poles often called *interpoles*.

18. The polarities of the interpoles of generators are the same as those of the succeeding main poles in the direction of rotation.
19. The speed of an alternating-current generator is fixed by the required frequency of the generated e.m.f.
20. The per cent voltage regulation of an alternator depends upon the character of the load. In general, it may be said that the more lagging the power factor of the load, the greater will be the drop in voltage between no load and full load.
21. Because the regulation of alternators is generally higher than direct-current generators, it is more essential that automatic regulators be used with the former. Moreover, alternators cannot be readily compounded as can direct-current generators.
22. In practice alternators feed longer transmission lines than do direct-current generators.
23. Modern power plants generally have several small generators rather than large single units capable of supplying the maximum peak loads. This practice generally results in higher operating efficiency and undisturbed continuity of service.
24. When two direct-current generators are to be connected in parallel, two important conditions must be fulfilled; namely, their voltages must be equal and their polarities must be correct.
25. When two alternators are to be connected in parallel, their voltages must be equal and their polarities must be correct. Obtaining the correct polarities involves an important synchronizing process.
26. Two shunt generators will generally operate satisfactorily in parallel if their voltage-load characteristics are approximately the same.
27. Two compound generators will generally operate satisfactorily in parallel if an equalizer connection is used between them.
28. When two generators are operated in parallel, load can

be shifted from one to the other by properly manipulating the field rheostats in the shunt-field circuits.

29. When two alternators are operated in parallel, load can be shifted from one to the other only by adjusting the power inputs to the prime movers.

QUESTIONS

1. Define a generator.
2. What types of prime mover are generally used for direct-current generators? for alternators?
3. Name the essential parts of a direct-current generator; an alternator.
4. Why is the generated e.m.f. in a direct-current generator alternating?
5. What determines the speed of an alternator?
6. How is the alternating e.m.f. changed to direct current in a direct-current generator?
7. Discuss the principle of generator action.
8. Describe a commutator and explain its action in conjunction with the brushes.
9. Distinguish between separate and self-excitation for direct-current generators.
10. Why must alternators be separately excited? How is this usually accomplished?
11. Describe an experiment for obtaining the saturation curve of a direct-current generator.
12. Upon what two factors does the value of the generated voltage depend?
13. Is it correct to say that "the generated voltage is directly proportional to the field current"? Give reasons for your answer.
14. Is it correct to say that "for a given field current the generated voltage is proportional to the speed"? Give reasons for your answer.
15. What conditions must be fulfilled if a self-excited shunt generator is to build up?

16. Upon what factors does the *value* of the final voltage to which a generator will build up depend?
17. What is meant by "flashing" the field? Under what conditions is this practice necessary?
18. What is meant by "critical resistance" when the building up of a self-excited shunt generator is referred to?
19. What is meant by "critical speed"?
20. How does a self-excited shunt generator behave when loaded?
21. Will the full-load voltage of a separately excited generator be higher or lower than the same machine operated as a self-excited generator? Give reasons for your answer.
22. Define voltage regulation.
23. Explain how the terminal voltage of a shunt generator may be controlled.
24. Explain the principle of the *Tirrill* regulator.
25. What important advantages are possessed by an automatic voltage regulator?
26. What is the constructional difference between a shunt generator and a compound generator?
27. In what two ways can the series field be connected with respect to the shunt field? Explain the action in both arrangements.
28. In which one of two circuits can the series field be connected?
29. Distinguish between a short-shunt and a long-shunt compound generator.
30. Why is a compound generator more desirable, in most applications, than a shunt generator?
31. Draw characteristic voltage-load curves for shunt, flat-compound, under-compound, and over-compound generators.
32. What is meant by the *degree* of compounding? What practical method can be used to adjust the degree of compounding of a generator?
33. Describe how a diverter is used and adjusted.

34. Carefully describe the commutation process.
35. Why does the commutator spark at the brushes as the load changes in a noninterpole generator?
36. What are interpoles? What important function do they have?
37. How does the voltage of an alternator change when the power factor of the load changes?
38. Why are automatic voltage-regulators more essential on alternators than on direct-current generators?
39. Why are power plants generally equipped with several generators instead of with a single large machine capable of taking care of the maximum demand?
40. Why is "continuity of service" so important in electrical systems? Give several examples where power failure would result in much loss.
41. Carefully explain how a generator is "put on the line" to operate in parallel with another generator.
42. Carefully explain how an alternator is connected in parallel with another alternator.
43. How can the load be shifted from one direct-current generator to another while two machines are operating in parallel?
44. How can the load be shifted from one alternator to another while two machines are operating in parallel?
45. What is meant by an *equalizer* connection?
46. What is the function of the equalizer connection?
47. What would happen if two compound generators were operated without an equalizer connection?

PROBLEMS

1. An alternator has 24 poles. At what speed must it be operated to generate 50 cycles? 40 cycles?
2. How many poles does a 30-cycle, 360-r.p.m. alternator have?
3. A 60-cycle motor is to be *directly coupled* to a 25-cycle alternator. Determine the fewest number of poles that

each machine must have and the speed of the motor-generator set.

4. Referring to Fig. 159*b*, assume that the saturation-curve data were obtained for a speed of 1,200 r.p.m. Using the method of proportion, calculate the speed at which the generator would have to operate for a voltage of E_H; for a voltage of E_L.
5. A shunt generator has a full-load rating of 50 kw. at 250 volts. The field resistance is 25 ohms. Calculate the full-load armature current.
6. A shunt generator has a no-load voltage of 140 and a regulation of 12 per cent. If the full-load current is 60 amp., calculate the kilowatt rating of the generator.
7. A 12.5-kw. compound generator has a full-load line current of 100 amp. If the shunt-field resistance is 15.6 ohms, what is the series-field current if the machine is connected (*a*) short-shunt, (*b*) long-shunt?
8. The series field of a 10-kw., 230-volt compound generator has a resistance of 0.05 ohm. If the diverter resistance is 0.15 ohm, determine the series-field current. (Assume a short-shunt connection.)
9. A 50-kw., 240-volt, over-compound generator has a no-load voltage of 220. Assuming a straight-line voltage rise between no-load and full-load current, calculate the kilowatt output when the load current is 150 amp.
10. The shunt field of a 120-volt generator has a resistance of 40 ohms. If a field rheostat of 25 ohms is connected in the field circuit, calculate (*a*) the power taken by the field winding, (*b*) the power lost in the rheostat.
11. Using the data of Prob. 10, determine how much power the field winding will take if a pair of contacts short-circuit the field rheostat.
12. A 25-kw., 125-volt, compound generator has a shunt field, each pole of which has 600 turns of wire. The series field has eight turns per pole. If the total shunt-field resistance is 20 ohms, calculate the total number of

ampere turns that produces flux at full load. (Assume a short-shunt connection.)

13. What is the per cent regulation of a flat-compound generator?
14. A transmission line has a resistance of 0.5 ohm. If the voltage at the load must be 120 under all load conditions, (*a*) what must be the generator voltage when the load takes 40 amp.? (*b*) What is the kilowatt rating of the generator?
15. The series field of a compound generator has a resistance of 0.04 ohm. If the full-load current of the generator is 140 amp. and it is necessary to divert 35 amp. in order to bring the full-load voltage down to a lower value, calculate (*a*) the diverter resistance, and (*b*) the length of a No. 6 gauge Manganin wire to be used for the diverter.
16. Two direct-current generators operate in parallel to deliver a total load of 840 kw. If generator 1 has a rating of 250 kw. and generator 2 has a rating of 750 kw., (*a*) what load should each machine deliver if the total load is to be divided in proportion to the ratings? (*b*) What current does each machine deliver if the line voltage at this load is 600?
17. Assuming constant field excitation, calculate the no-load voltage of a separately excited shunt generator at a speed of 1,800 r.p.m. if its 1,600-r.p.m. voltage is 222.
18. A 200-kw. compound generator has a no-load voltage of 250. If the line resistance between generator and load is 0.025 ohm, calculate the full-load voltage at the generator if the load voltage is 250 when the machine delivers its rated output.
19. Calculate the power loss in the line wires when the generator in Prob. 18 is delivering its rated output.
20. Two 50-kw. shunt generators are operated in parallel. Generator *A* has a no-load voltage of 250 and a full-load voltage of 210. Generator *B* has a no-load voltage of

240 and a full-load voltage of 220. (*a*) At what terminal voltage will both machines deliver equal loads, and what will these loads be? (*b*) When the terminal voltage is 220, what loads will the two machines deliver? (*c*) When the terminal voltage is 240, what loads will the two machines deliver?

CHAPTER 10

MOTORS—DIRECT AND ALTERNATING CURRENT

Differences between Generators and Motors.—In Chap. 9 our attention was centered upon the electric generator, the machine that converts mechanical energy into electrical energy. It will now be our object to study *the machine that converts electrical energy into mechanical energy—the electric motor.*

When a *generator* is in operation, it is driven by a mechanical machine and develops a *voltage,* which in turn can produce a current flow in an electric circuit; when a *motor* is in operation, it is supplied with current and develops *torque,* which in turn can produce mechanical rotation. The load on a generator constitutes those electrical consuming devices that convert electrical energy into other forms of energy; the load on an electric motor constitutes the force that tends to oppose rotation and is called "countertorque." The voltage of a generator in operation tends to change when the load changes; in the case of the motor, the speed tends to change when the load changes. The voltage of a generator can always be adjusted by changing the speed of the mechanical driving unit or by changing the strength of the magnetic field; the speed of a direct-current motor can be adjusted by changing the strength of the magnetic field or by changing the voltage impressed across the armature; whether or not the speed of an alternating-current motor may be adjusted depends upon its type. The speed of rotation of a generator is usually quite constant, and in the case of alternators absolutely so; the voltage impressed across the terminals of a motor is substantially constant, except in the case of some special motors that are supplied with power from an independent source of supply. Generators can be, and frequently are, operated in parallel with others to supply power to one or more loads; motors usually operate as single independent units to drive their individual loads, although in special cases (streetcars, trains, excavators) they may be operated in series or parallel to drive their loads. Generators are always started without electrical loads; motors may or may not be started with a mechanical load. (In connection with the latter point, a motor must frequently be able to develop more torque during the starting period than when performing its normal operating function.) From the standpoint of construction direct-current generators and motors are practically identical; they may, in fact, be operated as either generators or motors with complete satisfaction if certain conditions, to be discussed later, are fulfilled. Except in the case of one type of machine, the synchronous machine, alternating-current generators differ greatly in construction from alternating-current motors.

Classification of Motors.—Strictly speaking, there are only one type of alternator and two general types of direct-current generator, namely, shunt and compound. There are, however, three general types of direct-current motor, namely, series, shunt, and compound, and four types of alternating-current motor, namely, series, induction, synchronous, and repulsion. As will be pointed out later, the series motor, when properly designed, will operate with complete satisfaction when connected to either a direct-current or an alternating-current source. Moreover, some motors start by the repulsion principle and after reaching rated speed continue to operate under load by the induction principle.

With the single exception of the constant-speed synchronous (alternating-current) type of motor, the speed of all of the others changes as the load changes. Obviously, the speed of a motor is higher at light loads than under heavy load. (A streetcar runs slower going uphill than when operating on level track; a drill press slows down when the drill begins cutting through heavy steel; when the pressure in the tank of an air compressor increases, the motor slows down.) Some types of motor slow down a great deal as load is applied, while the speed of others changes very little with similar load changes. For the purposes of classification, therefore, it is convenient to indicate how a motor behaves between no load and full load by using such terms as "constant" speed and "variable" speed. Thus, if a change from no load to full load results in a drop in speed of approximately 8 per cent or less, the motor is said to be of the constant-speed type. Direct-current shunt motors and squirrel-cage induction motors generally fall into this classification. Where the speed changes by greater values than that indicated above, the motors are generally regarded as falling into the variable-speed classification. Understand that the 8 per cent figure is just an arbitrary value used merely as a guide to differentiate motors on the basis of speed classification. In some cases an engineer might even consider a 5 per cent speed variation as excessive, while in other applications a motor might be regarded as falling into the constant-speed class when the variation is as much as 10 per cent. The point is that the terms "variable speed" and "constant speed" are relative and must be applied advisedly to the application. In some cases, however, there is no question about the classification; a series motor, or a compound motor with a strong series field, is definitely of the variable-speed type; a synchronous motor is unquestionably of the constant-speed type.

Whenever the speed of a motor can be controlled by an *operator* who makes a manual adjustment, the motor is said to be of the *adjustable-speed type*. Note the important difference between the variable-speed and the adjustable-speed types; in the former the speed changes inherently as a result of the load, while in the latter the speed changes only because an operator has made a manual adjustment of some sort. It is, therefore, possible to have a constant-speed–adjustable-speed motor, or a variable-speed–adjustable-speed motor. As will be pointed out later, a shunt motor with field-rheostat control would fall into the first classification, while a series motor with a rheostat connected into the line would fall into the second classification. The common kitchen food mixer equipped with an adjustable speed governor is an excellent example of the constant-speed–adjustable-speed combination.

The Direct-current Motor Principle.—A direct-current motor develops torque. Basically, a current-carrying conductor will experience a force action when it is properly placed in a magnetic field. This force action will be greatest when

FIG. 185.—Direct-current armature completely wound, dipped in insulating varnish, and baked. (*The Louis Allis Co.*)

the conductor occupies a position perpendicular to the direction of the magnetic field and will be zero when the field and the conductor are parallel to each other. When this force action is such that there is a tendency to produce rotation, then torque is developed. In the actual motor many copper conductors are placed near the surface of a laminated steel core structure, having a cylindrical shape. The latter is mounted securely on a steel shaft that is free to turn, in bearings, between the poles of powerful electromagnets. Figure 185 shows a completely wound, properly dipped and baked direct-current armature for a modern type of motor.

Consider one pair of conductors of such an armature in a two-pole field. These conductors are shown placed in two diametrically opposite slots under the centers of the poles marked *north* and *south*. If only the field is energized, the flux distribution is quite uniform and symmetrical as shown in Fig. 186*a*. If the conductors carry currents as indicated in Fig. 186*b* (no field excitation), the magnetic fluxes surrounding both conductors are approximate circular paths. However, when the field is excited and the currents flow in the two conductors, the flux distribution is far from uniform, as represented by Fig. 186*c*. Notice particularly that the flux tends to concentrate on the bottom of the left conductor

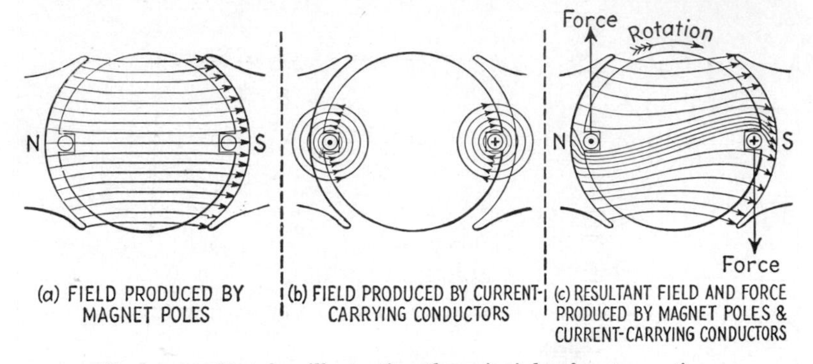

FIG. 186.—Sketches illustrating the principle of motor action.

and the top of the right conductor. The flux lines, which tend to act like rubber bands, endeavor to contract, with the result that the armature tries to rotate in a clockwise direction. Notice particularly that the flux, the current-carrying conductor, and the force exerted on the conductor are mutually perpendicular.

If the directions of the currents in the two conductors are reversed so that the current will be away from the observer in the left conductor and toward the observer in the right conductor, the armature will tend to turn in a counterclockwise direction. Or, if the polarity of the field is reversed, the armature will likewise tend to rotate counterclockwise. Thus, it is seen that the direction of rotation of a direct-current motor can be reversed by changing the direction of the current flow through the armature conductors *or* by changing the polarity of the field. A motor will not reverse its direction of rotation by changing both the field polarity and the current flow through the armature. Interchanging the two line wires to the motor does exactly this; therefore, the motor will not reverse if such a change is made.

Force and Torque Developed by a Direct-current Motor.—A current-carrying conductor will experience a force only if it is placed in a magnetic field. Assuming that the conductor and the magnetic field are perpendicular to each other—the usual case in practice—it should be obvious that the magnitude of the force will depend directly upon the strength of the field and the value of the current. If either or both of these quantities change, the force will change. No force will be created if the conductor carries no current or if the current-carrying conductor is placed in a "fluxless" space.

Actually, the force exerted upon a conductor is directly proportional to (1) the current in the wire, (2) the flux density of the magnetic field, and (3) the length of the wire. In equation form this becomes

$$F = \frac{B \times I \times l}{11{,}300{,}000} \text{ lb.} \tag{55}$$

where B = flux density in lines per square inch
I = current in conductor in amperes
l = length of conductor in inches

Example 1.—A conductor 9 in. long carries a current of 160 amp. and is placed at right angles to a magnetic field whose intensity is 60,000 lines per square inch. Calculate the force exerted upon the conductor.

Solution:

$$F = \frac{60{,}000 \times 160 \times 9}{11{,}300{,}000} = 7.65 \text{ lb.}$$

Example 2.—The armature of a motor contains 160 conductors, 70 per cent of which are directly under the poles, where the flux density is 48,000 lines per square inch. If the core diameter is 4 in., its length is 5 in., and the torque developed by the motor is 30 ft.-lb., calculate the current flowing in each conductor.

Solution:

$$\text{Torque} = 30 \text{ ft.-lb.} = 30 \times 12 \text{ in.-lb.} = 360 \text{ in.-lb.}$$

$$\text{Force} = \frac{\text{torque}}{\text{radius}} = \frac{360 \text{ in.-lb.}}{2 \text{ in.}} = 180 \text{ lb.}$$

$$180 = \frac{(160 \times 0.7) \times 48{,}000 \times I \times 5}{11{,}300{,}000}$$

$$I = \frac{180 \times 11{,}300{,}000}{(160 \times 0.7) \times 48{,}000 \times 5} = 75.7 \text{ amp.}$$

As the above examples illustrate, the turning moment or torque of a motor is created by the combined action of many current-carrying conductors in a strong magnetic field. Moreover, only those conductors that are directly under the pole faces contribute to the tendency of the armature to rotate; the conductors that lie between the pole tips, in the interpolar spaces, are in very weak fields and are, therefore, more or less inactive. That is why only 70 per cent of the total number of conductors were used in the calculation of Example 2.

Direct-current generators, studied in the previous chapter, will operate satisfactorily as direct-current motors. In the four-pole motor represented by Fig. 187 current is fed to the positive brushes A and A' and leaves the negative brushes B and B'. Entering the armature conductors through the commutator, the currents then flow in directions indicated by dots and crosses. Note particularly that between a and b and between c and d the current is away from the observer; between b and c and between d and a the current is toward the observer. With the polarities of the poles as indicated the direction of rotation will be clockwise if the armature is free to turn. Since only those wires that are directly under the pole faces will be active, it will be observed that 16 out of a total of 64 conductors will not develop torque, although they carry currents. Furthermore,

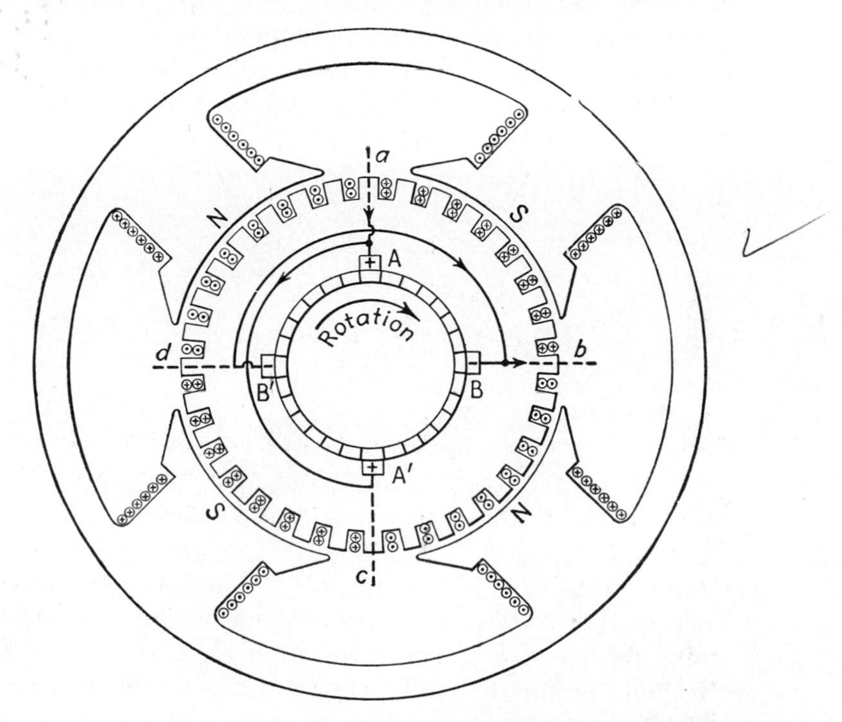

Fig. 187.—Sketch representing an elementary direct-current motor.

as the armature conductors rotate, the currents through them will be continually changing direction, being away from the observer when under a *south* pole and toward the observer when under a *north* pole. Thus, it is seen that rotation is maintained in one direction because the current in the conductors is alternating even though the source of supply is direct. In a motor, therefore, the commutator and the accompanying brushes change the externally applied direct current to alternating current in the conductors.

Counter Electromotive Force Developed by a Motor (C.E.M.F.).—As the armature of a direct-current motor rotates owing to motor action, voltages are *generated* in the very same conductors that receive current from the source of supply. This means that both motor action and generator action take place simultaneously in the armature conductors. With the armature conductors located in a magnetic field, motor action is developed when the brushes are connected to a source of supply and *current flows* in the

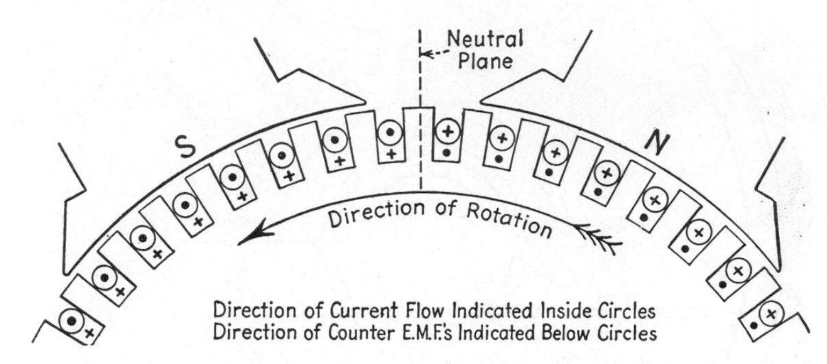

FIG. 188.—Sketch representing the relation between the direction of current flow and the direction of the c.e.m.f. in a direct-current motor.

armature winding. Moreover, as the armature rotates, *voltages are generated* in the very same armature conductors because the latter cut across the same lines of force that are responsible for the motor action. And since the generated voltage is always in such a direction that it tends to oppose the current flow, it is called a *counter electromotive force*, abbreviated c.e.m.f.

Referring to Fig. 188, which represents the armature conductors and two poles of a direct-current motor, note that rotation is counterclockwise. The current directions are indicated by the dots and crosses inside the circular conductors. From the right-hand rule (see Chap. 9), it is found that the generated voltages in the conductors are oppositely directed with respect to the current flow; these are indicated by the crosses and dots directly below the circular conductors in the slots. Obviously, *the c.e.m.f. can never be equal to, and must always be less than, the voltage impressed across the armature terminals*, because the direction in which the current flows determines first the direction of rotation and then the direction of the c.e.m.f. This can mean only that the armature current is *controlled* and *limited* by the c.e.m.f. Therefore, by Ohm's law,

$$I_a = \frac{E_T - E_c}{R_a} \tag{56}$$

where I_a = armature current
E_T = impressed voltage across armature
E_c = c.e.m.f. generated in armature
R_a = resistance of armature

Since the c.e.m.f. E_c is a generated voltage and depends only upon the flux ϕ per pole and the speed S in revolutions per minute, it follows that

$$I_a = \frac{E_T - k\phi S}{R_a} \tag{57}$$

where k is a factor (or constant) that depends upon the total number of armature conductors, the manner in which the armature is wound, and the number of main poles in the motor.

Example 3.—The speed of a motor is 1,200 r.p.m. when the voltage impressed across the armature terminals is 120. If the flux per pole is 560,000 maxwells and the armature resistance is 0.25 ohm, calculate the c.e.m.f. and the armature current. (For this motor k is 1.71×10^{-7}.)

Solution:

$$E_c = (1.71 \times 10^{-7}) \times 560{,}000 \times 1{,}200 = 115 \text{ volts}$$

$$I_a = \frac{120 - 115}{0.25} = 20 \text{ amp.}$$

Example 4.—If the load upon the motor of Example 3 is increased so that the armature current rises to 40 amp., at what speed will the machine operate?

Solution:

$$S = \frac{E_T - I_a R_a}{k\phi} = \frac{120 - (40 \times 0.25)}{(1.71 \times 10^{-7}) \times 560{,}000}$$

$$= \frac{11{,}000}{9.57} = 1{,}150 \text{ r.p.m.}$$

The c.e.m.f. developed in the armature of a motor is usually between 80 and 95 per cent of the voltage impressed across the armature terminals; the larger percentages generally apply to the larger motors while the smaller percentages apply to fractional-horsepower sizes. From the standpoint of practical operation, it is desirable to have as high a value of E_c as possible because it is a measure of the power output of the motor. Or to put it another way, the difference between the terminal voltage E_T and the c.e.m.f. E_c is a measure of the power loss in the armature. Thus,

$$E_T - E_c = I_a R_a \tag{58}$$

In order to convert this voltage equation into one involving terms of power (watts), both sides will be multiplied by I_a. Thus,

$$E_T I_a - E_c I_a = I_a^2 R_a \tag{59}$$

which shows that the armature power loss $I_a^2 R_a$ is the difference between the power input to the armature $E_T I_a$ and the power developed by the armature $E_c I_a$. Note particularly that two important advantages result from a high value of E_c, namely, high power output and low armature copper loss.

Example 5.—The armature of a motor has a resistance of 0.20 ohm and takes 65 amp. when operating from a

230-volt source while delivering a certain mechanical load. Calculate (*a*) the c.e.m.f. E_c, (*b*) the power developed by the armature, (*c*) the copper loss in the armature.

Solution:

a. $E_c = 230 - 65 \times 0.2 = 217$ volts

b. Power developed by armature $= E_c I_a = 217 \times 65$
$= 14,105$ watts

c. Armature copper loss $= I_a^2 R_a = (65)^2 \times 0.2 = 845$ watts

FIG. 189.—Completely disassembled direct-current, four-pole, commutating-pole motor. (*The Louis Allis Co.*)

Types of Direct-current Motor.—From the standpoint of construction direct-current generators and motors are similar in all respects. In fact, it is quite possible to operate a generator as a motor and a motor as a generator. Figure 189 shows a completely disassembled four-pole direct-current motor of modern design and construction. Note the cooling fan, the ball bearings, the brush rigging, and one of the two interpoles. Like generators, direct-current motors differ as to type by the way in which the field winding is (or the field windings are) excited.

If the field winding is connected directly *across* the armature terminals, it is said to be in shunt (or parallel) with the latter; the machine is then called a *shunt motor*. If the field winding is connected directly *in series* with the armature, the machine is called a *series motor*. Figure 190 represents both types of motor schematically. To understand thoroughly why these two types of motor differ in operating characteristics it is necessary to recognize the fol-

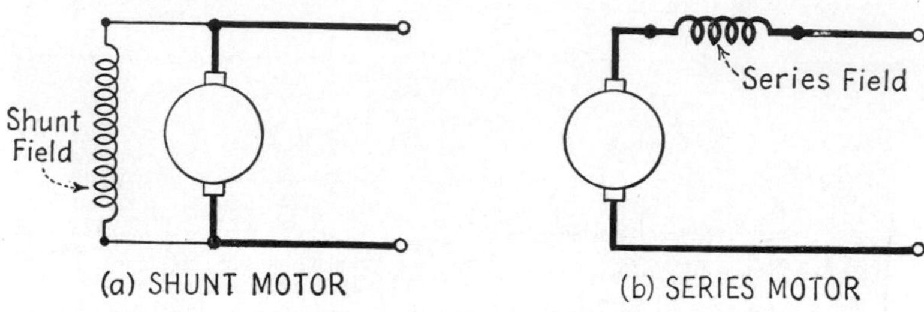

FIG. 190.—Elementary shunt and series motor connections.

lowing important differences between the two kinds of field winding:

1. The shunt winding is a comparatively high-resistance winding; the series winding is a very low-resistance winding.
2. The voltage across the shunt winding is the full line potential; the voltage drop across the series field is very low, being several per cent of the line potential.
3. The current through the shunt field is independent of the armature current; the current through the series field is the same as that in the armature winding, which in turn depends upon the mechanical load on the motor.
4. The excitation of the shunt field can be readily controlled by inserting a rheostat in series with the former; the excitation produced by the series field is determined only by the current taken by the motor, which in turn depends only on the mechanical load upon the motor.

If a machine is provided with both shunt-field and series-field excitation, it is called a *compound motor*. Figure 191 illustrates two ways in which these field windings may be connected with respect to each other and the armature. If the shunt field is connected directly across the armature terminals with the series field in the line feeding the motor (Fig. 191*a*), the following two points should be noted: (1) the voltage across the shunt field is slightly less (several

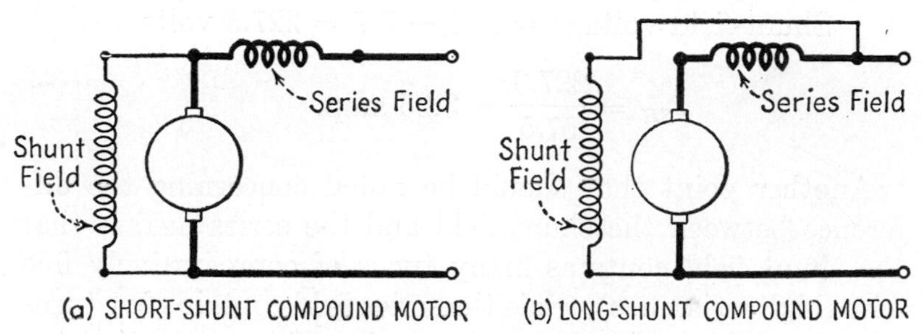

FIG. 191.—Elementary compound-motor connections.

per cent less) than the line potential, and (2) the current through the series field is the sum of the high armature current and the low shunt-field current. If the shunt field is connected directly across the line, with the armature and series field connected in series (Fig. 191*b*), the following two points should be noted: (1) the shunt field receives full line voltage, and (2) the series-field current is slightly less than the line current, being equal to the high total current fed to the motor *minus* the low shunt-field current. Since there is very little difference in the operating characteristics between the short-shunt connection (Fig. 191*a*) and the long-shunt connection (Fig. 191*b*), either one may be used with complete satisfaction.

Example 6.—A 230-volt compound motor has a shunt field whose resistance is 57.5 ohms and a series-field resistance of 0.05 ohm. If the normal full-load line current is 54 amp., calculate the shunt-field current and the series-field current for (*a*) the long-shunt connection, (*b*) the short-shunt connection.

Solution:

a. Long-shunt $I_{SH} = \frac{230}{57.5} = 4$ amp.

$$I_{SE} = 54 - 4 = 50 \text{ amp.}$$

b. Short-shunt $I_{SE} = 54$ amp.

Voltage drop across series field $= 54 \times 0.05 = 2.7$ volts
Shunt-field voltage $= 230 - 2.7 = 227.3$ volts

$$I_{SH} = \frac{227.3}{57.5} = 3.95 \text{ amp.}$$

Another point that should be noted concerning the difference between the shunt field and the series field is that the shunt field contains many turns of comparatively fine wire (high resistance), while the series field contains few turns of rather heavy wire (low resistance). This means that the shunt field can create much flux with a low current, while the series field must carry a considerable current before it can have an effect upon the shunt-field flux (see Chap. 6 where it is shown that flux is determined by ampere turns).

Starting a Direct-current Motor.—At the instant a direct-current motor is started, the c.e.m.f. is zero because the armature is not turning. As the armature accelerates to full speed, the c.e.m.f. increases. Since the c.e.m.f. E_c limits the current in the armature circuit [Eq. (56)], it should be clear that, at the instant of starting, when E_c is zero, the current would be extremely high unless some resistance were added to offset the lack of E_c. In other words, if the c.e.m.f. is zero, or very small as the motor is coming up to speed, a resistance must be inserted to take the place of E_c; as the speed increases, resistance may be cut out gradually because E_c rises; finally, when the motor has attained its normal speed, all resistance can be cut out of the armature circuit. This reasoning is made clear by the following example:

Example 7.—The armature of a shunt motor has a resistance of 0.22 ohm. If the line voltage is 115 and the armature current is not to exceed 46 amp., calculate (*a*) the resistance that must be inserted in the armature circuit at the instant of starting; (*b*) the value to which this resistance can be reduced when the armature accelerates until E_c is 46 volts.

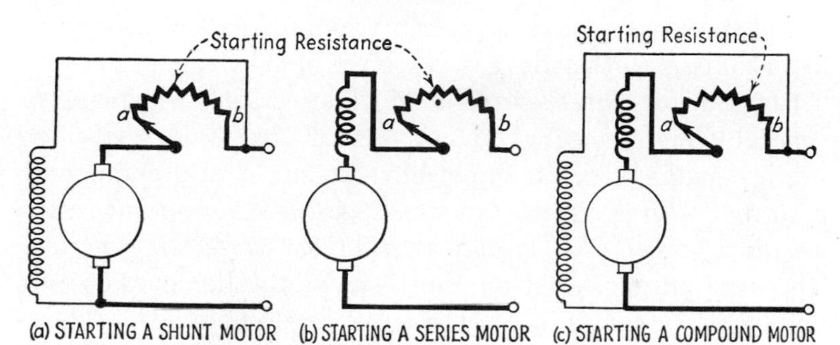

FIG. 192.—Elementary starting-resistance connections for three types of motor.

(*c*) Determine the armature current at the instant of starting if no resistance is inserted in the armature circuit.

Solution:

$$a.\ I_a = \frac{E_T - E_c}{R_a + R};\ R = \frac{115}{46} - 0.22 = 2.28 \text{ ohms}$$

$$b.\ R = \frac{115 - 46}{46} - 0.22 = 1.28 \text{ ohms}$$

$$c.\ I_a = \frac{115}{0.22} = 523 \text{ amp.}$$

Figure 192 shows how the starting resistance is inserted in the armature circuit in the three types of motor previously discussed. In all cases the motor must be started with the movable arm at *a*, to be gradually moved to *b* as the armature accelerates to full speed.

Fractional-horsepower motors up to about $\frac{3}{4}$ hp. may be started without the use of an external armature resistance. There are two reasons for this practice: (1) the resistance and the inductance of the armature winding are generally high enough to limit the initial rush of current to values that are not particularly serious, and (2) the inertia of a small armature structure is generally so low that it comes up to full speed very quickly, thereby minimizing the serious effect that might otherwise result from a high sustained current.

Starters for Direct-current Motors.—Motor starters are generally manufactured in convenient sizes and styles for use as auxiliaries with direct-current shunt and compound motors. *Their primary function is to limit the current in the armature circuit during the starting or accelerating period.* They are always rated on the basis of the horsepower and voltage of the motors with which they are to be used. There are two general types of motor starter for shunt and compound motors, namely, the *three-point* type and the *four-point* type. Three-point starters are not entirely satisfactory when used with motors whose speed must be controlled by inserting resistance in the shunt-field circuit. However, many of them are used with shunt and compound motors where the applications require no manual speed adjustment.

A three-point starter with its internal wiring is shown connected to a shunt motor in Fig. 193. Note that the starter has three terminals marked L, F, and A. The line terminal L must be connected to either one of the line terminals on the main switch—wire a; the field terminal F must be connected to either one of the motor shunt-field terminals—wire b; the armature terminal A must be connected to either one of the motor armature terminals—wire c. The final connection must then be made from the other line terminal on the switch to the junction of the remaining two armature and field terminals to the motor. If it is desired that the speed of the motor be controlled, a field rheostat should be inserted in series between the field terminal on the box and the field terminal on the motor—wire b'. It is well to remember that *under no circumstances must any other wires be connected to the ends of wires a, b, b′*, and *c* in Fig. 193. With the motor at rest the starting arm is held in the *off* position by a strong spiral spring. To start the motor one hand is held on the handle of the *open* main switch while the starter arm is moved to the first stud with the other hand;

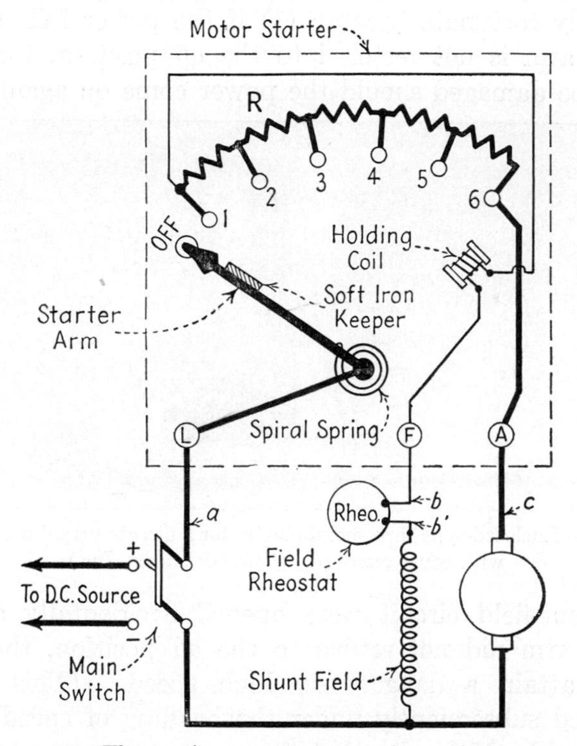

FIG. 193.—Three-point starter connected to a shunt motor.

the main switch is then closed. If all the wiring is correct and the armature is free to turn, the motor will start. Note particularly that there are *two* circuits: (1) through resistor *R* in series with the armature, and (2) through the holding coil in series with the shunt field and its rheostat. After the armature has accelerated sufficiently on the first stud, the starter arm is moved to studs 2, 3, 4, 5, 6, etc., until the soft iron keeper rests firmly against the iron poles of the holding coil. The whole starting process should take from 5 to 10 sec. In the final position the electromagnetic pull exerted by the holding coil will overpower the force exerted by the spiral spring. The starter arm will fall back to its *off* position only if the power supply should fail or if the field circuit should be opened accidentally. This action of the starter is especially fortunate because (1) if the power fails and the starter arm is not restored to the *off* position, the motor might be damaged should the power come on again; (2) if

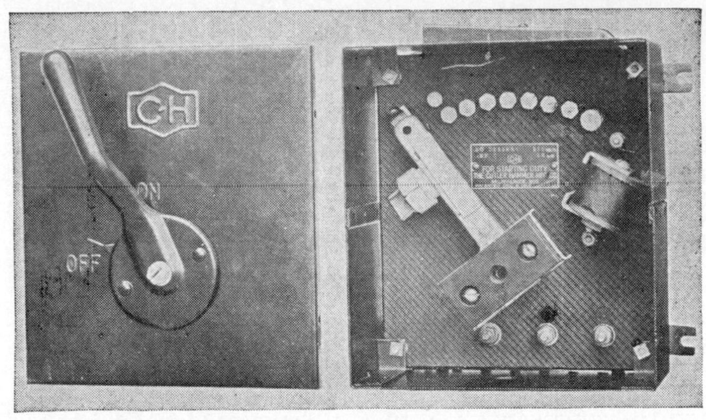

FIG. 194.—Enclosed-type three-point starter for a direct-current motor, shown with cover removed. (*Cutler-Hammer, Inc.*)

the shunt-field circuit were opened accidentally and the starter arm did not return to the *off* position, the motor might attain a dangerously high speed. (This will be discussed subsequently under the heading of speed control of motors.) Note also that the current through the shunt-field circuit is the *same* current that flows through the holding coil. Thus, if sufficient resistance is *cut in* by the field rheostat so that the holding-coil current is no longer able to create enough electromagnetic pull to overcome the spring tension, the starting arm will fall back to the *off* position. It is this undesirable feature of the three-point starter that makes it unsuitable for use with speed-controlled motors and has resulted in the widespread application of four-point starters. Figure 194 shows a three-point enclosed type of motor starter with the cover removed. With the cover in place no live parts are exposed. Note particularly the eight studs on the face plate, the electromagnet holding coil, and the three terminals at the bottom.

A four-point starter with its internal wiring is shown connected to a long-shunt compound motor in Fig. 195. If

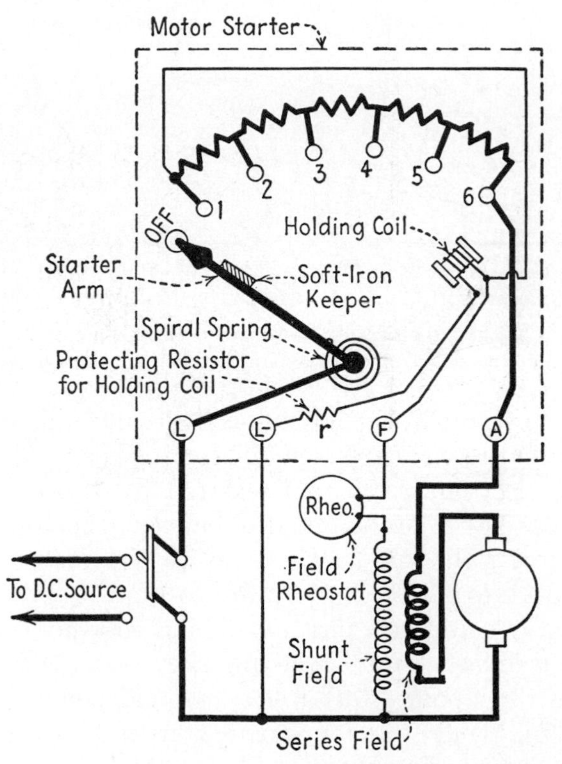

FIG. 195.—Four-point starter connected to a long-shunt compound motor.

this starter is compared with the three-point type (Fig. 193), it will be observed that one important change has been made; the holding coil has been taken out of the shunt-field circuit and placed in a separate circuit. Thus, when the starter arm is on the first stud, the line current divides into *three* parts: (1) one circuit through the starting resistance R, the series field, and the armature, (2) the second circuit through the shunt field and its field rheostat, and (3) the third circuit through the holding coil and a current-protecting resistor r. Note particularly that with this arrangement any change in current in the shunt-field circuit does not

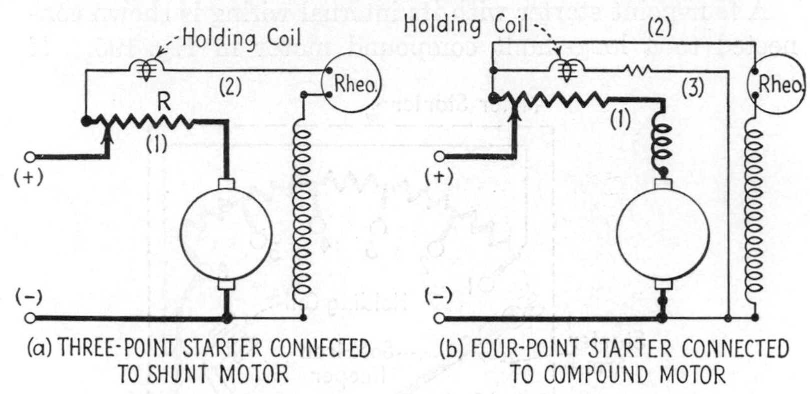

FIG. 196.—Schematic wiring diagrams showing three-point and four-point motor starters connected to shunt and compound motors.

affect the current in the holding-coil circuit; these two circuits are entirely independent of each other. This means that the electromagnetic pull exerted by the holding coil will always be sufficient and will prevent the spiral spring from restoring the arm to the *off* position no matter how the field rheostat is adjusted. In order to emphasize further the difference between the three-point and four-point starters, Fig. 196 is given. In these wiring sketches it will be noted that the three-point starter has two independent circuits (Fig. 196*a*), while the four-point starter has three independent circuits (Fig. 196*b*).

Series motors are generally started with another device known as a *drum controller*. The wiring connections are rather simple and are given in Fig. 192*b*. The word "controller" is used for this device because it performs the basic function of accelerating the motor to its normal speed and in addition provides a means for reversing the direction of rotation. Other features, such as safety protection against an open field, overloads, and a temporary failure of the power supply, are frequently included with this type of controller. Figure 197 illustrates such a drum controller for a series motor. It is designed for starting, reversing, and speed-

FIG. 197.—Drum-type controller used principally with speed-controlled motors employing resistance in the armature circuit. (*Cutler-Hammer, Inc.*)

controlled applications and may even be arranged for use with shunt and compound motors.

Loading a Motor—Effect upon Speed and Armature Current.—When a *generator* delivers electric power to a load, its terminal voltage *tends* to change. And, as was learned in

Chap. 9, the operator (or the designer of the machine) has complete control over this tendency on the part of the generator to change its terminal voltage. Briefly stated, *voltage control of a generator is exercised through the medium of flux adjustment or control.*

In practice an electric motor generally receives its electric power ($E \times I$) at substantially constant voltage. It then converts this electric power into mechanical power, doing so by developing torque as it rotates its load. If the mechanical load on the motor changes, either the torque or the speed, or both, must tend to change. And here again it will be learned that the *control of the speed of a motor is exercised through the medium of flux adjustment or control.*

When a load is applied to a motor, the natural tendency of the latter is to slow down because the opposition to motion (*i.e.*, resisting torque) is increased. Under this condition the c.e.m.f. decreases for the reason that E_c is proportional to the speed. This reduction in the c.e.m.f. immediately results in an increase in armature current, since, by Eq. (56), I_a equals $(E_T - E_c)/R_a$. Obviously, this increase in armature current is exactly what is required because *any increase in the mechanical driving power must be met by a corresponding increase in electrical power input to the armature.* Moreover, since the electrical power input to the armature equals $E \times I_a$, it follows that only I_a must increase for the reason that the impressed voltage E is, as stated above, substantially constant. Thus, it is seen that loading a motor always results in (1) a reduction in speed, and (2) an increase in armature current. And, vice versa, unloading a motor causes its armature to take less current while it speeds up.

The speed at which a motor operates when it is driving its rated load, its so-called "rated horsepower" (hp.), is called the *normal speed.* If the load is completely removed from a *shunt motor* so that it is merely overcoming its own bearing, brush, and wind friction, it will operate at a speed only slightly higher than the normal speed; this will usually be between 2 and 8 per cent higher than the normal speed.

Doing the same thing to a *compound motor* will result in a rise in speed of about 10 to 25 per cent. In both shunt and compound motors the no-load speed is very definite and stable; these motors do not attempt to operate at excessive unsafe speeds when running idle. The *series* motor, on the other hand, does attempt to race, or operate at a very high speed, when the load is removed. This fact is so well recognized in practice that a series motor is always geared or coupled to its load so that an opposing torque will always exist; it is never belted to the load because the accidental "throwing" of the belt will instantly result in a dangerous, racing motor, a motor that is said to "*run away*."

Torque Characteristics of Direct-current Motors.—The *torque* developed by a motor, *i.e.*, *the tendency of a motor to produce rotation*, depends upon two factors: (1) the flux created by the stationary field, and (2) the current flowing in the armature winding. This statement can be written in equation form thus:

$$T = k\phi I_c \tag{60}$$

where T = torque (usually in foot-pounds)
ϕ = flux per pole in maxwells
I_c = current in each armature conductor in amperes
k^* = a constant depending upon the total number of armature conductors and the number of poles

A study of Eq. (60) in connection with the three types of motor, represented in Fig. 198, should make it clear how the torque of such machines behaves under varying conditions of load. In the shunt and compound motors the current through the shunt field is constant and is fixed only by the shunt-field resistance and the terminal voltage E_T;

$$I_{SH} = E_T/R_{SH}.$$

This means that the shunt-field flux is independent of

* $k = \left(\frac{0.1173}{10^8}\right) \times Z \times p$, where Z = total number of armature conductors and p = number of poles.

the load and is substantially constant, because the flux depends only upon the field current. In the series and compound motors the current through the series field changes with the load, because, as was pointed out in the previous articles, the armature current is determined by the load; at light loads the armature current is small, whereas at heavy loads the armature current is high. It follows, therefore, that the series-field flux will change with the load.

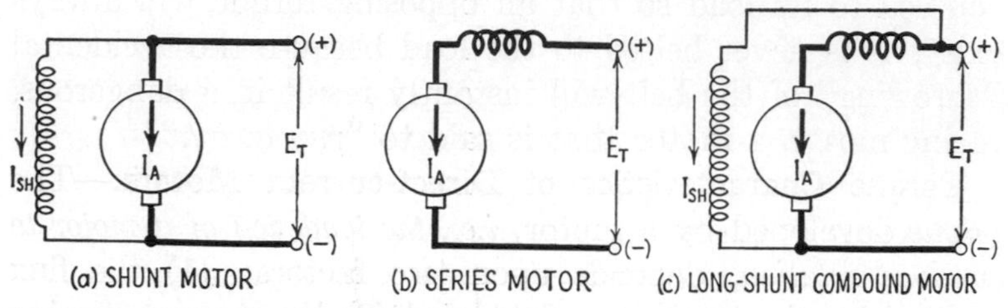

FIG. 198.—Armature and field currents in three types of direct-current motor.

This reasoning leads to the following conclusions regarding the manner in which the torque developed by a motor varies with the horsepower output (load) of the motor:

1. The torque of a *shunt motor* depends only upon the armature current; assuming that the shunt-field current is not changed by field-rheostat adjustment, the torque is independent of the flux. A graph indicating the relation between torque and load should, therefore, be a straight line ($T = k_1 I_a$).

2. The torque of a series motor depends upon the armature current *and* the flux that it produces when it passes through the series field. At light loads when the magnetic circuit iron is not saturated the field flux is directly proportional to the load current. Under this condition a graph indicating the relation between torque and load should be an approximate parabola ($T = k_2 I_a^2$). At heavy loads when the magnetic circuit iron is saturated, the flux will change very little or not at all with changes in load; under this condition the graph will tend to become a straight line. Thus, a complete graph of torque versus load for a series motor will start out as a parabola and become a straight line.

3. The torque of a *compound motor* (cumulative only, where the shunt and series field aid each other) combines the torque-load characteristics of the shunt and series motors. As the load on the motor increases, the armature, or load, current passing through the series field creates flux that adds to the constant shunt-field flux. The resultant flux thus tends to give the motor a rising torque curve (concave

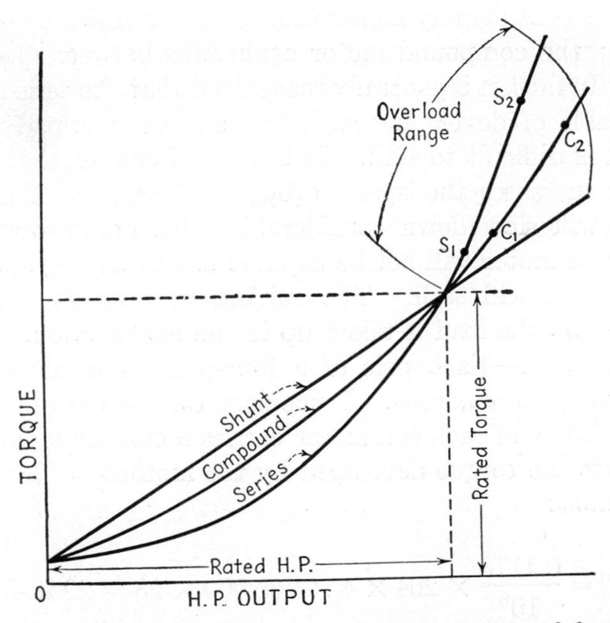

FIG. 199.—Torque-versus-horsepower-output characteristics of three types of direct-current motor.

upward) at light loads when the iron is not saturated; when the iron becomes saturated at heavy loads, the graph tends to become a straight line as in the case of the series motor.

These torque-versus-load curves are given in Fig. 199 for the three types of motor discussed above. For comparative purposes these were drawn for motors having the same torque at the same horsepower output. It should be noted that between no load and full load the shunt motor develops the greatest torque while the series motor develops the least; the torque developed by the compound motor falls between these two. However, it is at overloads, *i.e.*, above rated horsepower, that the differences between these motors show up most prominently. Observe first that the series and compound motor curves become straight lines between s_1 and s_2 and between c_1 and c_2. And, second, it is particularly significant that the overload torque of a series motor is considerably higher than that developed by a shunt motor; the compound motor again falls between the other two. In fact, it is generally recognized that the series motor is capable of developing such tremendous overload torque that it is difficult to stall. It is true, of course, that as the torque increases the speed drops; but whereas the series motor will slow down considerably with heavy overloads, the shunt motor will not be capable of developing sufficient torque and will stall. The subject of how the speed is affected by the load is taken up in the next section.

Example 8.—Each pole of a four-pole shunt motor produces 700,000 maxwells. If the armature has a total of 264 conductors and each conductor carries a current of 23 amp., calculate the torque developed by the motor.

Solution:

$$T = \frac{0.1173}{10^8} \times 264 \times 4 \times 700{,}000 \times 23 = 20 \text{ ft.-lb.}$$

Example 9.—To change the shunt motor of Example 8 into a compound motor it is equipped with a series field that increases the total flux by 18 per cent when each armature conductor carries 30 amp. What torque does the compound motor develop?

Solution:

$$T_2 = T_1 \times \frac{I_{c_2}}{I_{c_1}} \times \frac{\phi_2}{\phi_1} = 20 \times \frac{30}{23} \times \frac{826{,}000}{700{,}000}$$

$$= 20 \times 1.305 \times 1.18 = 30.8 \text{ ft.-lb.}$$

Example 10.—A series motor develops 62 ft.-lb. torque when the current is 48 amp. Assuming that the flux varies directly with the current, calculate the torque if the load increases so that the motor takes 60 amp.

Solution:

$$T_2 = T_1 \times \frac{I_2}{I_1} \times \frac{\phi_2}{\phi_1} = 62 \times \frac{60}{48} \times \frac{k \times 60}{k \times 48} = 97 \text{ ft.-lb.}$$

Speed Characteristics of Direct-current Motors.—It was previously pointed out that (*a*) the speed of a shunt motor rises about 2 to 8 per cent when the rated load is completely removed; (*b*) the speed of a compound motor rises approximately 10 to 25 per cent when the rated load is completely removed; (*c*) the speed of a series motor rises very rapidly when load is removed and must, therefore, always drive *some* load if it is to be prevented from racing dangerously, *i.e.*, "running away." In order to understand why these conditions prevail it will be desirable to study Eq. (57) by rewriting it in the form

$$S = \frac{E_T - (I_a \times R_a)}{k\phi} \tag{61}$$

where the meanings of the various terms are as already given. Assuming that the impressed terminal voltage E_T is constant, it is seen at once that the only factor affected when the load upon a *shunt motor* changes is I_a. And since the maximum change in the product of $I_a \times R_a$ between no load and full load is about 2 to 5 per cent of E_T, it follows that the maximum change in speed must be of the same order. The following example makes this clear:

Example 11.—The armature of a 230-volt shunt motor has a resistance of 0.25 ohm and takes 40 amp. when driving its rated load at 1,600 r.p.m. At what speed will the motor operate if the load is completely removed, *i.e.*, when it is running idle, under which condition the armature current drops to 8 amp.? The flux is assumed to remain constant.

Solution:

$$S_{FL} = \frac{230 - (0.25 \times 40)}{k\phi}; \quad S_{NL} = \frac{230 - (0.25 \times 8)}{k\phi}$$

$$\frac{S_{NL}}{1{,}600} = \frac{(230 - 2)/k\phi}{(230 - 10)/k\phi} = \frac{228}{220}$$

$$\text{Therefore, } S_{NL} = 1{,}600 \times \frac{228}{220} = 1{,}660 \text{ r.p.m.}$$

In this typical shunt-motor example it is seen that the rise in speed is 60 r.p.m., or 3.75 per cent, when the rated load is completely removed from the motor so that it runs idle.

When the rated load is removed from a *compound motor*, two factors are affected, namely, the armature current I_a and the flux ϕ. Unlike the shunt motor, where the flux remains unchanged for all conditions of loading, the flux created by the series field of a compound motor does drop when the load is removed. Thus, at full load the total flux is due to the constant shunt field and an added strong series field, while at no load the total flux is due to the same shunt field and a greatly weakened series field. It follows, therefore, that the speed of a compound motor varies much more between full load and no load than does the shunt motor, because (1) I_aR_a changes, and (2) the flux changes. The following example is given to illustrate this reasoning:

Example 12.—A 230-volt, long-shunt compound motor (Fig. 198*c*) has an armature resistance of 0.25 ohm and a series-field resistance of 0.03 ohm. The full-load speed is 1,200 r.p.m. when the armature current is 71.5 amp. At what speed will the motor run at no load if the armature current drops to 14.3 amp. and the flux is reduced to 90 per cent of its full-load value?

Solution:

$$S_{FL} = \frac{230 - (0.28 \times 71.5)}{k\phi_{FL}}; \quad S_{NL} = \frac{230 - (0.28 \times 14.3)}{k\,(0.90 \times \phi_{FL})}$$

$$\frac{S_{NL}}{1{,}200} = \frac{\dfrac{226}{k(0.90 \times \phi_{FL})}}{\dfrac{210}{k \times \phi_{FL}}} = \frac{226}{210 \times 0.9}$$

$$\text{Therefore, } S_{NL} = 1{,}200 \times \frac{226}{210 \times 0.90} = 1{,}435 \text{ r.p.m.}$$

Note that in this typical compound-motor example the speed rises from 1,200 to 1,435 r.p.m., *i.e.*, it changes 235 r.p.m., between full load and no load. This change represents a rise of 19.6 per cent, as compared with 3.75 per cent for the example given above for the shunt motor.

In operating a *series motor* great care must be taken not to permit the load to be reduced to such an extent that the speed becomes excessive. To understand why this is so, the following points should be recognized: (1) the speed of any motor is *inversely* proportional to the flux [see Eq. (61)]; (2) the flux produced in a given series motor depends entirely upon the load current; (3) when the load is heavy, the current is proportionately large and as a consequence the flux is high; this results in a low speed; (4) when the load is lightened, the current drops and with it the flux; this causes a rise in speed. Moreover, the voltage drop in the armature circuit consisting of the armature resistance and the series-field resistance also affects the speed in the same way although not to the same extent. Thus, when the load is heavy, the $I(R_a + R_{SE})$ drop is relatively high; this also causes the speed to drop. When the load is lightened, the $I(R_a + R_{SE})$ drop is reduced; this causes the speed to rise. The extremely large change in speed of a series motor with variation in load is illustrated by the following example:

Example 13.—A 25-hp., 240-volt, series motor takes 93 amp. when driving its rated load at 900 r.p.m. The armature resistance is 0.12 ohm and the series-field resistance is 0.08 ohm. At what speed will the motor operate if the load is partially removed so that the motor takes 31 amp.? (Assume that the flux is reduced by 50 per cent for a current change of $66\frac{2}{3}$ per cent.)

Solution:

$$S_{FL} = \frac{240 - 93\,(0.12 + 0.08)}{k\phi_{FL}}; \quad S_x = \frac{240 - 31\,(0.12 + 0.08)}{k\,(0.5 \times \phi_{FL})}$$

$$\frac{S_x}{900} = \frac{\dfrac{233.8}{k\,(0.5\,\phi_{FL})}}{\dfrac{221.4}{k\phi_{FL}}} = \frac{233.8}{221.4 \times 0.5}$$

$$\text{Therefore, } S_x = 900 \times \frac{233.8}{221.4 \times 0.5} = 1{,}900 \text{ r.p.m.}$$

This represents a rise in speed of 1,000 r.p.m., or more than 110 per cent increase. A further reduction in load would cause the speed of the motor to increase by an even greater percentage because, with the iron unsaturated at light loads, the reduction in flux would be almost directly proportional to the drop in load.

In order to emphasize the importance of the speed-versus-load characteristics of the three types of motor, typical curves are shown in Fig. 200. For the purpose of comparison the three motors are assumed to have the same speed when delivering the same horsepower output. In studying these curves particular note should be made of the fact that the speed of a shunt motor is substantially constant and has a very definite no-load value; the speed of a compound motor varies considerably and also has a very definite no-load value; the series motor operates over an extremely wide speed range and tends to "run away" at light loads—it should never be used with a belt drive or where the load is such that the torque might drop below 15 per cent of full-load torque.

Speed Regulation of Direct-current Motors.—It is customary to speak of the natural, or inherent, change in speed of a shunt or compound motor between full load and no load as the *regulation*. And when this regulation is referred

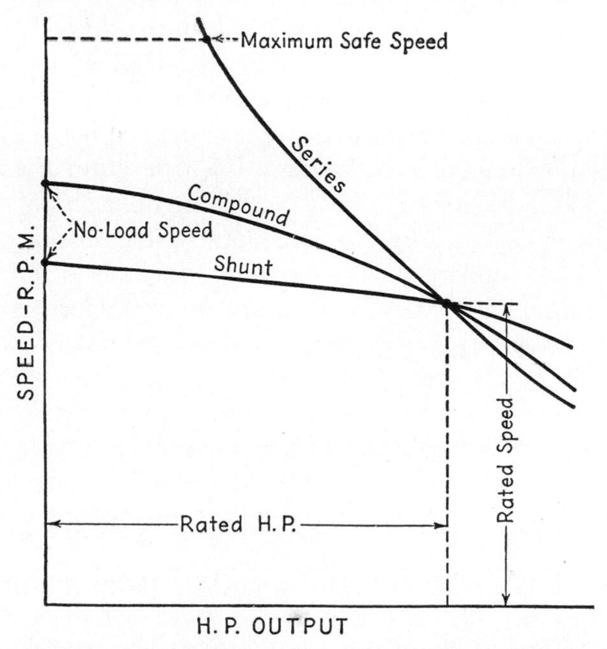

FIG. 200.—*Speed-versus-horsepower-output* characteristics of three types of direct-current motors.

to the full-load or rated speed of the motor expressed in per cent, it is called the *per cent speed regulation*. In equation form this becomes

$$\text{Per cent speed regulation} = \frac{S_{NL} - S_{FL}}{S_{FL}} \times 100 \qquad (62)$$

In the shunt motor of Example 11 the speed regulation was 60 r.p.m., or 3.75 per cent, while in the compound motor of Example 12 the regulation was 235 r.p.m., or 19.6 per cent. It should be thoroughly understood that these speed changes are due only to the load changes imposed upon the motors and are not the result of any manual or automatic adjustment on the part of an operator or a control mechanism. *Shunt motors* are generally regarded as *constant-speed motors* because the per cent speed regulation is very small. Of course, they are not constant-speed motors in the strictest sense (as are synchronous motors), but the speed varies so little between no load and full load that they are so termed for practical reasons. *Compound motors* are properly considered to be *variable-speed motors* because the per cent speed regulation is comparatively high. To be sure, there may be considerable variation between the regulations of motors of different design, but this is generally due to the number of series-field ampere turns as compared with the shunt-field ampere turns. If very few turns are used for the series field, the regulation will tend to become that of a shunt motor; if many series-field turns are used, the regulation tends to depart greatly from the shunt-motor characteristic. In any case the regulation of a compound motor is always high enough so that it may be classed as a variable-speed motor. The *series motor* certainly has a *variable-speed* characteristic, and it, too, is classed as such.

Example 14.—The full-load speed of a 10-hp. shunt motor is 1,800 r.p.m. (*a*) If the per cent speed regulation is 3 per cent, calculate the no-load speed. (*b*) Assuming a straight-line speed-load variation, determine the speed of the motor when it delivers a load of 7.5 hp. and 5 hp.

Solution:

$$a.\ 0.03 = \frac{S_{NL} - 1{,}800}{1{,}800};\ S_{NL} = 1{,}800 + (0.03 \times 1{,}800) = 1{,}854 \text{ r.p.m.}$$

$$b.\ \text{R.p.m.}_{7.5} = 1{,}800 + \left(\frac{2.5}{10} \times 54\right) = 1{,}813.5 \text{ r.p.m.}$$

(by similar triangles)

$$\text{R.p.m.}_{5} = 1{,}800 + \left(\frac{5}{10} \times 54\right) = 1{,}827 \text{ r.p.m.}$$

(by similar triangles)

Example 15.—The no-load speed of a compound motor is 1,150 r.p.m. At what speed will it operate at full load if the per cent regulation is 15 per cent?

Solution:

$$0.15 = \frac{1{,}150 - \text{r.p.m.}_{FL}}{\text{r.p.m.}_{FL}}; \quad 1.15\ \text{r.p.m.}_{FL} = 1{,}150;$$

$$\text{r.p.m.}_{FL} = 1{,}000$$

The arbitrary classification of motors on the basis of how the speed varies with load is especially important in connection with the problem of selection and application. In some applications such as wood planers, circular saws, grinders, polishers, and line shafts it has been found that constant-speed shunt motors perform most satisfactorily. Variable-speed compound motors should, however, be applied to loads requiring considerable torque upon starting or where the loads are subject to rapid changes. Good examples of such applications are compressors, pumps, and pressure blowers. Series motors are most desirable in those applications requiring considerable starting torque or severe accelerating duty or where very high-speed variations are advantageous. They are commonly used in such applications as streetcars, turntables, cranes, bucket and mine hoists, and the operation of large valves.

Adjustable-speed Direct-current Motors.—It is frequently necessary to adjust the speed of a motor to some other value than that at which it will normally operate its load. This can readily be done with direct-current motors in one or more of three different ways. These are (1) by inserting a field rheostat in the shunt-field circuit of a shunt or compound motor; (2) by inserting a resistance in the armature circuit of a shunt, compound, or series motor; (3) by varying the voltage across the armature circuit of a shunt or compound motor while at the same time maintaining constant voltage across the shunt field. Method 1 is illustrated in Figs. 193, 195, and 196. In this method *the speed* *increases as resistance is "cut in" by the field rheostat.* Method 2 is illustrated by Fig. 192*b* for a series motor where the starting resistance might also be used for speed-adjustment purposes. This method is likewise represented by Fig. 192*a* for a shunt motor and by Fig. 192*c* for a compound motor. In either case the starting resistance might be used for controlling the speed of the motor as well as for starting purposes. In this method *the speed decreases as resistance is*

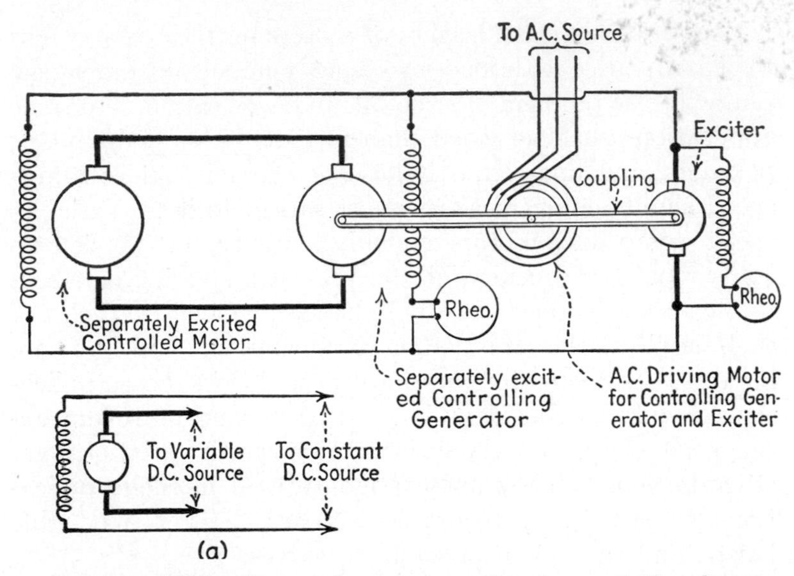

FIG. 201.—Wiring diagram showing connections for a variable-voltage control system.

inserted in the armature circuit. A wiring diagram illustrating method 3 is given in Fig. 201 for the control of a shunt motor, although the scheme applies equally well to the compound motor. Sketch *a* shows the simplified connections of the motor in which the armature and field are connected to two independent direct-current sources of supply; note that the armature is supplied with power by a variable-voltage source, while the field is excited from another constant-voltage source. In the main diagram the variable-voltage supply is a separately excited, field-controlled shunt generator driven at constant speed by an alternating-current motor; this combination of driving motor and control generator is called an *M-G control set.* Speed control of the motor is accomplished simply by adjusting the field rheostat in the control generator. When the generator voltage is low (high field resistance), the motor speed is low; when

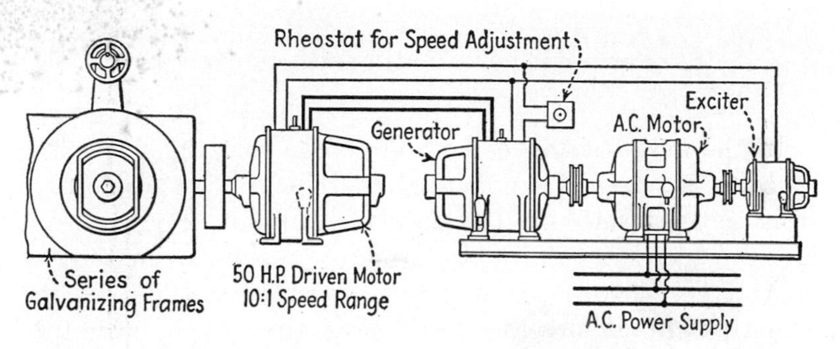

FIG. 202.—Schematic wiring diagram of Ward Leonard system used to provide a 10:1 speed range to a 50-hp. motor applied to a galvanizing take-up frame.

the generator voltage is high (low field resistance), the motor speed is high.

This variable-voltage control system has many important applications where extremely wide speed ranges are desired. It is called the *Ward Leonard* system and is illustrated again in the schematic diagram of Fig. 202. In this setup three units are mounted on a solid base and are coupled together as shown. The center machine is an alternating-current motor driving the control generator on the left and a small exciter on the right. The latter machine supplies excitation power to both the control generator and the main motor. The application here depicted is a galvanizing take-up frame in which rods in a wide range of sizes are pulled through galvanizing pots or tempering furnaces. A speed range of 10 to 1 is readily attained with this system.

The three methods of speed control discussed above are best understood by analyzing Eq. (61), rewritten in the following ways:

$$S = \frac{E_T - I_a R_a}{k(\phi_{\text{variable}})} \qquad \text{field-resistance control} \qquad (61a)$$

$$S = \frac{E_T - I_a\,[R_a + (R_{\text{variable}})]}{k\phi} \qquad \text{armature-resistance control} \qquad (61b)$$

$$S = \frac{(E_{T_{\text{variable}}}) - I_a R_a}{k\phi} \qquad \text{armature-voltage control} \qquad (61c)$$

In the field-resistance method of control [Eq. (61*a*)] the speed is inversely proportional to the flux. Therefore, if resistance is inserted in the shunt-field circuit, the flux drops and the speed rises. In the armature-resistance method of control [Eq. (61*b*)] the insertion of a resistance R in the armature circuit increases the voltage drop in the armature circuit and thereby decreases the speed. And by the armature-voltage control method [Eq. (61*c*)] the speed can be raised or lowered by simply manipulating the field rheostat in the generator; increasing the field resistance lowers the generated voltage with a corresponding drop in speed of the controlled motor; lowering the field resistance raises the generated voltage and with it the speed of the controlled motor.

Classification of Motors on Basis of Speed-load Changes. When the speed of a motor is adjusted to a given value for a certain load, it does not necessarily follow that it will not change when the load changes. In order to distinguish between motors whose speeds do and do *not* change with variations in load, the National Electrical Manufacturers Association (N.E.M.A.) has classified adjustable-speed motors in the following ways: An *adjustable-speed* motor is one in which the speed can be varied gradually over a considerable range, but, once adjusted, remains practically unaffected by the load. A shunt motor with field-rheostat control, method 1 [Eq. (61*a*)], designed for a considerable range of speed adjustment would fall into this classification. An *adjustable varying-speed* motor is one in which the speed can be varied gradually over a considerable range, but in which the speed, once adjusted to a given load, will vary in considerable degree with change in load. Good examples of such applications are the following: a series motor with a variable resistance inserted in the line for speed-control purposes; a shunt motor with armature-resistance control, method 2 [Eq. (61*b*)]; a compound motor with field-resistance or armature-resistance control, methods 1 and 2 [Eqs. (61*a*) and (61*b*)].

It is also well to recognize the important difference between the terms "speed regulation" and "speed control." Speed regulation always refers to the change of armature rotation, caused by a change in load upon the motor. *Speed control* has reference to changing the rate of armature rotation by external means such as the insertion of resistance in the field or armature or by varying the voltage across the armature. Sometimes operators use such terms as "good" speed regulation or "close" speed regulation when referring to motor performance. "Good" speed regulation indicates that a motor will maintain a set speed within desired or allowable limits under load fluctuations. With "close" speed regulation a motor will hold a set speed with slight change in spite of considerable load variations.

Reversing the Direction of Rotation of a Motor.—There are two general methods for reversing the *direction* of rotation of a direct-current motor. These are (1) changing the direction of current flow through the armature, *or* (2) changing the direction of current flow through the field circuit or circuits. The direction of rotation of a direct-current motor *cannot* be reversed by interchanging the line wires connected to the starting switch. The principle underlying the *direction* of the force action exerted upon a current-carrying conductor when placed perpendicularly to a magnetic field was discussed previously (see Fig. 186 and pages

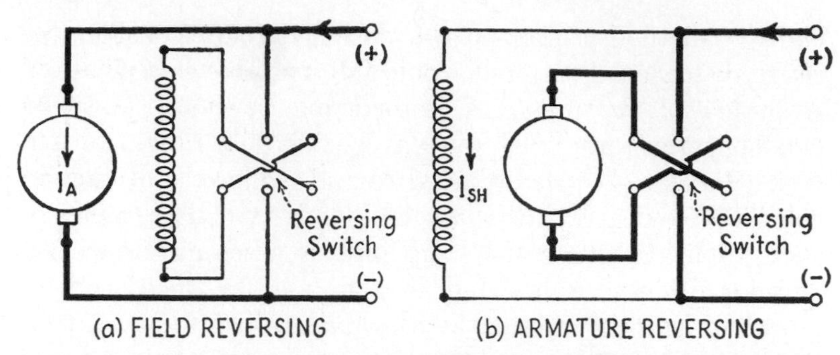

FIG. 203.—Wiring diagrams showing methods for reversing the direction of rotation of a shunt motor.

403–405). Figure 203 shows how the reversal of the direction of rotation of a shunt motor may be accomplished by both methods using a d.p.d.t. reversing switch. In Fig. 203*a* the reversing switch is connected to the shunt field while in Fig. 203*b* it is connected to the armature. When the switch is closed to the left, the current will be *down* through both the field and armature. When the switch is closed to the right, the current will be *up* through one of the elements and *down* through the other.

To reverse the direction of rotation of a compound motor it is necessary to reverse the current flow through the armature winding only (Fig. 204*a*) or through *both* series and shunt fields (Fig. 204*b* and *c*). Note that the wiring is

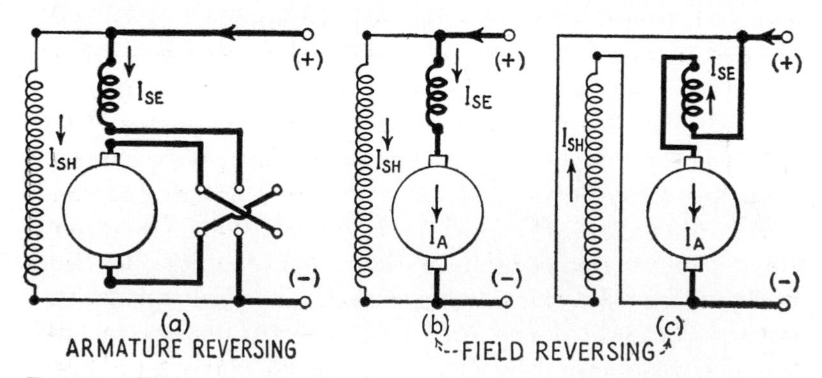

FIG. 204.—Wiring diagrams showing methods for reversing the direction of rotation of a compound motor.

much simpler when the first of the two methods is used because the reversal of the current through a single element is involved; a reversing switch can be used if frequent reversals are desired. If the second of the two methods is to be used, it is necessary to reverse the current through two field windings as shown in Fig. 204*b* and *c*. Obviously, the armature-reversal method is preferred because the wiring is simplified somewhat.

Commutating Poles for Direct-current Motors.—As in the case of direct-current generators, the magnetic neutral tends to shift when a motor is loaded. The reason for this tendency is the fact that the armature current creates a magnetic field of its own, apart from that created by the stationary poles, whose magnetic axis is exactly halfway between the centers of the main poles. The two fields then react with each other to produce a resultant magnetic field whose axis lies somewhere between the center of a main pole and the axis of the armature field. And since the armature current in a motor is opposite to that of a generator for the same direction of armature rotation, it follows that the shift of the magnetic axis is opposite to that produced in the generator. The result is that *the magnetic neutral in a motor always tends to shift in a direction opposite to that of the armature rotation.* For good commutation, therefore, the brushes should be shifted to a new neutral plane with every change in load. Obviously, such brush-shifting practice is inconvenient and unsatisfactory because load changes generally occur quite frequently in the operation of motors. A much more satisfactory practice, universally employed, is to equip motors with commutating poles (often called *interpoles*). These poles are similar to those discussed in the previous chapter under Commutation and Commutating Poles. Their windings are always in series with the armature and produce polarities that are opposite with respect to those in generators (see Fig. 168). *The polarities of the interpoles of direct-current motors are always the same as the preceding main poles with respect to direction of rotation.* In motors of rather small horsepower ratings, up to perhaps 15 hp., it is usually possible to use half as many commutating poles as main poles and still provide good commutation. Figure 205 shows the connections for a four-pole motor with two interpoles. The

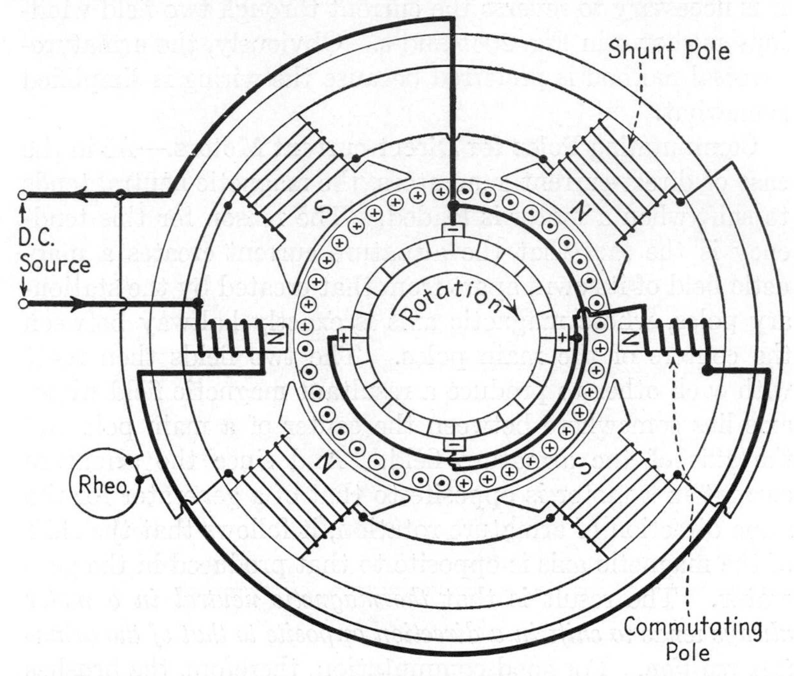

Fig. 205.—Internal wiring connections of shunt motor with two commutating poles.

following points should be noted particularly in studying this interpole shunt-motor diagram: (1) the positive terminal is the one from which the current *enters* the motor and the negative terminal is the one from which the current *returns* to the source; (2) the conductors with the dots are under the *north* poles and the conductors with the crosses are under the *south* poles for clockwise rotation; (3) the polarities of the two interpoles are *north* and are the same as the *preceding* main poles with respect to the direction of rotation; (4) the two positive brushes are connected together by a "jumper" and the two negative brushes are connected by a "jumper";

(5) the two interpoles are in series with the armature. Figure 206 is a photograph of the field structure of a direct-current motor in which one of the two interpoles is plainly visible.

Direct-current Motor Applications.—Direct-current motors are not used as widely as are those designed for alternat-

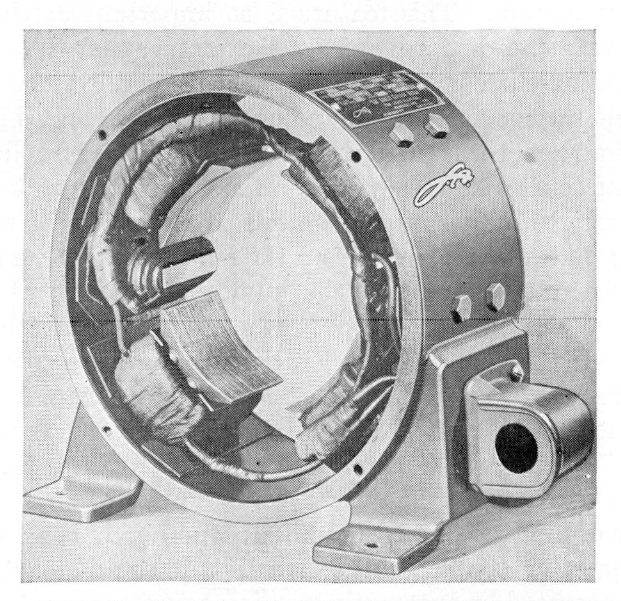

FIG. 206.—Field-pole assembly of a four-pole, direct-current motor. Note the two commutating poles. (*The Louis Allis Co.*)

ing-current service. There are several reasons for this practice, most important of which are the following: (1) direct-current motors have commutators that are subject to sources of trouble, resulting from sparking, brush wear, arc-over, and contaminated surrounding air; (2) direct-current electrical service for power applications is found in comparatively few localities, and then only when the transmission distances are short or where direct-current motors would operate more satisfactorily than alternating-current motors; (3) direct-current motors are generally more expensive than alternating-current motors for the same operating conditions.

Direct-current motors are nevertheless used in a large number of applications, especially when their excellent torque and speed operating characteristics cannot be duplicated by alternating-current motors. Moreover, speed control of direct-current motors is far more flexible and satisfactory than that which can be provided for alternating-current motors. This feature is so important at times, in steel mills and on excavators, for example, that the existing alternating-current service is frequently rectified into direct-current service so that direct-current motors may be used.

Before a motor is properly selected for a given application, it is, of course, necessary to know several important things. A thorough study is often desirable to determine the requirements that are to be met from the standpoint of the following: the duty cycle, *i.e.*, the number of times the motor must be started and stopped; whether the motor must be reversed; the required acceleration of the application; the required starting torque; the speed range; whether or not the motor must be stopped quickly; whether the motor should be enclosed or open. In addition to these factors it is also necessary to know the voltage of the power source; how the motor is to be mounted; whether it is to have a belt gear, or coupled drive; whether it should have manually operated or automatic starting equipment.

Obviously, such information can be obtained by those who not only are familiar with the various types of motor and their operating characteristics, but who also have had actual experience with the mechanical machines to which they are applied. In order that the student may have some idea of the problems involved in motor selection, Table XIII is given to illustrate a few of the applications and the types of motor that have generally been found to give satisfactory service.

Alternating-current Motors. Single-phase Types.—Great numbers of motors of comparatively small horsepower rating are designed to operate when connected to a two-wire alternating-current source. The latter is generally referred

TABLE XIII.—APPLICATIONS OF SHUNT, COMPOUND, AND SERIES DIRECT-CURRENT MOTORS

SHUNT				COMPOUND		SERIES
Constant speed	Adjustable speed			Variable-adjustable speed		Variable-adjustable speed
Plain	Field control	Armature control	Multivoltage control	Field control	Armature control	Line-resistance control
Line shaft	....	....	....	Compressor		Crane
Vacuum cleaner	....	....	....	....	Door lift	Coal and ore bridge
Large blower				Stamping machine		Mine hoist
Pressure blower		....	....	Pressure blower		Continuous conveyer
Centrifugal pump Constant head		....	....	Centrifugal pump Variable head		Valve operation
Displacement pump		....	....	Displacement pump		Turntable
....	Compressor	....	....	Rotary press		Motor vehicle
....	Small print press		....	Flat-bed press		Bucket hoist
Circular saw	....	....	....	....	Circular saw	......
Wood planer	....	....	....	Metal planer	....	......
Grinder	....	....	....	Shearing machine	....	......
Polisher	....	....	....	Punch press	....	......
....	Milling machine	....	Milling machine	Rolling mill		......
....	Lathe	....	Lathe	....	Freight elevator	......
....	Passenger elevator		....	Passenger elevator		......
....	Continuous conveyer	....	Continuous conveyer	Continuous conveyer		......
Laundry washing machine	....	....	....	Hydroextractor		......

to as a *single-phase* source because a *single* alternating e.m.f. (see Chap. 5) appears between the conductors of such a system. *Single-phase motors*, as these machines are called, are usually built in fractional-horsepower sizes and, in such ratings, are designated *small-power motors;* a *small-power motor* is defined as "a motor in a frame smaller than that having a continuous rating of 1 hp, open type, at 1,700–1,800 r.p.m.* Accordingly a $\frac{2}{3}$-hp., 900-r.p.m. motor would *not* be classified as a small power machine, because a similar frame, designed for a speed of 1,800 r.p.m., would have a rating greater than 1 hp. Moreover, a $1\frac{1}{2}$-hp., 3,600-r.p.m. motor would be classified as a small-power machine, because a 1,800-r.p.m. motor in a similar frame would have a rating less than 1 hp. Single-phase motors perform a great variety of useful services in the home, the office, the factory, in business establishments, on the farm, and many other places where electricity is available. Since the requirements of the numerous applications differ so widely, the motor-manufacturing industry has developed several types of such machines, each type having operating characteristics that meet definite demands. For example, one type operates satisfactorily on direct current or any frequency up to 60 cycles; another rotates at absolutely constant speed, regardless of load; another develops considerable starting torque; and still another, although not capable of developing much starting torque, is nevertheless extremely cheap to make and very rugged.

The type of motor that performs with about equal satisfaction on direct or alternating current up to 60 cycles is the familiar direct-current *series motor* (see Fig. 190*b*). Motors of this type are generally constructed in small sizes, operate at high speed, and include special design features so that good commutation will result when its source of power is either direct or alternating current. Since they may be connected

* American Standards Association (ASA) and National Electrical Manufacturers Association (NEMA).

to any of the commonly available electrical systems, they are appropriately called *universal* motors.

The principle of electromagnetic induction (see Chap. 8) is applied to several types of single-phase motor. These include (1) the *shaded-pole* motor, an extremely popular small motor used in low starting-torque applications; (2) the *reluctance-start* motor, made in rather limited numbers and small sizes; (3) the *split-phase* motor, made in various styles to fulfill a great variety of starting-torque and operating requirements; (4) *repulsion*, *repulsion-start*, and *repulsion induction* motors, that develop excellent performance characteristics; (5) the *synchronous* motor, constructed to operate at a speed that is absolutely constant regardless of load; (6) special types of synchronous motors that are generally referred to as *reluctance* motors, *hysteresis* motors, and *subsynchronous-reluctance* motors.

A number of the more commonly used single-phase motors are discussed in succeeding articles.

The Universal (Series) Motor.—The direct-current series motor will operate if connected to an alternating-current source of supply. This is so because the direction of the torque is determined by *both* the field polarity and the direction of the current through the armature. And since the *same* current passes through the field windings and the armature, it follows that the alternating-current reversals from positive to negative will simultaneously affect both the field polarity and the direction of the current in the armature conductors. Figure 207 represents an elementary series motor in which the torque produces clockwise rotation for both directions of current flow. From Fig. 207*a* and *b* it is seen that (1) when the top terminal is plus and the bottom terminal *minus*, the upper pole is *south*, the lower pole is *north*, and the current in the armature is from right to left with the resulting *crosses* and *dots* in the conductors as indicated; (2) when the bottom terminal is *plus* and the top terminal *minus*, the lower pole is *south*, the upper pole is *north*, and the current in the armature is from left to right with the *crosses* and *dots* in the conductors interchanged. Applying the rules previously explained, it is seen that the armature will rotate as shown, *i.e.*, clockwise.

When the series motor is comparatively large, the inductive effects of the field and armature tend to create serious commutation difficulties, which, if allowed to remain uncorrected, will cause the motor to operate unsatisfactorily when

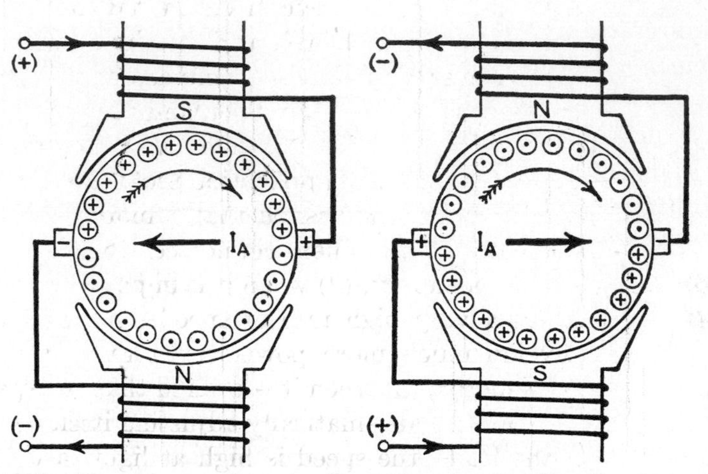

Fig. 207.—Elementary series motor illustrating that the direction of rotation is unchanged when the line polarity is reversed.

used on alternating-current circuits. It is for this reason that large series motors, for direct-current *and* alternating-current operation, are specially designed and constructed. However, when the series motor is *small*, it will have essentially the same operating characteristics whether used on direct-current or alternating-current sources up to 60 cycles. And if a particularly high grade of performance is desired on alternating current, when commutation might be serious, such motors are equipped with special windings known as *compensating* windings. The American Standards Association has formerly designated "a series motor that may be operated either on direct current or single-phase alternating current at approximately the same speed and output" as a *universal* motor. It further specifies that ". . . these conditions must be met when the direct-current and alternating-current voltages are approximately the same and the frequency of the alternating current is not greater than 60 cycles per second."

Small-power universal motors range in output between values of about $\frac{1}{500}$ hp. to perhaps $\frac{1}{2}$ hp. and are used in an unusually large number of applications in the home, in business offices, in stores, and in factories. Just as in the case of many other everyday electrical conveniences such as flatirons, incandescent lamps, and telephones, these fractional-horsepower motors perform a wide range of services. They have their widest fields of application under the following conditions: (1) when it is desired that a motor perform with complete satisfaction when connected to direct *or* alternating sources of supply; (2) when it is important that a motor operate at a very high rate of speed—a high-speed motor can develop much more power per unit of weight than a low-speed motor; (3) when it is desired that the speed of a motor be capable of automatically adjusting itself to the magnitude of the load—the speed is high at light load and low at heavy load. An excellent example of the last two points is the portable drill; here the motor must be light in weight to be portable and must be capable of developing sufficient power when the drill is large and is cutting heavy material; also, the speed of the motor automatically adjusts itself to the size of the drill.

The field structure of the universal type of motor is always a stack of laminations bolted together, fitted with field windings and placed inside a ring yoke. The armature is similar to the large direct-current-motor armature with the exception that the stack of laminations are pressed on a shaft so that the slots are skewed, *i.e.*, set at an angle with respect to the axis. This latter construction helps to keep the motor quiet and eliminates a tendency on the part of the armature to lock when started. Figure 208 illustrates several sets of field and armature laminations, and Fig. 209 shows a disassembled universal motor.

A few of the more common applications of universal motors are the following: electric shavers, hair driers, sewing machines, vacuum cleaners, drink mixers, hair clippers, dishwashers, motion-picture outfits, portable drills, pipe threaders, calculating machines, small grinders, routers, wood

FIG. 208.—Field and armature laminations for fractional-horsepower series motors. (*Carnegie-Illinois Steel Corporation.*)

shapers, saws, and kitchen food mixers.[1] The motor armatures generally operate at very high speeds, up to perhaps 30,000 r.p.m.; this makes it possible for comparatively lightweight motors to develop considerable power. Such high speeds cannot, of course, be applied directly to the mechanical tools, such as the drill, the beater in a food mixer, or the pipe threader; for this reason gears are usually interposed between the armature shaft and the rotating mechanism. These gears are generally well made and have ratios of 10 to 1 to as much as several hundred to one. Figure

[1] See C. S. Siskind, A Study of Food Mixer Performance, Purdue University, *Bulletin*, 72.

FIG. 209.—Disassembled $\frac{1}{15}$-hp. series motor.

FIG. 210.—Cutaway view of a gear train on a fractional-horsepower motor. Considerable speed reduction is accomplished in this way, permitting the motor to operate at an efficient high speed, and the load at the desirable low speed. (*Bodine Electric Co.*)

210 shows such a gear train for a small motor. Another mechanism sometimes used in universal motors, particularly in food mixers, is the constant-speed governor. This is mounted on the rapidly moving armature shaft and consists essentially of a set of spring-controlled weights, which, for given spring tensions applied by the turning of a dial, permit

the opening and closing of two sets of electrical contacts. The latter may be permitted to open or close the line circuit very rapidly, under which condition the speed of the motor is maintained between two closely held speeds. Another type of governor operates on the principle that the flux produced by an inductively coupled field winding, which is opened or short-circuited by a pair of contacts, tends to keep the motor speed within closely set limits.

The Induction-motor Principle.—Thus far our discussion of motors has been limited to the type in which current is "fed" to the rotating part of the machine through brushes and a commutator. In this respect it may be said that the electrical energy, to drive the motor, is *conducted directly* to that part of the machine where it is converted into mechanical energy.

Another type of motor makes use of the principles of electromagnetic induction and transformer action, studied in Chap. 8. It will operate satisfactorily only when connected to an alternating-current source of the frequency for which it is designed. A stationary winding properly wound around a laminated iron core, called a *stator*, receives electrical energy from the source of supply. This energy, except for the losses that occur in the stator, is then transferred to the rotating part of the machine, called the *rotor*, *by transformer action*. Note particularly that the electrical energy that produces rotation is transmitted to the rotor *inductively*. Such a machine is, therefore, a special type of transformer, a transformer in which the primary (stator) is generally stationary and the secondary (rotor) rotates. Transformer action, in which electrical energy is transferred from the primary to the secondary, takes place *across an air gap*. Motors of this type are extremely popular and are extensively used for the following reasons: (1) they are simple in construction, rugged, and virtually trouble-free—there are no moving contacts, no commutation problems; (2) they are comparatively inexpensive—they are doubtless the cheapest of all motors manufactured; (3) they can be made to operate with complete satisfaction in any location—if properly insulated they will operate in atmospheres charged with corrosive fumes or explosive mixtures, or even under oil or water; (4) they operate at substantially constant speed regardless of the load—a large percentage of applications require a type of motor whose speed regulation is low.

The principle of the induction motor was first discovered by Arago in 1824 when he observed the following interesting phenomenon: if a nonmagnetic disk and a compass are pivoted with their axes parallel so that one (or both) of the compass poles is (are) located near the edge of the disk, the compass will rotate if the disk is made to spin, or the disk will rotate if the compass is made to spin. The direction of the *induced* rotation is always the same as that imparted to the other. Such an experiment can be readily performed if a simple copper or aluminum disk and a rather large compass are both mounted on the same vertical stem so that each may be rotated in its own bearing independently of the other. There is no more effective way to demonstrate the *principle* of the induction motor, of which there are several types. If the disk is rotated, the compass will follow at a speed always less than the former; if the compass is rotated, the disk will follow the former at a lower speed.

Consider Fig. 211. Assume that a *north* pole is moving from left to right, and that it is close to a free-to-move nonmagnetic disk. In (*a*) the lines of force are shown to bend around a small element of the disk; in (*b*) the motion of the flux with respect to the small conductor element causes a voltage to be generated in the latter toward the *observer;* in (*c*) the current (eddy current) that flows in the conductor element as a result of the generated voltage creates a flux of its own in a counterclockwise direction; in (*d*) the resultant flux produced by the moving pole and the current in the disk conductor element creates a dense field on the left and a weak field on the right—this causes the conductor element and the rest of the *disk to move in the same direction as the pole.* It is never possible for the disk to move as rapidly as the pole.

If it did, there would be no relative motion between the pole and the disk, there would be no generated voltage in the disk, and no flux would be created by the disk; this would immediately cause the disk to slow down until sufficient current flowed to develop the necessary power of rotation.

In the actual motor the rotor is not a disk but a well-designed structure called a *squirrel cage.* It consists essentially of a stack of circular laminations mounted on a shaft. These laminations have holes or slots punched near the outer edge. In assembling the laminations on the shaft the holes

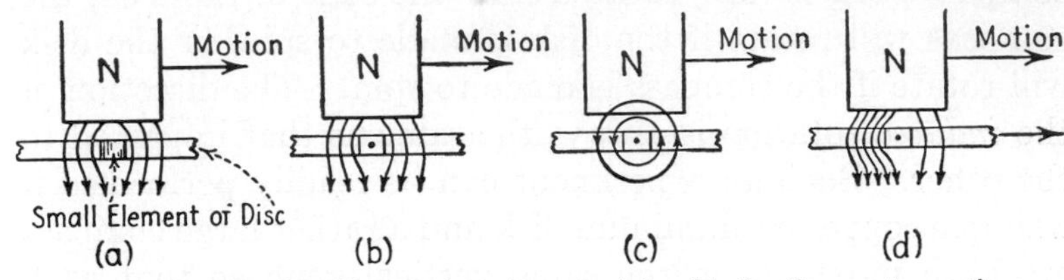

FIG. 211.—Sketches illustrating the principle of induction-motor action.

are lined up with a *skew,* after which copper or aluminum bars are driven through the holes and short-circuited by nonmagnetic rings at both ends.

As explained above, the principle of induction-motor action requires that poles rotate. Actually, of course, the poles do not move physically but are made to appear to do so in the sense that the axes of the magnet poles change position around the inside periphery of the stator. This rotation of the pole axes is accomplished electromagnetically in several ways. In single-phase motors the revolving field is commonly produced by the *shaded-pole* principle and the *split-phase* principle.

The speed of rotation of the revolving field is constant and depends only upon the supply frequency and the number of poles in the motor; it is called the *synchronous speed.* It may be calculated from Eq. (52) by rewriting it in the form

$$\text{R.p.m.}_{\text{syn}} = \frac{120 \times f}{p} \tag{63}$$

The speed of the rotor is always less than the synchronous speed by several per cent; the amount of this difference is called the *slip* and is indicated by the symbol s. The equation for the motor speed can, therefore, be written as follows:

$$\text{R.p.m.}_{\text{motor}} = \frac{120 \times f}{p}(1 - s) \qquad (64)$$

Example 16.—Calculate the speed of a two-pole, a four-pole, a six-pole, and an eight-pole motor when connected to a 60-cycle source, assuming a 4 per cent slip in each case.

Solution:

$$\text{R.p.m.}_2 = \frac{120 \times 60}{2}(1 - 0.04) = 3{,}456$$

$$\text{R.p.m.}_4 = \frac{120 \times 60}{4}(0.96) = 1{,}728$$

$$\text{R.p.m.}_6 = \frac{120 \times 60}{6}(0.96) = 1{,}152$$

$$\text{R.p.m.}_8 = \frac{120 \times 60}{8}(0.96) = 864$$

The Shaded-pole Motor.—One of the simplest ways to produce a magnetic field that shifts its position from one side of a pole to the other is to use a construction similar to that represented by Fig. 212. Each one of the poles of the stator has a slot cut *across* the laminations about one-third the distance from one edge. Around the smaller of the two rectangular sections formed by this slot is placed a heavy copper short-circuiting coil called a *shading* coil; the iron around which the shading coil is placed is called the *shaded part* of the pole. The free portion of the pole is the *unshaded part*. The exciting coil, not shown in the sketch, surrounds the entire pole.

When the exciting winding is connected to an alternating-current source of supply, *the magnetic axis will shift from the unshaded part of the pole to the shaded part of the pole.* This shift of the magnetic axis is, in effect, equivalent to moving the pole physically; the result is that the squirrel-cage rotor will rotate in a direction from the unshaded part to the shaded part. In order to understand how this comes about,

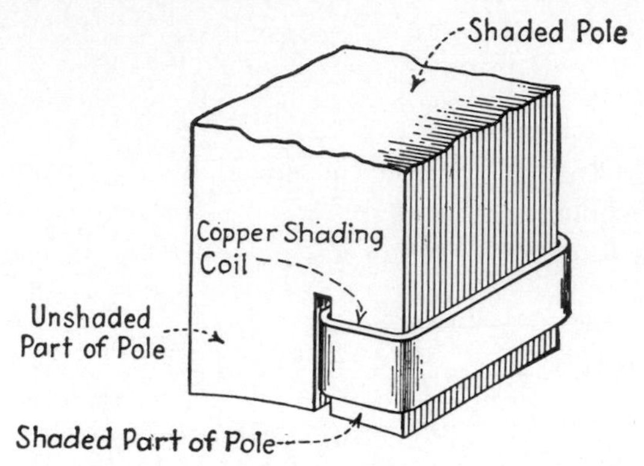

FIG. 212.—Sketch showing the construction of a shaded pole.

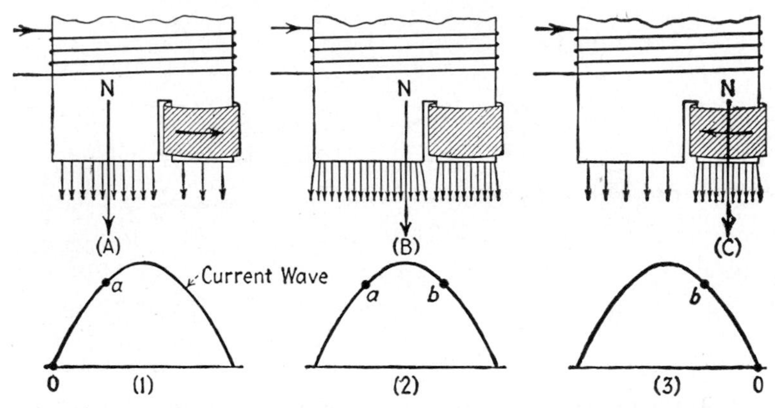

FIG. 213.—Sketches illustrating how the magnetic axis shifts across the pole from the unshaded to the shaded parts of a shaded pole in a shaded-pole motor.

consider Fig. 213. Assume first that the current in the exciting coil follows a sine wave and is in such a direction that a *north* pole will be formed. The discussion is divided into three parts for changes in current from O to a, a to b, and b to O.

Part 1. The current rises very rapidly from O to a along the sine curve; under this condition a voltage will be induced in the shading coil that will send a comparatively large current through the low-resistance turn; this current will be in such a direction that it will oppose the rapidly changing flux that creates it (Lenz's law); the field flux is, therefore, shifted mostly to the unshaded part of the pole; the magnetic axis will then be along the large arrow near the center of the unshaded part of the pole.

Part 2. The current changes very little from a to b along the top of the sine curve; under this condition practically no voltage will be induced in the shading coil; no current will, therefore, flow in the shading coil; the flux created only by the main exciting coil will be a maximum and will be uniformly distributed over the entire face of the pole; the magnetic axis will now be moved to the center of the pole as indicated by the large arrow.

Part 3. The current drops very rapidly from b to O along the sine curve; under this condition a voltage will be induced in the shading coil that will send a comparatively large current through the low-resistance turn; this current will be in a direction that it will try to prevent the flux from drying out, *i.e.*, it will create a strong north pole in the shaded part of the pole; the magnetic axis will thus be shifted to the center of the shaded part of the pole as indicated by the large arrow.

Note particularly that the magnetic axis shifts across the pole from A to B to C, from the unshaded part to the shaded part of the pole. This shift actually takes place gradually, not in steps, from one side to the other; and as the negative half of the wave is applied to the exciting coil, a south pole trails along. The effect is as though real poles were sweeping across the space from left to right. Simple motors of this type cannot be reversed and must be constructed so that the rotor shaft extends from the proper end of the motor to drive the application in the right direction. Specially designed shaded-pole motors have been constructed for reversing service but are too complicated for general use.

In order to demonstrate the action of a shaded-pole motor in full view of his students the author constructed a simple shaded pole like that illustrated in Fig. 212. This was placed on top of the center pole of the E-core electromagnet of Fig. 96. A squirrel-cage rotor from an actual motor was then fitted with ball bearings. If the equipment is set up

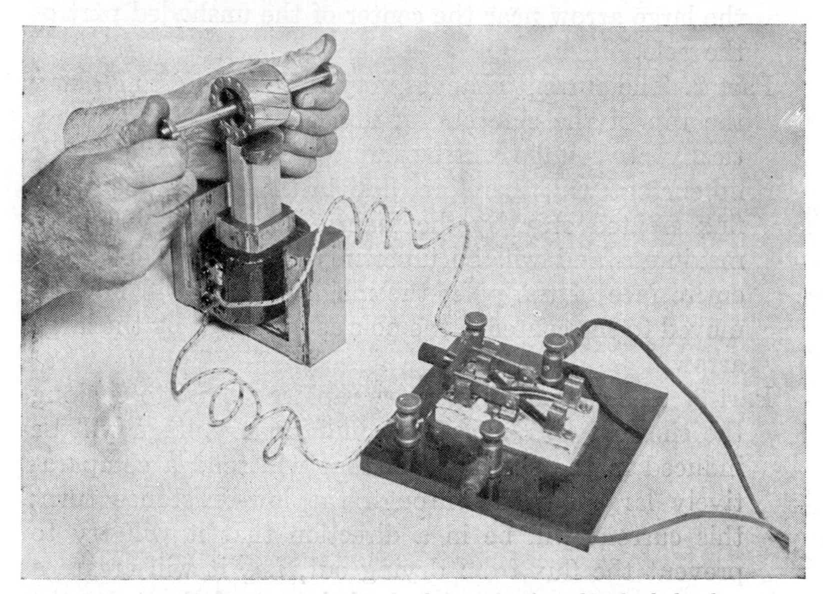

Fig. 214.—Arrangement of apparatus demonstrating the shaded-pole motor. Note the shaded pole mounted on the center leg of an E-type alternating-current electromagnet. Fingers hold the ball bearings supporting the squirrel-cage rotor above the pole face.

as shown in Fig. 214 and the coil is excited from a 115-volt, 60-cycle, the rotor will rotate at high speed when held by the bearings so that the lower part of the rotor is a fraction of an inch above the surface of the shaded pole.

Figure 215 is a photograph showing a completely disassembled four-pole shaded-pole motor. It is interesting to note that in a motor as small as this, $\frac{1}{30}$ hp., more than 30 separate parts are necessary. Plainly visible are the laminated stator and rotor cores, the four field coils, the four shading coils, the shaft, the bearings, the cooling fan, two

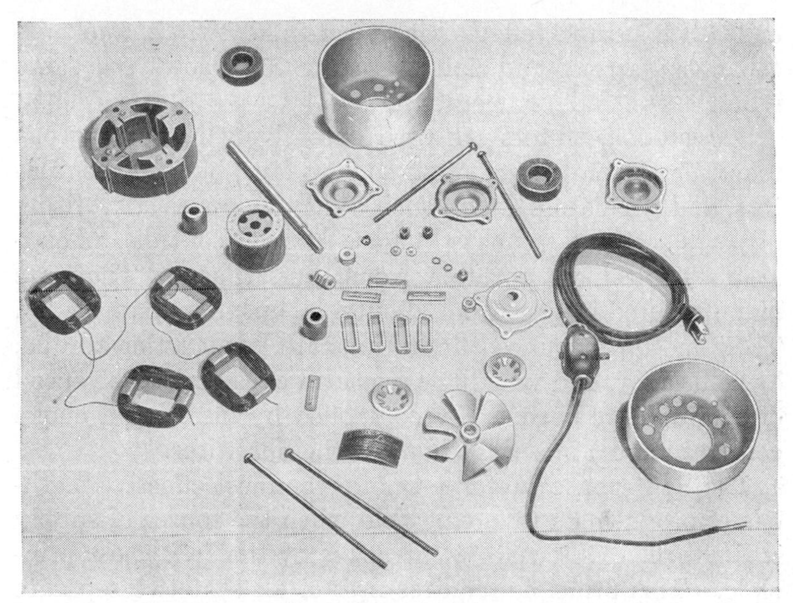

FIG. 215.—Completely disassembled shaded-pole motor. (*Victor Electric Products, Inc.*)

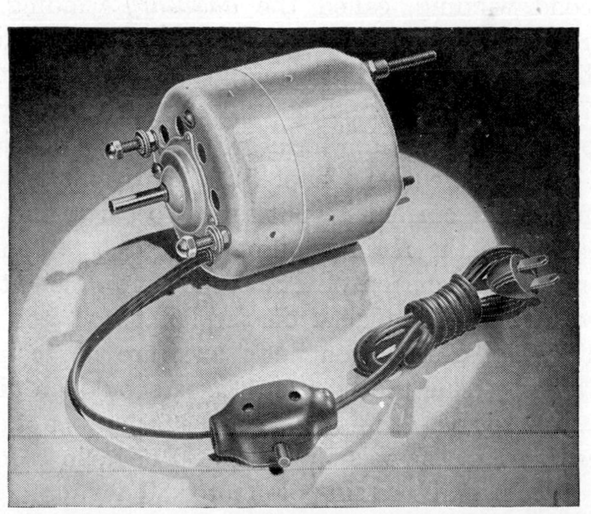

FIG. 216.—Completely assembled $\frac{1}{30}$-hp., 115-volt, 60-cycle shaded-pole motor ready for operation. (*Victor Electric Products, Inc.*)

end-bell housings, felt oil wicks, cord and switch, and miscellaneous screws and bolts. Figure 216 shows the same motor assembled for operation.

Shaded-pole motors are used extensively in applications requiring the movement of air such as fans, blowers, ventilators, and circulators and in such other devices as advertising displays, churns, animated signs, furnace controls, phonograph turntables, portable irons, and timers. They are manufactured in sizes from about $\frac{1}{500}$ hp. to perhaps $\frac{1}{10}$ hp. Their most pronounced limitations are low starting torque, low efficiency, and very little overload capacity. The speed of such motors is generally controlled by inserting a choke coil (reactance) in series in one of the line wires.

The Split-phase Motor.—One of the most effective methods of producing a revolving field when the source of supply is single-phase alternating current is by the *split-phase* principle. This principle requires first of all that two separate windings, connected in parallel, be used to magnetize the laminated iron core. One winding, called the *main* winding, has a comparatively low resistance and a high inductance; the second winding, called the *auxiliary* winding, has a comparatively high resistance and a much lower inductance than the other. When both windings are excited, the current in the auxiliary winding is nearly in phase with the voltage, while the main winding current lags considerably behind the voltage (see Chap. 5). The result is that the single-phase line current is split into two parts, and in such a manner that the main winding current lags behind the auxiliary winding current. The second requirement is that the two windings be placed on the laminated iron core in such a way that their magnetic axes are not coincident. For the best result the magnetic axes should be displaced with respect to each other by the greatest number of degrees; in a two-pole motor this would be 90 deg., in a four-pole motor 45-deg., and in a six-pole motor 30 deg.

It should, therefore, be understood that two conditions must be fulfilled if motor operation is to result by the split-phase principle. These are (1) time displacement between the two currents, resulting from the comparatively different values of resistance and inductance in the main and auxiliary windings, and (2) space displacement between the positions of the main and auxiliary windings.

The shift of the magnetic axes in a split-phase motor comes about in much the same way as it does in a shaded-pole motor because the same essentials are present in both. The shaded-pole motor has two windings; one of them is connected directly to the supply source, while the other, the shading coils, receives its power by induction. The split-phase motor has two windings, both of which (main and auxiliary) receive their power from the same supply source. In both motors the two windings are displaced in space with respect to each other; in the shaded-pole motor one winding surrounds the entire pole while the shading coil surrounds about one-third of the pole; in the split-phase, four-pole motor the two windings are generally 45 deg. apart. In both motors the currents in the two windings are always out-of-phase with each other, *i.e.*, there is a time displacement between the two currents.

However, from the standpoint of construction and operation there is considerable difference between the two types of motor. In the shaded-pole motor the windings are placed around salient (shaped) poles; in the split-phase motor the windings are distributed completely around the core in slots. In the shaded-pole motor the magnetic axis shifts from one side of a pole to the other; no action takes place in the interpolar space. In the split-phase motor the magnetic axes revolve completely around the entire cylindrical core; the magnetic field is, in this respect, a true revolving field. And whereas the shaded-pole motor is incapable of developing much starting torque and overload power, the split-phase motor can be designed and constructed to perform admirably on the basis of starting and running characteristics. Furthermore, the efficiency of a split-phase motor is generally two or more times as much as that of a shaded-pole motor; the efficiency of a split-phase motor may be as high as 60 to 70 per cent, while that of a shaded-pole motor rarely exceeds 25 to 30 per cent.

During the starting period a split-phase motor must have both windings in operation, but when the speed has reached about 75 per cent of its rated value, the main winding alone will develop nearly as much torque as both windings acting together. And when the speed of the motor reaches its rated value, the torque developed with both windings in the circuit is less than when only the main winding is energized. It seems logical, therefore, to provide some sort of mechanism, actuated by a centrifugal device or an electromagnetic relay, that will cut out the auxiliary winding at the proper time. Many such mechanisms have been developed. In the common applications of this motor, centrifugally operated governors are employed wherein a set of spring-loaded weights, mounted on the shaft, fly out at a predetermined speed; in doing so a switch mechanism fastened to the end bell disconnects the auxiliary winding from the circuit. Figure 217 is a cutaway view of a split-phase motor in which the windings, the squirrel-cage rotor, and the *centrifugal switch*, at the right end, are plainly visible. When it becomes necessary to seal hermetically a split-phase motor, as in a refrigerator, a centrifugally operated switch is not permissible inside the refrigerant. Under such conditions an electromagnetically actuated relay is employed. A photograph of one such switch of recent development is shown in Fig. 218.

The split-phase motor principle can be demonstrated very effectively if equipment previously described is set up as shown in Fig. 219. The E core if fitted with two exciting coils, one on the center leg and the other on either of the outside legs. The center coil is connected directly to the alternating-current source, while the outer coil is connected in series with a 150-watt lamp or a space-heater unit to the same supply. With both coils energized, a squirrel-cage rotor, fitted with ball bearings at the ends of the shaft, will rotate at high speed if held, as indicated, slightly above the core about halfway between both coils. In this arrangement space displacement is provided by separating the two coils so that one of them is on the center leg while the other is on the outer leg. Time displacement is introduced because the outer coil circuit has less inductance (smaller coil) and more resistance (lamp in series) than the center coil.

When a capacitor is connected in series with the auxiliary winding, the split-phase motor can be made to develop

Fig. 217.—Cutaway view of a split-phase, fractional-horsepower motor. Note stator windings, squirrel cage, and centrifugal switch. (*Century Electric Co.*)

considerable starting torque. There are several reasons for this, most important of which are the following: (1) the time displacement between the main and auxiliary winding currents is increased; (2) the main and auxiliary winding currents can be larger for the same line current; (3) more auxiliary winding turns can be used. These factors make it possible to design split-phase motors with capacitors so that the starting torque can be as much as 3.5 to 5 times as much as those without capacitors. Machines of this type are known as *capacitor-start motors* since the centrifugal switch acts in the same way as previously described. They are extensively used where the applications require extremely

FIG. 218.—Cutaway view of electromagnetically actuated starting relay for a $\frac{1}{4}$-hp. capacitor-start, hermetically sealed motor. Note disk contactor mounted on the vertical plunger. (*Westinghouse Electric Corporation.*)

FIG. 219.—Arrangement of apparatus to demonstrate the principle of the split-phase motor.

high values of torque during the starting period. In most cases the capacitor is mounted on the outside of the frame, although in special cases, where streamlined appearance is desired, it may be placed inside the motor housing. Figure 220 shows a cutaway view of a capacitor-start split-phase motor in which the specially constructed spiral-wound capacitor is placed in the left end bell. Plainly seen in the

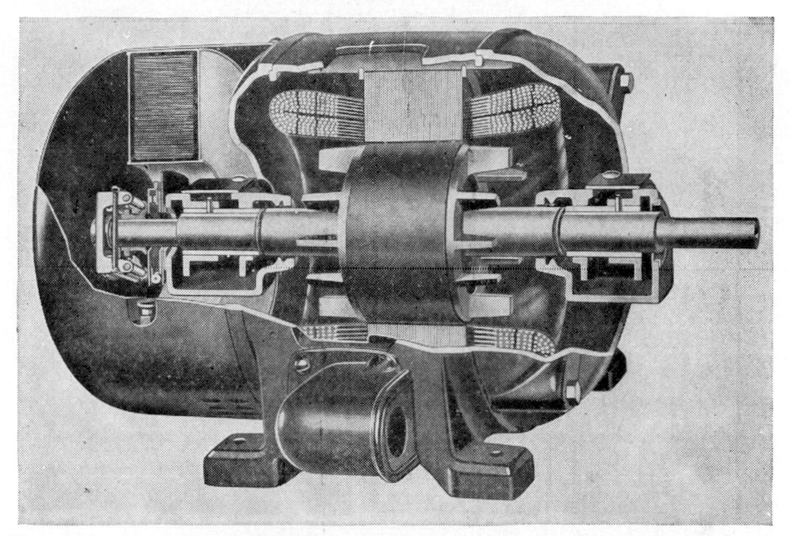

FIG. 220.—Cutaway view of a capacitor-type single-phase motor. Note particularly the spiral-wound capacitor mounted inside the left end bell directly surrounding the centrifugal switch. (*The Louis Allis Co.*)

photograph are the centrifugal switch, the stator winding, and the fan-cooled squirrel-cage rotor.

Split-phase motors with and without capacitors have many applications. In fact, it has been estimated that more fractional-horsepower motors of this construction are used than all others combined. Some of the more common applications are washing machines, refrigerators, small drill presses, grinders, blowers, milking machines, silage cutters, concrete mixers, cream separators, milk churns, floor sanders and waxers, stokers, water pumps, small circular saws, compressors, and air circulators. Figure 221 shows a cutaway view of a split-phase motor of $\frac{1}{50}$-hp. capacity in which the normal 1,730-r.p.m. speed of the rotor is reduced to 2.4 r.p.m. at the load by means of a special gear train having a ratio of 720:1.

The Repulsion-induction Motor.—Before capacitor-start split-phase motors came into common use for applications requiring high starting torque, the repulsion-start induction

Fig. 221.—Cutaway view of a $\frac{1}{50}$-hp., 1,730-r.p.m., split-phase motor equipped with a gear train for a speed reduction to 2.4 r.p.m. (*Bodine Electric Co.*)

motor was the accepted standard. Manufactured in integral- as well as fractional-horsepower sizes, this type of motor was used at one time in larger numbers than any of the others for single-phase service. Although it is a more costly machine, and one most likely to develop trouble, it does nevertheless possess two extremely desirable characteristics, namely, high starting torque and low starting current. Its rotor construction is much more complicated than the squirrel cage of the split-phase motor; it has a standard direct-current armature winding, a commutator of very special design, and a centrifugal mechanism for short-circuiting the commutator when the motor reaches its rated speed. The stators of both the split-phase and the repulsion-induction types are, however, quite similar with the exception that only one winding is used in the latter.

The repulsion principle was first employed in a practical motor by E. Arnold in Germany and was commercially

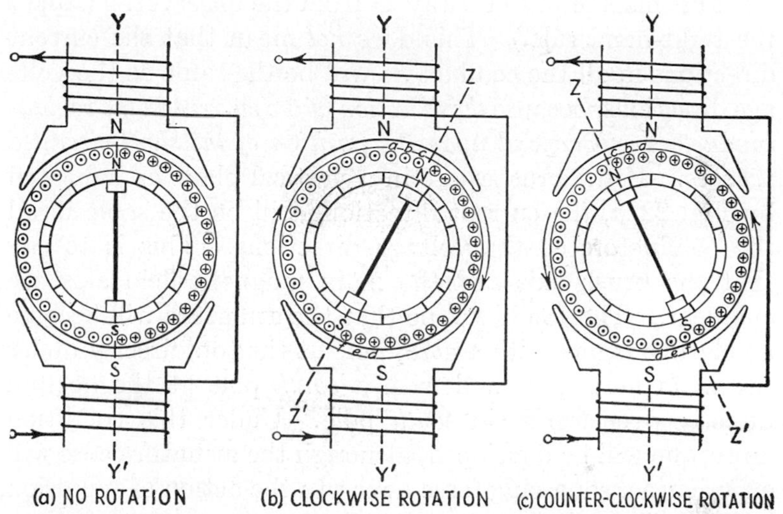

Fig. 222.—Sketches representing the principle of operation of a repulsion motor.

adopted in this country for some applications about 1896. Since that time it has been steadily improved both mechanically and electrically. It is still used in large numbers, although, as pointed out above, it has been replaced to a great extent by the more rugged, less costly capacitor-start split-phase motor. To understand how torque is developed by the repulsion principle consider Fig. 222. Imagine a two-pole salient (shaped) pole motor with the magnetic axis vertical. The armature is of standard direct-current construction with commutator and brushes, but with the latter connected together, *i.e.*, short-circuited. Assume that the *alternating current* flows in such a direction that it creates a *north* pole on top and a *south* pole on the bottom. Voltages will be induced in all the armature conductors by transformer action; and by Lenz's law the direction of these induced voltages will be such that they will tend to create a current flow in the conductors so that the main field will be opposed. This means that the voltages in all the conductors to the left of the vertical line YY' will be directed toward ⊙ the observer, and the voltages in all the conductors to the right of this line will be away ⊕ from the observer. (Apply the right-hand rule.) This does *not* mean that the current directions in all the conductors will be the same as the voltage directions, because *the direction of the current in the various conductors will depend upon the position of the short-circuited brushes.* If the brushes are in a vertical plane as indicated by Fig. 222*a*, the current directions will be the same in all the conductors as the voltage directions. This is to say that the brush axis and the main magnetic-field axis are collinear. The result will be that the armature will become an electromagnet with a *north* pole at the top directly under the main *north* pole and with a *south* pole at the bottom directly over the main *south* pole. Under this condition no torque will be developed, although the armature core will experience a squeezing force owing to the action of repulsion between like poles.

If the short-circuited brushes are now moved over to position ZZ' as indicated by Fig. 222*b*, torque *will* be developed. The reason is that the magnetic axis of the armature is no longer collinear with respect to the vertical axis of the main poles; it will be along axis ZZ' with the *north* and *south* poles shifted around by exactly as many degrees as the brushes are shifted. It is true that the induced voltages in conductors a, b, and c will oppose the other conductors above the brush axis, and the induced voltages in conductors d, e, and f will oppose the other conductors below the brush axis. But the net voltage acting at the brushes to produce current flow will still be sufficient to make the armature core into a powerful electromagnet. Obviously, the armature *north* pole will now be *repelled* by the main *north* pole, and the armature *south* pole will likewise be *repelled* by the main *south* pole so that torque will be created. Thus, rotation will be produced by the action of *repulsion* (like poles repel) if the armature is free to turn. The designation *repulsion-induction* motor is therefore a proper one since the armature gets its power by induction and torque is developed by the repelling action between like poles.

In practice it is customary to shift the brushes about 15 to 20 deg. in two-pole motors, $7\frac{1}{2}$ to 10 deg. in four-pole motors, and 4 to 5 deg. in six-pole motors. Furthermore, if the brushes are shifted clockwise from the main magnetic neutral (Fig. 222*b*), the armature will rotate clockwise; if shifted counterclockwise (Fig. 222*c*), the motor will rotate counterclockwise. It should be clear, therefore, that the direction of rotation is independent of the stator or armature winding connections and depends only upon the brush position when the motor is started.

As in the case of split-phase motors, the repulsion-induction type has the slotted-stator construction and not the salient-pole arrangement described above; the latter was assumed only because the principle of operation can be explained more simply. Motors having stator cores with slots develop more uniform torque, are not likely to have dead spots when started, and more particularly can be wound for several different speed combinations. This latter point is very important in manufacture from the standpoint of cost because a single lamination can frequently be used in the design of two-, four-, six-, or eight-pole motors [see Eq. (64)]. Figure 223 shows a 24-slot completely wound stator for a repulsion type of motor. Clearly visible are the four groups of concentric coils for operation at about 1,720 r.p.m. when connected to a 60-cycle source.

In the so-called "repulsion-start induction" motor, the armature winding is converted into an equivalent squirrel cage by short-circuiting the commutator bars after the motor has reached a predetermined speed. This is done by means of a centrifugally operated short-circuiter cleverly concealed inside the hollow commutator or along the outside face. There are many ingenious designs for this mechanism, but they all operate in essentially the same way. In one arrangement a large number of copper segments is restrained by a garter spring from moving radially outward against the inside of a section of the commutator. When centrifugal force has caused these segments to overcome the spring tension, they fly out and wedge themselves against a grooved

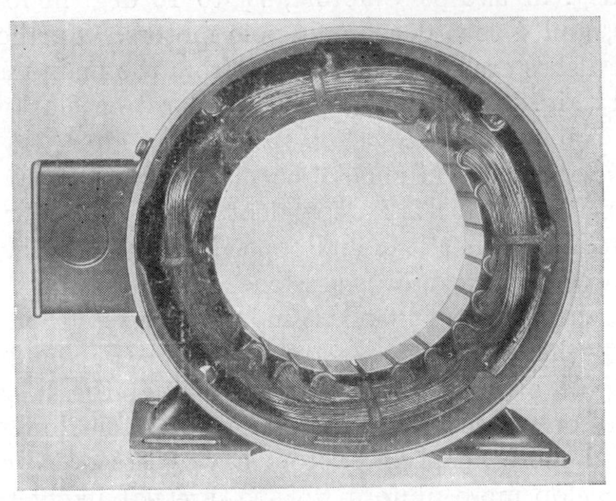

FIG. 223.—Stator with its winding for a repulsion-induction-type single-phase motor. (*Century Electric Co.*)

track on the inside of the commutator, thereby short-circuiting it. The motor then continues to operate like a squirrel-cage induction motor and is to all intents and purposes a simple induction motor. In some designs the centrifugally operated mechanism also causes the brushes to be raised from the commutator so that the frictional losses and the unnecessary brush wear can be eliminated entirely. Figure 224 shows the rotor of a repulsion-start induction motor in which the commutator is of the radial type. In this design there is a short-circuiting ring inside a hollow commutator. A sort of necklace of copper segments is placed inside the ring on a spring barrel. As the motor starts, the necklace is not in contact with the commutator; but when the motor accelerates to its proper speed, a set of governor weights causes the spring barrel to be forced forward against a stiff spring. This action is accompanied by the short-circuiting of the commutator and the lifting of the

FIG. 224.—Rotor with its winding for a repulsion-start induction single-phase motor. (*Century Electric Co.*)

FIG. 225.—Inside view of end bell for a repulsion-start induction motor. Note the brush arrangement and method for shifting brushes. (*Century Electric Co.*)

brushes. The radial commutator is clearly seen in Fig. 224, and the brush rigging with its mechanism for being shifted is observed in Fig. 225. Figure 226 shows a cutaway view of a completely assembled repulsion-start induction motor.

Polyphase Systems and Types of Motor.—Alternating-current motors having ratings that are generally higher than the single-phase types considered in the foregoing articles usually operate from polyphase systems. In this country the latter are, for the most part, *three-phase* systems, although a comparatively few two-phase systems still exist. The distinguishing feature of a three-phase system of voltages, as contrasted with *single* phase, is that *three* alternating e.m.f.'s, displaced by 120 electrical degrees with respect to one another, are made available. This implies (1) that three independent voltage waves appear between pairs of wires of

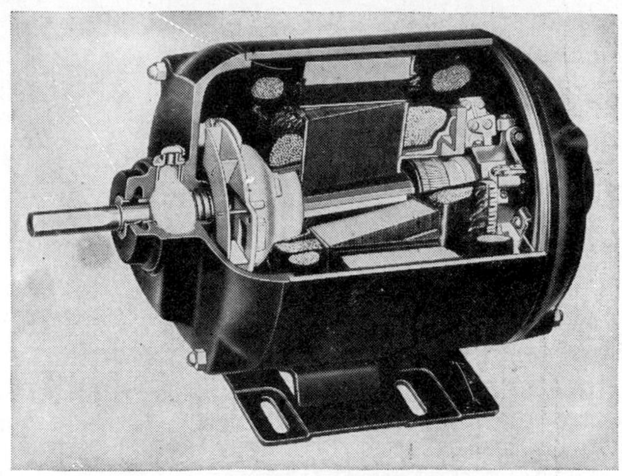

FIG. 226.—Cutaway view of a fractional-horsepower repulsion-start induction motor. (*Century Electric Co.*)

the three-wire service, (2) that the zero values and the maximum values of the three waves always occur, *in time*, exactly one-third of a cycle apart, and (3) that the three *effective* voltages between pairs of wires are equal. In a two-phase system two equal effective voltages are provided, their independent voltage waves being displaced, in time, by exactly one-quarter of a cycle or 90 electrical degrees.

Alternators in power plants are nearly always constructed to provide three-phase service, because such machines are much more economical, and operate much more satisfactorily than those which supply single-phase power. Furthermore, the transmission lines, transformers, circuit breakers, lightning arresters, and other items of necessary equipment in modern electrical installations are capable of maintaining a high grade of performance at low cost.

Polyphase motors used on polyphase systems may, in general, be divided into three classifications, namely, (1) induction type, (2) synchronous type, and (3) commutator type. The first of these, the *induction motor*, is the most widely used and is available with either of two kinds of rotor construction; the latter involves the so-called *squirrel-cage* or *wound-rotor* design, the stator being identical for both. The *synchronous motor*, as its name implies, operates at a constant speed—the synchronous speed (Eq. 63)—and is constructed with a stator core and winding similar to that used on induction motors (squirrel-cage or wound-rotor). The rotor consists of a set of salient poles and windings (as in the alternator of Fig. 158), with the field excitation provided by a small shunt generator which may be an exciter mounted on an extension of the motor shaft or by a separate source of direct current. The *commutator motor* is a rather complex type of machine, designed for adjustable-speed operation, having a stator that is identical with that found on induction motors, but a rotor that differs greatly from those already described. The rotor in one such design—the Schrage motor—has two windings, one above the other, placed in deep slots; one of them, the so-called *primary winding*, is connected to slip rings and fed by polyphase power, and the other, the *secondary winding*, is connected to a commutator. Speed adjustment is effected through the circumferential shifting of three sets of brushes.

Induction Motors.—The induction-motor principle discussed under the heading of single-phase machines applies equally well to those operated from polyphase systems. A true revolving field, constant in magnitude and rotating at exactly synchronous speed (Eq. 63), is developed by a polyphase winding placed in the stationary part of the machine. As previously mentioned, there are two general rotor constructions, namely, the *squirrel cage* and the *wound rotor;* these are shown in Figs. 227 and 228.

The *stator*, consisting of a properly insulated and connected winding in a laminated core, is first dipped in an insulating varnish and baked, and then pressed into a frame; Fig. 229 illustrates such a complete unit. Both types of

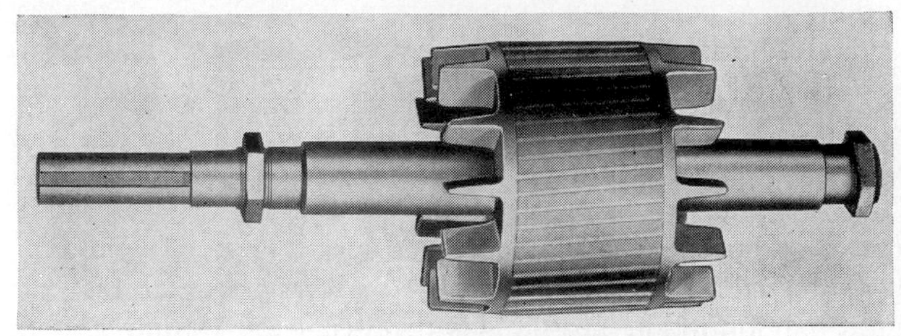

FIG. 227.—Squirrel-cage rotor for three-phase induction motor. Note the cooling fins. (*The Louis Allis Co.*)

FIG. 228.—Wound rotor for a three-phase induction motor. Note the three slip rings and the cooling fans at both ends. (*The Louis Allis Co.*)

rotor construction—the squirrel cage and wound rotor—employ a slotted, laminated core tightly pressed on a shaft. A common manufacturing practice in constructing the squirrel cage is to place the assembled core in a mold and force molten metal—often aluminum—into the slots under pressure. End rings, and projecting fins for cooling purposes, short-circuit the conducting bars at both ends. Practically speaking, rotors of this type are virtually indestructible; there is no insulation to burn out if the motor becomes overheated. The wound-rotor assembly is employed when it is necessary to control the speed of the motor or to provide the machine with a high starting torque. An insulated winding, similar to that used on the stator, is placed in the rotor slots and connected to slip rings; brushes riding on the

FIG. 229.—Stator and its winding for a three-phase induction motor. (*The Louis Allis Co.*)

rings are then wired to a resistance controller which is used for speed or starting-torque control.

The operating characteristics of a polyphase motor with a squirrel-cage rotor are such that the speed is substantially constant regardless of the load; variations of perhaps 3 to 10 per cent may be expected depending upon the resistance of the rotor. When the wound rotor is employed, it is possible to lower the speed as much as 50 per cent below synchronism by manipulating the resistance controller; moreover, for a given setting of the resistance controller, the speed will change approximately 10 to 25 per cent between no load and full load.

As a general rule, an induction motor is subjected to the most severe service during the starting and accelerating period; it is during this interval that an extremely high current tends to flow unless steps are taken to keep its value down to a reasonable level. Remembering that the induction motor with a squirrel-cage rotor is, in effect, a transformer with a short-circuited secondary, it follows that a high rotor (secondary) current will, by transformer action, have to be matched by a correspondingly large stator (primary) current. Of course, as the motor speeds up, the generated voltage in the rotor decreases, so that both rotor and stator currents drop to values determined only by the mechanical load.

In starting induction motors several methods are commonly used to limit the current during the accelerating period. A popular scheme is to employ a *compensator* between motor and source; this is merely a set of autotransformers, properly interconnected, that performs the function of reducing the motor voltage during the starting period. In operation a handle is thrown in one direction to start the motor; this action applies about 50 per cent voltage to the stator winding. Then, after full speed is attained the lever is quickly moved to "run," in which position the motor receives full voltage and the compensator is disconnected. Two other arrangements, similar in many respects to the procedure used for direct-current motors, is to insert variable line resistances or line reactances between motor and source. In each case a handle is slowly moved across a set of studs to bring the machine up to speed; in the starting position maximum resistance or reactance is inserted in the line wires, and as the motor gains speed these are gradually cut out. Still another practice is to design the rotor of the motor to have a high resistance during the starting period and a comparatively low ohmic value after full speed is reached; such machines, called *line-start* motors, are widely employed, because they dispense with the need for auxiliary starting equipment. And finally, the wound rotor has its own built-in current-limiting rotor resistors in the resistance controller; the latter serves to keep both rotor and stator current low during the accelerating period, as well as to adjust speed.

Figure 230 shows a completely disassembled squirrel-cage type of polyphase motor in which all parts are clearly visible.

FIG. 230.—Completely disassembled 10-hp., three-phase, four-pole, squirrel-cage motor. Note the ribbed outside stator surface and the fan for cooling purposes. (*The Louis Allis Co.*)

In this design it is particularly significant that the motor is entirely closed and yet cools quite readily. Note the cooling fins on the outside of the motor, the dummy housing that restricts the cooling air to the outside fin passages, the two fans, and the ball bearings.

Figure 231 shows a completely assembled motor of this type ready for operation. This motor is arranged for operation on 230 or 460 volts three-phase. Nine wires are brought out of the motor at the outlet box shown, where the electrician makes the proper connections for the voltage source available.

Synchronous Motors.—This type of polyphase machine is usually made in the larger horsepower-output ratings and, as the name implies, operates at absolutely *average con-*

stant speed regardless of load; it departs from this average speed only instantaneously, during load changes. The speed regulation of the synchronous motor is, therefore, zero. Should the countertorque exceed the maximum torque that can be developed by the motor at the average constant speed, the motor will come to rest because the average torque then drops to zero. Two factors only determine the speed

FIG. 231.—Completely assembled three-phase squirrel-cage induction motor. (*The Louis Allis Co.*)

of such a motor; these are (1) the frequency of the supply source, and (2) the number of poles in the machine; the speed is directly proportional to the frequency and inversely proportional to the number of poles.

Unlike the induction motor, the excitation of which must come solely from the alternating-current supply lines to which it is connected, the synchronous motor receives its excitation from *two* sources of supply: (1) the alternating-current source through its stator winding, and (2) the direct-current source through its rotor field. And whereas the power factor of the induction motor is always lagging and fixed by the magnitude of the load, that of the synchronous motor is variable over very wide limits by changes in the direct-current excitation. When the motor power factor is unity, the direct-current excitation is said to be normal; overexcitation causes the motor to operate at a leading power factor, underexcitation at a lagging power factor.

The starting torque of a synchronous motor, as such, is practically zero. For this reason it is necessary to employ one of several methods to bring the machine up to synchronism (synchronous speed) before it is capable of assuming load. The starting method most commonly used, and one that endows the motor with starting torques that may be as much as 150 per cent of rated torque, is to incorporate a squirrel cage in the pole faces of the rotor; this practice permits the synchronous motor to be started as an induction motor. The revolving-pole structure of a 600-hp., 40-pole, 60-cycle, 180-r.p.m. synchronous motor is illustrated in Fig. 232; note particularly the squirrel-cage winding in the pole faces, with four bars near the surface of each pole. Also clearly visible are the two slip rings and the connections between the latter and the field winding; when the motor is completely assembled, brushes will rest on the rings so that direct-current excitation can be supplied to the winding. As in the case of squirrel-cage induction-motor starting, it is customary to employ a compensator between synchronous motor and source, or other voltage-reducing scheme, when the machine is started in the manner indicated. To prevent extremely high induced voltages in the field windings, which act as the secondary of a step-up transformer, the field is generally short-circuited during the starting period. After the rotor reaches a speed that is close to synchronous, the direct-current excitation is applied; this action causes the revolving poles to pull into step with the revolving stator field, after which the machine continues to rotate at synchronous speed.

The fact that the power factor of a synchronous motor is adjustable over extremely wide limits suggests the possibility that it be employed for power-factor correction. This is, in fact, one of the most useful functions of this type of motor because, by overexcitation of the field, the power factor can be made sufficiently *leading* to compensate for normal lagging power-factor loads. Moreover, if the synchronous motor is operated without mechanical load, as it

FIG. 232.—Revolving field structure—without shaft—of a 600-hp., 40-pole, 60-cycle, 180-r.p.m. synchronous motor. (*General Electric Co.*)

sometimes is, the machine can be made to act just like a capacitor to take current that leads the voltage by nearly 90 deg.; when operated in this way the machine is called a *synchronous condenser* and is said to "float" on the line.

Figure 233 shows the assembled stator and rotor, without shaft, of the motor whose rotor is depicted in Fig. 232. Observe the horizontal pipe, fastened to the stator frame, that supports the brush rigging for the direct-current field. Also seen are the stator-winding leads emerging from the bottom, to which the three-phase power supply would be connected.

Commutator Motors.—Modern industrial practice requires an increasingly large number of polyphase motors whose speeds may be controlled over wide limits. The induction

Fig. 233.—Assembled stator and rotor (without shaft) of a synchronous motor whose rotor is shown in Fig. 232. (*General Electric Co.*)

motor, although admirable in many ways, is at a disadvantage in this respect. The speed of a squirrel-cage motor cannot be changed unless the motor is equipped with special windings and auxiliary devices, and speed control of the wound-rotor motor is accomplished at a considerable sacrifice in efficiency. The commutator motor, of which there are several types, overcomes the objections indicated, since speed adjustments are readily made by the operation of a lever that simultaneously moves three sets of brushes; moreover, the speed may be changed as little or as much as desired to provide a sort of stepless control.

The principle of operation of the commutator motor involves the creation of a voltage that is injected into the secondary circuit, the value of this voltage being a measure of the change in speed; this voltage must, of course, have exactly the same frequency as that which already exists in the secondary circuit. Furthermore, if the injected voltage opposes the induced voltage, the speed will drop; on the other hand, an aiding injected e.m.f. will cause the motor to speed up. It is thus possible to adjust the motor speed to values that are both below and above synchronous speed.

The important design feature of the commutator motor is a winding, properly disposed with respect to the usual stator and rotor windings, that (1) always generates a voltage having the same frequency as that already existing in the circuit into which it is injected, and (2) is easily adjusted. This is accomplished by a motor developed by Schrage in which the special winding is placed in the rotor directly over another winding that is connected to the three-phase power supply; the special winding—the adjustable voltage winding—is connected to a commutator upon which three sets of brushes ride. The brushes are wired to a conventional three-phase stator winding.

Referring to Fig. 234, which is a schematic diagram of the Schrage motor, note that the primary winding is on the rotor and the secondary winding, on the stator; these two windings have interchanged positions with respect to standard induction motors. Also observe that the adjusting winding, connected to the commutator, provides the secondary winding with a voltage determined by the position of the three sets of brushes aa', bb', and cc'. The farther apart these brushes are moved, the lower will be the speed; conversely, the closer together they are moved, the higher the speed. Also, by an ingenious arrangement of brush connections the brushes may, in effect, be shifted to occupy positions on opposite sides of one another, in which event the motor speed may be increased to values that are above synchronous speed. Another feature of this motor is that the power factor may be adjusted by simultaneously moving all brushes circumferentially.

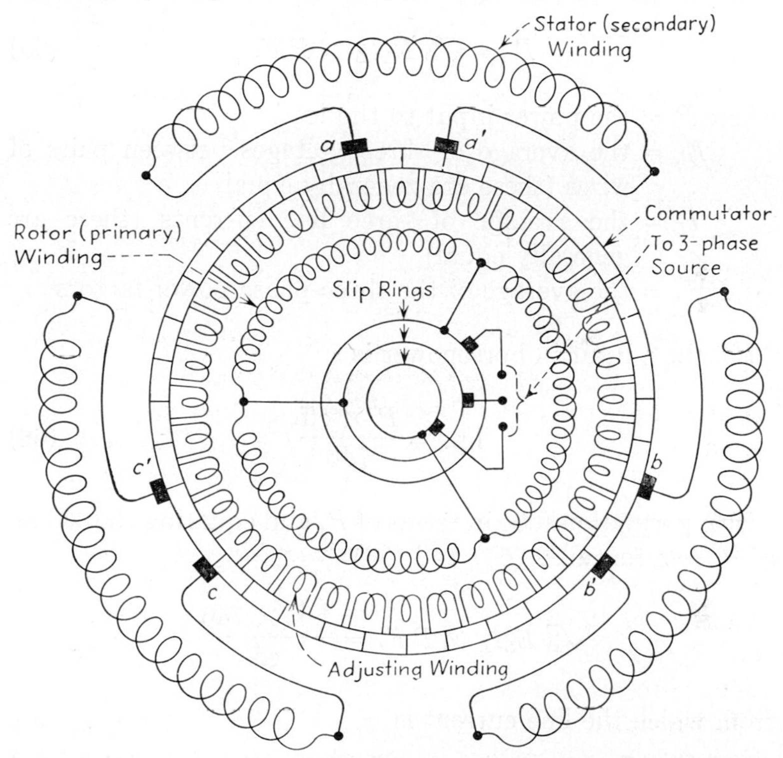

Fig. 234.—Schematic diagram of a Schrage three-phase adjustable-speed motor.

The motor is somewhat larger and more expensive than conventional induction-type machines having comparable ratings.

Polyphase Motor Power Input.—The total power taken by a polyphase balanced load such as a motor is equal to $nE_{PH}I_{PH} \times P.F.$, where n is the number of phases, E_{PH} is the voltage per phase, I_{PH} is the current per phase, and $P.F.$ is the power factor. Since polyphase motor windings are usually interconnected, and these discussions are limited to three-phase motors, phase voltages and currents may or may not be equal to line voltages and currents. Fundamental theory, however, indicates that whatever the interconnection between windings, the power input to a three-phase motor is given by the equation

$$P = \sqrt{3}\, E_L I_L \times P.F. \tag{65}$$

where P = the power input to the load
E_L = the average of three voltages between pairs of wires (these are generally equal)
I_L = the average of three line currents (these are generally equal)
$P.F.$ = the average of the three-phase power factors

Also, the output in horsepower is

$$\text{hp.} = \frac{P \times \text{eff}}{746} \tag{66}$$

Writing equation (66) in terms of P, and equating the values of P from formulas (65) and (66)

$$\sqrt{3}\, E_L I_L \times P.F. = \frac{\text{hp.} \times 746}{\text{eff}}$$

from which the line current is

$$I_L = \frac{\text{hp.} \times 746}{\sqrt{3}\, E_L \times P.F. \times \text{eff}} \tag{67}$$

Example 17.—A 5-hp. 230-volt three-phase induction motor operates at full load (*i.e.*, its output is 5 hp.) at an efficiency of 91 per cent and a power factor of 0.89. Calculate (*a*) the power input to the motor, (*b*) the current in any of the three line wires. (*c*) How much current would a single-phase motor take, assuming the same voltage, efficiency, power factor, and horsepower output?

Solution:

$$a.\ P_{\text{input}} = \frac{5 \times 746}{0.91} = 4{,}100 \text{ watts}$$

$$b.\ I_L = \frac{4{,}100}{\sqrt{3} \times 230 \times 0.89} = 11.6 \text{ amp. (three-phase)}$$

$$c.\ I_L = \frac{4{,}100}{230 \times 0.89} = 20 \text{ amp. (single-phase)}$$

Experiment 37. Starting and Reversing Shunt Motors

Objectives: To learn how to connect, start, and reverse a shunt motor (*a*) using a three-point starter, (*b*) using a four-point starter.

Procedure:

Part 1. *Three-point Starter.*—Following the wiring connections represented by Fig. 193, connect a shunt motor to a three-point starter, omitting the field rheostat for the present. Start the motor in accordance with the instructions given under *Starting a Direct-current Motor* (page 416). Do this several times, making sure that the motor accelerates smoothly from rest to its operating speed.

Since one of the most serious defects in the wiring connections may be an *open field* (the motor "runs away" under this condition), it is desirable to make a simple test to determine whether or not the field circuit is intact. This can be done as follows: disconnect the wire on the armature terminal on the starter, which will open the armature circuit; move the starter arm to the first stud; then quickly close and open the main switch, observing if there is a spark. If a spark occurs at the switch blades when the latter are opened, the field is complete; if not, the field is open.

The motor should next be reversed first by interchanging the armature terminals with respect to the field and then by interchanging the field terminals with respect to the armature. If a reversing switch is available, it will be desirable to do this by following the wiring connections given in Fig. 203*a* and *b*. *Great care should be used in making this change because it is easily possible to interchange the leads so that an open field will result.* When all wiring connections are made, be sure they are carefully checked before the motor is started.

Part 2. *Four-point Starter.*—Omitting the series field and the field rheostat of Fig. 195, connect the shunt motor to a four-point starter. Again practice starting and stopping the motor several times as in Part 1.

Reverse the direction of rotation of the motor, first by armature-current reversal and then by field-current reversal. This should be done using a reversing switch if one is available.

No data need be taken in this experiment because its object is to familiarize the student with the technique of starting, stopping, and reversing a direct-current motor.

EXPERIMENT 38. STARTING AND REVERSING COMPOUND MOTORS

Objectives: To learn how to connect, start, and reverse a compound motor (*a*) using a three-point starter, (*b*) using a four-point starter.

Procedure:

Part 1. *Three-point Starter.*—Following the same plan as outlined in Experiment 37, wire a compound motor to a three-point starter. Omit the field rheostat as before. *Be sure the series field is connected to aid the shunt field.* This is important because a differentially connected motor tends to become unstable and "run away." Try connecting the motor *long-shunt* and then *short-shunt*.

Finally, reverse the direction of rotation of the motor. This should be done first by armature-current reversal as in Fig. 204*a* and then by field-current reversal as in Fig. 204*b* and *c*. In the latter method be sure that *both* series and shunt fields are reversed; if only one field is reversed, the motor will be connected *differentially*, which, as mentioned above, will tend to make the motor unstable.

Part 2. *Four-point Starter.*—The same plan as that outlined for the three-point starter in Part 1 should now be followed using a four-point starter. Great care should always be taken to check all connections before the motor is started. Always be sure that the motor starts when the starter arm is on the first stud; if it does not, open the main switch, release the starter arm, and locate the trouble before proceeding further.

Experiment 39. Demonstrating the Existence of a C.E.M.F. in a Motor

Objective: To demonstrate experimentally that a c.e.m.f. is generated in the armature of a direct-current motor and that its value is only slightly less than the impressed voltage.

Procedure: Connect a shunt motor to a three-point starter (Fig. 193) or to a four-point starter (Fig. 195). Insert a single-pole single-throw (s.p.s.t.) switch in the connection between the *A* terminal on the starter and the armature terminal (wire *c* in Fig. 193). Start the motor in the usual way with the s.p.s.t. switch closed. If the motor is a 115-volt machine, connect an incandescent lamp and a 150-volt voltmeter *directly across the armature terminals* of the motor. If it is a 230-volt motor, connect two incandescent lamps in series and a 300-volt voltmeter directly across the motor armature terminals.

While the motor is running, record the voltmeter deflection and observe the brilliancy of the lamp or lamps. Now, as the s.p.s.t. switch is quickly opened, watch the voltmeter carefully. It will be observed that the deflection will drop slightly *at the instant the switch is opened* and will continue to drop to zero as the armature slows down. It will also be observed that the lamp brilliancy will change only slightly at the instant the switch is opened but will become dimmer and will be finally extinguished as the armature slows down to zero.

Since the field is still excited when the s.p.s.t. switch is opened, it should be clear that *the voltage that deflects the voltmeter needle* (in the same direction as does the line voltage) *and keeps the lamp lighted is a generated voltage in the armature.* It is a c.e.m.f. because the needle deflection is *not* reversed.

Experiment 40. Field-resistance Speed Control of Shunt and Compound Motors

Objectives: (*a*) To increase the speed of shunt and compound motors by inserting resistance (field rheostat) in the shunt-field circuit. (*b*) To determine the relationship between the speed and the relative value of resistance inserted in the shunt-field circuit.

Procedure:

Part 1. *Shunt-motor Speed Control.*—Following the wiring connections shown in Fig. 193 or Fig. 195 without the series field, connect a shunt motor to a starter. Set the field rheostat in the *all-out* position before the motor is started. Bring the motor up to full speed in the usual manner. Gradually cut in resistance in the shunt-field circuit by turning the knob of the field rheostat. Note how the speed of the motor increases as this is done. After practicing this method of speed control several times, proceed to take data in the following manner to determine how much the speed varies with changes in field-rheostat resistance.

Starting with the field rheostat in the *all-out* position, successively increase the field-rheostat resistance *in steps* until the maximum safe speed is reached. For each setting of the rheostat take readings of speed in revolutions per minute, voltage across the shunt field E_f, and voltage across the field rheostat E_{RH}. Record these values in a neat table. Since the same current flows through the entire shunt-field circuit, it follows that $E_{RH}/E_f = R_{RH}/R_f$. The second term R_{RH}/R_f merely indicates the value of the field-rheostat resistance with respect to the constant field-winding resistance. Thus, if this ratio is zero, no resistance is inserted; if it is 0.25, then R_{RH} is one-quarter of R_f; if 0.5, it is one-half of R_f, etc. Therefore, a curve plotted with revolutions per minute as ordinate and R_{RH}/R_f as abscissa should clearly indicate the manner in which the speed rises with *relative* increases in field-rheostat resistance with respect to the field-winding resistance.

A table similar to that illustrated below should be prepared in which the data may be recorded. After the experiment is performed and the necessary calculations are made, plot a curve of revolutions per minute (ordinate) versus R_{RH}/R_f (abscissa).

R.p.m.	Voltages		$\frac{R_{RH}}{R_f}$
	E_{RH}	E_f	

Part 2. *Compound-motor Speed Control.*—The same plan as outlined for the shunt-motor speed-control procedure should be followed using a compound motor. Refer to the wiring connections of Fig. 195. The student is again cautioned to make sure that the shunt and series fields are connected *aiding*. The data to be taken should be the same as in Part 1 and a similar curve should be plotted for the compound motor.

After studying the plotted curves the student should try to explain why they are not straight lines.

Experiment 41. Armature-resistance Speed Control of a Shunt Motor

Objectives: (*a*) To decrease the speed of a shunt motor by inserting resistance in the armature circuit. (*b*) To show that the armature-resistance method of speed control involves a considerable power loss in the rheostat and a comparatively high speed regulation.

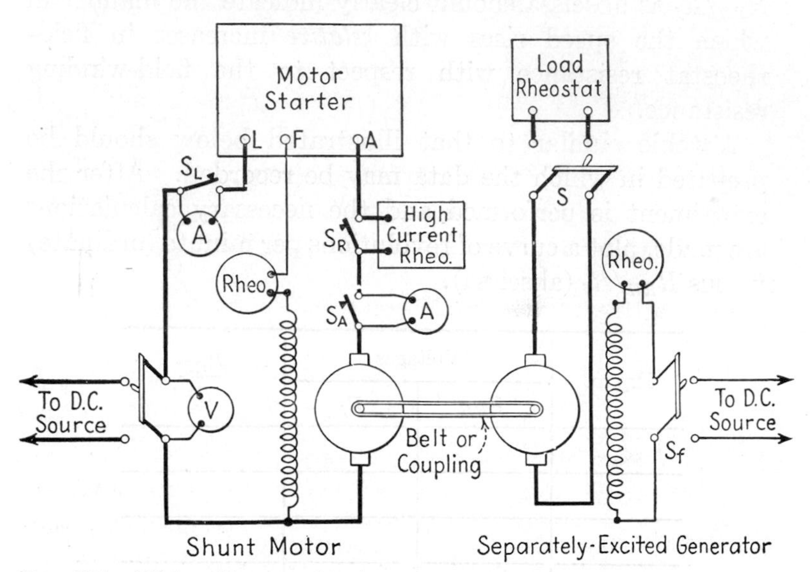

Fig. 235.—Wiring diagram showing connections for testing a shunt motor with armature-resistance speed-control arrangement.

Procedure: A shunt motor should first be wired to a three- or four-point starter, with a rheostat and an ammeter in the armature circuit and an ammeter in the line. The rheostat (Fig. 177) and the two ammeters should be capable of carrying a current somewhat in excess of the normal full-load motor current (name-plate value). Short-circuit switches S_R, S_L, and S_A across the rheostat and ammeters, respectively, should also be included. The motor should be coupled or belted to a *separately excited* shunt generator in a manner similar to the procedures outlined in Chap. 9. Follow the wiring diagram represented by Fig. 235.

With everything in readiness for the performance of the test, proceed in the following order:

1. Close switches S_R, S_L, and S_A; open the generator-field switch S_f and the load switch S.
2. Start the motor in the usual way. Measure and record the speed with the motor operating at no load. (Assume the motor to be operating at no load when the generator field is not excited.)
3. Close the generator-field switch and adjust the armature voltage to rated value (or approximately 115).
4. Close the load switch S and proceed to load the generator until the line ammeter in the motor circuit equals the rated motor current (ammeter across S_L). Measure and record the full-load motor speed.

Calculation:

Per cent regulation (no armature resistance)

$$= \frac{\text{r.p.m.}_{NL} - \text{r.p.m.}_{FL}}{\text{r.p.m.}_{FL}} \times 100 \qquad (a)$$

5. Now adjust the speed of the motor, using the rheostat in the armature circuit for this purpose, until it is 60 per cent of the full-load value obtained in (4), and *at the same time adjusting the line current to rated value.* This double adjustment will take some little time before both speed and line amperes are correct.
6. Record the following: line amperes I_L, armature amperes I_A, volts across armature E_A, volts across rheostat E_R, line volts E, and r.p.m.$_{FL}$.
7. Without disturbing anything else, merely open the generator-field switch. Measure and record the r.p.m.$_{NL}$.

Calculations:

Per cent regulation (with armature resistance)

$$= \frac{\text{r.p.m.}_{NL} - \text{r.p.m.}_{FL}}{\text{r.p.m.}_{FL}} \times 100 \qquad (b)$$

Power delivered to motor $= E \times I_L$ (c)
Power delivered to armature $= E_A \times I_A$ (d)
Power loss in rheostat $= E_R \times I_A$ (e)
Per cent of total power delivered to armature

$$= \frac{E_A \times I_A}{E \times I_L} \times 100 \qquad (f)$$

Per cent of total power lost in rheostat

$$= \frac{E_R \times I_A}{E \times I_L} \times 100 \qquad (g)$$

The above calculations from the test results should verify the following facts:

1. The per cent regulation is increased when resistance is inserted in the armature circuit [compare (*a*) and (*b*)].
2. The per cent power loss in the rheostat is a large part of the total power input [see (*c*), (*e*), and (*g*)].
3. The useful power delivered to the armature is much less than the total power input [see (*c*), (*d*), and (*f*)].

EXPERIMENT 42. SPEED REGULATION OF SHUNT AND COMPOUND MOTORS

Objectives: To determine the relation between the speed and the input current of (*a*) a shunt motor, and (*b*) a compound motor.

Procedure:

Part 1. *Shunt-motor Test.*—Using essentially the same wiring scheme employed in Experiment 41, make the connections shown in Fig. 235, omitting the rheostat, ammeter, and switches in the armature circuit.

Beginning with zero generator load, increase the load in steps until the motor line current registers full-load value. For each step record the speed of the motor and the motor line current I_L. Use a table similar to that given below.

Part 2. *Compound-motor test.*—Connect the series field in either the line or the armature circuit (short-shunt or long-shunt). Be sure the two fields are connected aiding.

Again, beginning with zero generator load, proceed to

load the motor-generator set as in Part 1 until the motor line current reaches name-plate value. For each step record the speed of the motor and the line current I_L. Use a table similar to that given below to record the test results.

Shunt		Compound	
I_L	R.p.m.	I_L	R.p.m.

Using the data obtained above, plot two curves *on the same sheet of graph paper*, for comparison, of revolutions per minute (ordinate) versus I_L (abscissa). These curves should be similar in shape to those given in Fig. 200. Calculate the per cent regulation for both types of motor.

Experiment 43. Shunt-motor Load Test

Objective: To determine the operating characteristics of a shunt motor.

Procedure: Equip the shaft of a shunt motor with a flanged pulley having a diameter of 2 to 4 in. depending upon the size of the motor. (A 2-in pulley works well with motors up to $\frac{3}{4}$ hp.) Make a rig to support a spring balance, and have a string, tied to the scale, line up with the face of the pulley. By wrapping one or more turns around the pulley it is possible to load the motor as desired. Figure 236 is a picture of the equipment described with a motor under test. It is necessary to make sure that the string is wrapped around the pulley so that it loads the spring scale.

Starting with no load, increase the motor load in steps until rated motor current is reached. Record motor volts E_L, line current I_L, revolutions per minute, and force on scale in pounds. Record the data in a table similar to

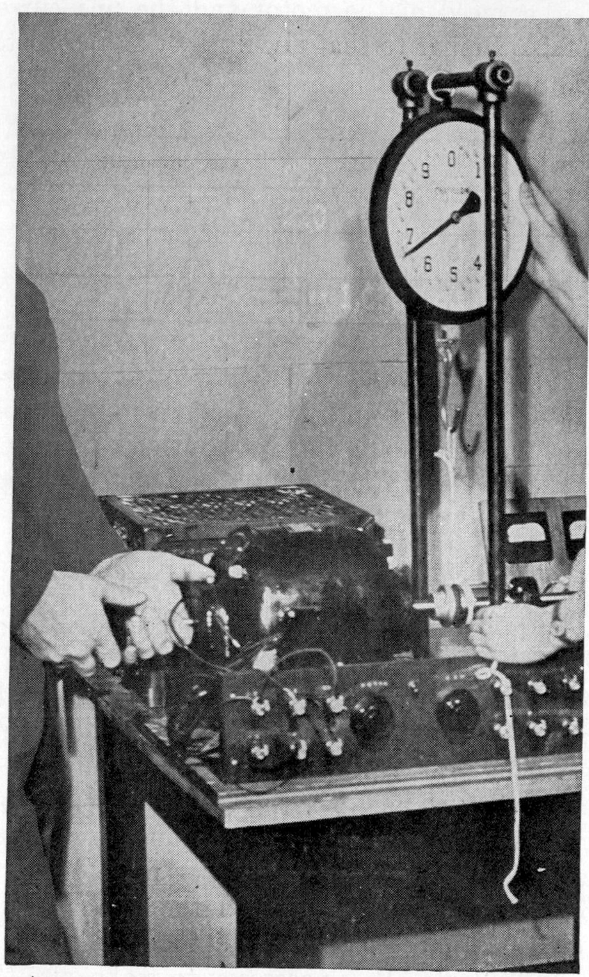

Fig. 236.—Arrangement of apparatus for performing a test upon a direct-current motor. Note the braking arrangement in the foreground and the rectifier in the background.

that given below, and make the necessary calculations indicated.

E_L	I_L	R.p.m.	Lb.	Power input ($E_L \times I_L$)	Torque (lbs. × R^1)	Hp.[2] output	Watts output (Hp. × 746)	Percentage efficiency $\frac{\text{Output}}{\text{Input}} \times 100$

[1] Radius of pulley in inches. [2] Horsepower $= \frac{T \times \text{r.p.m.}}{12 \times 5{,}250}$

Curves should next be plotted of revolutions per minute, torque, and efficiency as ordinate versus horsepower output.

Alternating-current Motors.—If several types of alternating-current motor are available, they should be completely disassembled like those illustrated in Figs. 209, 215, and 230. Each part should be carefully examined and notes should be made of the constructional details, the materials used, the functions, the possible troubles they might develop, etc. They should then be reassembled, operated at no load, and if possible under load. It is particularly important in connection with fractional-horsepower alternating-current motors to determine the starting current and starting torque. This should be done if facilities for doing so are available.

SUMMARY

1. An electric generator converts mechanical energy into electrical energy; an electric motor converts electrical energy into mechanical energy.
2. There are three general types of direct-current motor, namely, shunt, series, and compound. There are four general types of single-phase alternating-current motor: series, induction, synchronous, and repulsion.
3. Except in the case of synchronous motors, the speed of all others changes with variations in load.

4. Variable-speed motors are those whose speed changes appreciably with changes in load; adjustable-speed motors are those whose speed is changed manually by an operator or by an automatic mechanism.
5. The principle of motor action requires that a current-carrying conductor be placed perpendicularly to a magnetic field. If this is done, the conductor experiences a force.
6. A direct-current ammeter or voltmeter is essentially a torque motor. A coil, carrying a pointer, rotates against the opposing force of a spiral spring when current passes through the coil.
7. The force acting upon a current-carrying conductor placed in a magnetic field is proportional to the flux density, the current, and the length of the conductor.
8. As the armature of a motor rotates, a counter e.m.f. is generated.
9. The armature current in a motor is equal to the difference between the impressed and c.e.m.f.'s divided by the armature resistance.
10. The speed of a motor is proportional to the c.e.m.f. and inversely proportional to the flux.
11. When a motor is started, the armature current must be limited to a reasonable value until the c.e.m.f. is developed. A motor starter is generally used to limit the current.
12. The primary function of the motor starter is to limit the current in the armature circuit during the starting period.
13. There are two general types of direct-current motor starter, namely, *three-point* starters and *four-point* starters.
14. Three-point starters are not generally suitable when used with motors whose speed must be controlled.
15. Series motors are usually started by using drum-type starters or controllers.
16. The speed of a direct-current motor is generally con-

trolled by varying the flux or by changing the voltage across the armature.

17. When a load is applied to a motor, it has the natural tendency to slow down. When the motor does slow down, the c.e.m.f. diminishes, thus causing the armature current to increase.
18. When the load on a series motor is reduced, its speed tends to rise very rapidly. Series motors will race, or "run away," if the load is removed. This is a dangerous condition and should be avoided.
19. The torque developed by a motor is proportional to the armature current and the flux. For a shunt motor the torque is practically proportional to the load; for a series motor it is approximately proportional to the square of the load, except for very heavy loads; for a compound motor it is between the series and shunt characteristic.
20. Shunt and compound motors have definite no-load speeds; a series motor has a runaway speed at no load.
21. Shunt motors may be considered constant-speed motors, for all practical purposes; the speed changes about 2 to 8 per cent between no load and full load.
22. Compound and series motors are regarded as variable-speed motors.
23. Per cent speed regulation refers to the per cent rise in speed of a motor (except series motors) when the normal full load is completely removed. *The rise is based on the full-load value.*
24. There are three methods of adjusting the speed of a direct-current motor, namely, field-resistance control, armature-resistance control, and armature-voltage control (Ward Leonard method).
25. The direction of rotation of a direct-current motor may be reversed by reversing the current through the armature *or* the field or fields; it cannot be reversed by changing the direction of the current through both armature and field.

26. Commutating poles for direct-current motors are quite as common, and necessary, as in direct-current generators. The polarities of the interpoles are always the same as the preceding main poles with respect to the direction of rotation.
27. Motors should be selected on the basis of the following: kind of current available, starting torque, duty cycle, speed regulation, location of the installation, reversibility, overload capacity desired, ventilation, acceleration desired, etc.
28. A universal motor will operate satisfactorily on direct-current and alternating-current sources up to about 60 cycles. It is a series, direct-current type of motor in construction.
29. Universal motors generally operate at very high speeds and are usually built in fractional-horsepower sizes.
30. Universal motors are frequently equipped with constant-speed governors for adjustable-constant-speed applications.
31. The induction motor operates by the principle of transformer action, wherein the rotor receives its electrical energy by electromagnetic induction.
32. The speed of rotation of an induction type of motor is always slightly less than the synchronous speed, the latter being the speed of the revolving field.
33. Shaded-pole motors are essentially induction motors, built in small sizes. They are simple and economical to build. The shading coils, acting together with the main exciting coils, create fields whose axes shift across the poles from the unshaded to the shaded portions.
34. Split-phase motors are also induction motors, usually built in larger sizes than shaded-pole motors. The axes of the magnetic fields in such motors rotate completely around the core.
35. Split-phase motors have two windings, namely, the main winding and the auxiliary winding. It is customary to open the auxiliary winding circuit when the speed

of the rotor reaches about 75 per cent of its rated value. This is accomplished by means of a centrifugally operated mechanism or an electromagnetic relay.

36. When a capacitor is connected in series with the auxiliary winding, more starting torque and less starting current will result. If the auxiliary winding circuit is opened as in the straight split-phase motor, the machine is called a *capacitor-start motor*.
37. The repulsion-induction motor has the usual slotted type of stator and a direct-current type of rotor. All brushes resting on the commutator are short-circuited.
38. Poles are created in the rotor of a repulsion motor by electromagnetic induction. These poles are repelled by the stator poles; hence the name "repulsion-induction."
39. Repulsion-induction motors develop great starting torque with comparatively low starting current. This type of motor is, however, being rapidly replaced by the less costly, more rugged, more trouble-free capacitor type of machine.
40. Polyphase alternating-current motors generally have ratings that are higher than those built for single-phase service.
41. Polyphase systems develop two or more e.m.f.'s that are electrically displaced with respect to one another. In two-phase systems two voltages are displaced by 90 electrical degrees, and in three-phase systems three voltages are displaced by 120 electrical degrees with respect to one another.
42. Alternators that supply power to polyphase systems are nearly always three-phase machines.
43. Polyphase systems are superior to single-phase systems because they are economical to operate and require less costly transmission lines, transformers, circuit breakers, lightning arresters and other necessary equipment.
44. There are three general types of polyphase motor; these are the induction type, the synchronous type, and the commutator type.

45. Two kinds of rotor are available for induction-type motors: the squirrel cage and the wound rotor.
46. Salient-pole constructions are used in the rotors of synchronous motors.
47. The commutator-type motor was developed for adjustable-speed operation. In one design the stator construction is standard, but the rotor is complex, with one winding connected to a commutator and another connected to slip rings.
48. A polyphase induction motor creates a true revolving field, constant in magnitude, that rotates at synchronous speed.
49. Modern squirrel-cage rotors are generally of the cast-aluminum construction; molten aluminum is forced under pressure into the slots of a laminated core to form bars, end rings, and often cooling fins.
50. Squirrel-cage motors operate at essentially constant speed; speed regulations are about 3 to 10 per cent.
51. Wound-rotor motors develop high values of starting torque and have speed regulations of the order of 10 to 25 per cent. The resistance controller in the rotor circuit may be used for speed adjustment as well as current limitation during the starting period.
52. A compensator is often used to start squirrel-cage motors; these reduce the starting voltage to about 50 per cent of line voltage.
53. Squirrel-cage motors are also started by employing line resistors or line reactors; they are sometimes designed for direct line-voltage starting.
54. Synchronous motors operate at an absolutely average constant speed.
55. A synchronous motor receives two kinds of excitation; these are alternating-current excitation through its stator winding and direct-current excitation through its rotor field.
56. The power factor of a synchronous motor is readily adjustable by altering the direct-current excitation;

overexcitation makes the power factor leading and underexcitation makes the power factor lagging.

57. Compensators are often used to start synchronous motors, functioning as they do in induction motors. The field is generally short-circuited during the starting period to limit the induced voltage in the field to reasonably low values.
58. When synchronous motors are used for power-factor correction purposes only, they are called *synchronous condensers*.
59. In the commutator-type polyphase motor power is delivered to a rotor winding through slip rings. An adjusting winding, also on the rotor, and connected to a commutator, provides a variable voltage to a stator winding. By an ingenious brush-shifting arrangement the voltage injected into the stator winding may be changed so that the speed can be varied; speed variations above and below synchronous rotational speed are attainable.
60. Polyphase induction motors are ideal from the standpoint of cost per horsepower, ruggedness, starting torque, speed regulation, and over-all good performance.

QUESTIONS

1. List several differences between generators and motors.
2. Classify motors on the basis of types, speed changes with load, variable and adjustable speed, and kind of excitation.
3. Describe the principle of the direct-current motor.
4. Define torque.
5. Explain how the *direction* of motion of a current-carrying conductor in a magnetic field can be determined. Illustrate by a sketch.
6. Why is a direct-current instrument (voltmeter or ammeter) a torque motor? Explain how such an instrument operates.

7. Upon what factors does the force acting upon a conductor depend? Illustrate by an example.
8. What is meant by *c.e.m.f.*? How can its existence be demonstrated experimentally?
9. What is the value of the c.e.m.f. compared with the impressed voltage? Why?
10. What determines the armature current in a direct-current motor? Write an equation that can be used to determine its value.
11. Explain why the armature current increases when a shunt motor is loaded.
12. List the several types of direct-current motor. Illustrate each type by a simple sketch.
13. What happens to the speed when the load is removed from a shunt motor? a compound motor? a series motor?
14. Explain why a series motor "runs away" when the load is removed.
15. What is a motor starter? What two important functions does it serve?
16. Make a sketch showing the internal wiring connections of a three-point starter.
17. Make a sketch showing the internal wiring connections of a four-point starter.
18. Carefully explain the procedure to be followed in starting a direct-current motor with a starter.
19. Why is it desirable that the starter arm fall back to the "off" position when the power supply fails?
20. Why is it undesirable to use a three-point starter with motors whose speed must be controlled?
21. Make simple sketches showing the electric circuits in a three-point starter connected to a shunt motor; in a four-point starter connected to a compound motor.
22. What is a controller? How does it differ from a starter?
23. Draw characteristic speed-load curves for a shunt motor, a compound motor, and a series motor.

24. Explain why a shunt motor is generally called a *constant-speed* motor.
25. Explain why a compound or series motor is generally called a *variable-speed* motor.
26. Upon what factors does the torque developed by a motor depend?
27. Draw characteristic torque-load curves for a shunt motor, a compound motor, and a series motor.
28. Explain why the torque of a series motor is proportional to the square of the load at light loads and only the first power of the load at heavy loads.
29. Why is it possible for a series motor to develop higher overload capacity than a shunt motor?
30. Distinguish between speed regulation and speed control.
31. What three important methods of speed control are possible with shunt motors? compound motors? series motors? Make sketches illustrating each method of control.
32. Under what practical operating conditions is it desirable to use a constant-speed motor? a variable-speed motor? an adjustable-speed motor? an adjustable-constant-speed motor?
33. Carefully describe how the Ward Leonard speed-control system operates. What are its advantages? its disadvantages?
34. How can a direct-current motor be reversed? Illustrate each method by a sketch.
35. Illustrate by a sketch the polarities of the main and commutating poles of a direct-current motor. Compare this with the polarities in a direct-current generator.
36. What functions are served by commutating poles in direct-current motors?
37. List several practical applications of shunt, compound, and series motors not included in Table XIII.
38. What important factors must be considered when selecting a direct-current motor for a given application?

39. What is a universal motor? Why is it so very important for household appliances?
40. Explain why the high speed of a universal motor is extremely desirable.
41. How is the high armature speed of a universal motor reduced to a reasonable load speed?
42. Explain how a constant-speed governor operates.
43. Describe the induction-motor principle.
44. List several types of single-phase induction motor.
45. Explain how the magnetic axis shifts across the pole face in a shaded-pole motor.
46. Upon what factors does the speed of an induction motor depend?
47. What important differences exist between the shaded-pole and the split-phase types of motor? List some of the similarities between them.
48. Why is it desirable to disconnect the auxiliary winding from the supply source after the motor reaches normal speed?
49. What are a centrifugal switch and an electromagnetic relay when applied to a split-phase motor? Explain the action of each.
50. What is a capacitor-start split-phase motor? What are its outstanding advantages?
51. Carefully explain the repulsion principle when applied to the repulsion-induction motor. Illustrate the discussion by sketches.
52. What are the two important advantages possessed by repulsion-induction motors?
53. Describe the centrifugal mechanism that short-circuits the commutator and raises the brushes in a repulsion-induction motor.
54. How is a shaded-pole motor reversed? a split-phase motor? a repulsion-induction motor?
55. What important advantages are possessed by polyphase induction motors? Why are they not generally used in small sizes?

56. Define a two-phase polyphase system; a three-phase polyphase system.
57. What kinds of polyphase alternators are generally used?
58. Why are polyphase systems superior to single-phase systems?
59. List three general types of polyphase motor.
60. Describe the construction of the squirrel-cage rotor; the wound rotor.
61. What type of rotor is used in synchronous motors? Describe its construction.
62. What important advantage is possessed by the commutator-type motor? Why is it similar, in this respect, to the wound-rotor motor?
63. At what speed does the revolving field of an induction motor operate? At what speed does the rotor operate?
64. What is a compensator? What is its function?
65. What is a line-start induction motor? How does it differ from a conventional induction motor?
66. What is meant by line-resistance and line-reactance starting when referring to induction-motor starting?
67. How does a synchronous motor receive its excitation?
68. What is meant by overexcitation and underexcitation when referring to a synchronous motor? What is the effect of each kind of excitation?
69. How are synchronous motors started?
70. What is meant by a synchronous condenser?
71. Describe the construction of the Schrage motor, and carefully explain its method of speed control.

PROBLEMS

1. Each of the conductors in the armature of a direct-current motor is 7.5 in. long. (*a*) What will be the force, in pounds, exerted on it when it carries 120 amp. and is in a field whose intensity is 58,000 lines per square inch? (*b*) What torque, in inch-pounds, will be exerted by it if the armature diameter is 8 in.?
2. There are a total of 260 armature conductors in a motor,

67 per cent of which lie directly under the poles where the flux density is 52,000 lines per square inch. If the torque developed by the motor is 84 ft.-lb., calculate the current in each conductor. (The armature diameter and length are 6 in. and 5 in., respectively.)

3. What torque will be developed by the motor of Prob. 2 if the current per conductor is increased by 50 per cent and the flux density rises by 10 per cent?
4. A 230-volt, direct-current shunt motor has an armature resistance of 0.32 ohm. (*a*) What c.e.m.f. is developed in the armature when the latter carries a current of 40 amp.? (*b*) What power is developed by the armature?
5. The speed of the motor in Prob. 4 is 1,200 r.p.m. (*a*) At what speed will it operate when the load is completely removed, under which condition the armature current drops to 5 amp.? (Assume no change in flux.) (*b*) What will be the per cent regulation between the two loads?
6. A compound motor operates at no load at 900 r.p.m. What is its full-load speed if the regulation is 12.5 per cent?
7. Calculate the copper loss in the armature of the motor of Prob. 4.
8. A 5-hp., 220-volt compound motor has a shunt-field resistance of 110 ohms and a series-field resistance of 0.10 ohm. The full-load efficiency is 89.2 per cent. (*a*) Determine the full-load line current and the armature current assuming the long-shunt connection. (*b*) Calculate the power loss in both fields.
9. The resistance of the armature circuit of a 115-volt shunt motor is 0.25 ohm. What resistance must be inserted in the armature circuit to limit the starting current to 85 amp.?
10. A 10-hp., 230-volt shunt motor has a full-load efficiency of 90 per cent. The armature resistance is 0.29 ohm and the shunt-field resistance is 57.5 ohms. If the initial armature current is to be limited to 1.5 times its full-load value, calculate the starter resistance.

11. What would be the initial line current to the motor of Prob. 10 if no starter were used?
12. A shunt motor has six poles each of which produces 5.2×10^5 maxwells. The armature has 288 conductors. What horsepower is developed by the motor if each conductor carries 50 amp. and the speed is 1,200 r.p.m.?
13. What torque, in foot-pounds, is developed by a 3-hp. series motor operating at 850 r.p.m.?
14. If the load on the series motor in Prob. 13 is reduced so that the current drops by 25 per cent, calculate the torque developed by the motor. (Assume that the flux varies directly with the current.)
15. A 115-volt, 1,750-r.p.m. compound motor (long-shunt connected) has an armature resistance of 0.12 ohm and a series-field resistance of 0.03 ohm. The full-load armature current is 48 amp. At what speed will the motor operate if the load is increased until the armature current rises to 60 amp.? (Assume a $12\frac{1}{2}$ per cent increase in flux for a 25 per cent increase in series-field current.)
16. A 15-hp., 550-volt series motor takes 23 amp. when operating at 1,400 r.p.m. The armature resistance is 0.65 ohm and the series-field resistance is 0.35 ohm. At what speed will the motor operate when it takes 11.5 amp.? (Assume that the flux varies directly with the series-field current.)
17. Assuming a 5 per cent slip in all cases, determine the full-load speeds of two-, four-, six-, and eight-pole 60-cycle induction motors.
18. The name plate of a split-phase motor indicates the following: $\frac{1}{4}$ hp., 60 cycles, 1,725 r.p.m., 4.6 amp., 115 volts. Calculate (*a*) the motor power factor; (*b*) the per cent slip; (*c*) the per cent regulation, assuming a no-load speed of 1,790 r.p.m.; (*d*) the full-load efficiency, assuming a power input of 340 watts.
19. A $\frac{1}{4}$-hp., 60-cycle, 115-volt split-phase motor takes 5.2 amp. and 375 watts when delivering a load 25 per

cent greater than its rated output. Calculate the power factor and the efficiency of the motor operating under these conditions.

20. A 100-hp., three-phase induction motor is connected to a 440-volt circuit. When it is delivering rated load, the efficiency is 87.0 per cent and the power factor is 0.88. Calculate the current in each of the three lines.
21. At what speed does a 60-cycle synchronous motor operate if it has 24 poles? 32 poles? 10 poles?
22. What are the upper and lower speed limits of a 6-pole, 60-cycle polyphase commutator-type motor if brush shifting will increase the speed 50 per cent above synchronous r.p.m. and decrease it 25 per cent below synchronous r.p.m.?
23. What full-load torque, in foot-pounds, is developed by a 5-hp., three-phase, 4-pole, 60-cycle induction motor whose rated-load slip is 5 per cent?
24. The starting current of a 15-hp., 440-volt, three-phase induction motor is 132 amp. when rated voltage is impressed. What current does the motor take if a compensator, used with the motor, reduces the starting voltage to 254 volts? (The starting current is directly proportional to the impressed e.m.f.)
25. What voltage should the compensator in Prob. 24 supply to the motor if the starting current is to be limited to 60 amp.?
26. The name plate of a squirrel-cage induction motor has the following information: 25 hp., 220 volts, three-phase, 60 cycles, 830 r.p.m., 64 amp. per line. If the motor takes 20,800 watts when operating at full load, calculate (*a*) slip; (*b*) per cent speed regulation if the no-load speed is 897 r.p.m.; (*c*) power factor; (*d*) torque; (*e*) efficiency.

LIST OF VISUAL AIDS

The following list of visual aids can be used to supplement the material in this book. This list is comprehensive rather than selective, and it is suggested that each film be previewed before using, as some may be too advanced and others too elementary.

These films can be obtained from the producer or distributor listed with each title (addresses are given at the end of this list). In many cases these films and filmstrips can be obtained from your local film library or film distributor; also, many universities have large film libraries from which films can be borrowed.

The running time (min), whether it is a motion picture (MP) or filmstrip (FS), and whether it is silent (si) or sound (sd) are listed with each title. All those not listed as color (c) are black and white. All of the motion pictures are 16 mm; filmstrips are 35 mm.

All of the U.S. Office of Education films have coordinated silent filmstrips and instructor's manuals. In many cases, other films also have accompanying instructor's manuals.

Each film has been listed only once, under the chapter to which it is most applicable, but many may be used advantageously with other chapters as well. The more recent films and those which are generally pertinent rather than specific to one chapter are listed at the end of the list under the head "General."

CHAPTER 1—ELECTRICITY—BASIC IDEAS AND EFFECTS

Story of Electricity (UWF 11 min sd MP). Shows discovery and progress, production and distribution, and various uses.

Sources of Electricity (Brandon 11 min sd MP). Describes production of electric phenomena by magnetic induction, friction, or chemical action; nature of electric currents.

Electricity (SVE FS). Illustrates electrical principles and operations; covers capacitors, dry cells, storage cells, electrical units, Ohm's law, resistance, fuses, and generators.

Chemical Effects of Electricity (EBF 15 min si MP). Shows making of dry cells, storage batteries, electric batteries; covers electrolysis, electroplating, electrotyping, etc.

Heat and Light from Electricity (EBF 15 min si MP). Deals with heating effects of electricity; shows manufacture and use of conductors, insulators, heating equipment, arc furnaces, lamps; presents Ohm's law; explains series and parallel circuits.

Magnetic Effects of Electricity (EBF 15 min si MP). Presents the electromagnet, the electric bell, the ammeter, the theory of permanent magnetism; uses the voltmeter to explain magnetism and magnetic induction.

Coils and Electric Currents (Edited 13 min si MP). Explores the nature of the fields of force about a current-carrying wire; theory of solenoids and electromagnets, induction coils and electric motors.

Elements of Electric Circuits (EBF 11 min sd MP). Depicts the flow of electrons, resistance and the ohm, current and ampere, electromotive force, Ohm's law.

The Electron—An Introduction (USOE 16 min sd MP). Explains the nature of electrons, electron flow in solid conductors, electromotive force, control of electron flow, electron flow and magnetic fields, types of electron flow, and induced electron flow.

Electrons (EBF 10 min sd MP). Pictures the conduction of electricity in liquids, gases, and vacuums, proving the hypothesis that electricity consists of a unit elementary charge, the electron.

CHAPTER 2—WIRES, CABLES, AND THEIR ELECTRICAL PROPERTIES

Resistance (SVE FS). Illustrates different forms of resistance, using subjects in everyday life; shows resistance by means of water and copper wires; explains the use of the rheostat and how resistance is measured.

Wire Sizes and Voltage Drop (USOE 13 min sd MP). Explains factors influencing the ability of conductors to carry electron flow; measurement of wire sizes, wire area in circular mils, voltage drop, and Ohm's law.

Measuring Electrical Units, Part 1 (Navy FS). Describes the use and care of instruments for measuring resistance, voltage, and current.

CHAPTER 3—DIRECT-CURRENT CIRCUITS

Series and Parallel Circuits (EBF 11 min sd MP). Presents relationship between resistance, current, and voltage in both types of circuits.

Primary Cell (EBF 11 min sd MP). Shows operation of dry cell in terms of electron action, including ionization of the electrolyte, polarization, and depolarizer; batteries and cells in series and parallel wiring.

Electricity and the Storage Battery, Part 1 (JH FS). Discusses the most fundamental aspects of electricity; principles of simple primary and secondary cell; Ohm's law; series and parallel connections.

Storage Battery Power (Edison 20 min si MP). A study of storage batteries and the unique features of Edison's product.

Principles of Electrical Measurement (DeVry 22 min sd MP). Explains construction and operation of electrical instruments; operations of a number of electrical measuring devices.

Electrical Measurement (DeVry 60 min si MP). Describes the construction and operation of electrical instruments; needs of different measuring quantities.

Electric Meters (JH FS). Construction and operation of various types of meters for electrical use.

Direct-current Voltmeters and Ammeters (SVE FS). Discusses how to measure flow of electricity; shows principles on which different meters operate; labels parts of portable meter; demonstrates uses of ammeter and voltmeter.

Electrical Measurements, Part 1 (SVE FS). Measurement —what it is; how we measure; principles of electrical measurement.

Electrical Measurements, Part 2 (SVE FS). Describes voltmeters and ammeters; construction principles; shunts, voltammeters; calibration of meters; "zero corrector" used in adjustments.

Electrical Measurements, Part 3 (SVE FS). Demonstrates principles on which voltmeter and ammeter coils operate; electrodynamometer type of instruments.

When You Can Measure (GE 40 min sd MP). Use of electrical measuring instruments; development of modern types; manufacture of parts and assembly.

CHAPTER 5—ALTERNATING-CURRENT ELECTRIC CIRCUITS AND MEASUREMENTS

Capacitance (Army 31 min sd MP). Demonstrates the flow of electrons through a circuit; shows the charging and discharging of capacitors; variations of a charge on a capacitor in relation to time and behavior of capacitance with alternating current.

Alternating Current (Army FS). Introduction to the principles of alternating current; demonstrates and explains Lenz's law, simple wave alternator; discusses frequency, effective value, voltage-current time relationship and power.

Alternating Current (JH FS). Shows inductance, capacitance, and impedance in a circuit—transformers and rectifiers.

Alternating-current Voltmeters and Ammeters (SVE FS). Demonstrates principles on which alternating-current meters work; principles of ammeters and voltmeters and their parts; other types of alternating-current meters including the oscilloscope.

Measuring Electrical Units, Part 2 (Navy FS). Describes the use and care of instruments for measuring capacity (capacitors) and alternating current.

CHAPTER 6—MAGNETISM AND ELECTROMAGNETISM

The Magnet (Edited 11 min sd MP). Shows how lodestone of ancient Greece has been developed into enormous electromagnets used by industry today.

Magnetism (JH FS). Describes the general properties and laws of magnets; magnetic effects; natural and artificial magnets; polarity and laws of magnetic attraction; magnetic fields; the compass; magnetic induction; theory of magnetism; magnetic materials.

Magnetism (SVE FS). Explains magnetism, furnishing historical background; presents theory of magnetism; defines lines of force and magnetic fields.

Magnetism (GE Slides). Describes elementary conceptions of magnetism and molecular theory of magnetism; contributions of Faraday and Steinmetz to the study of the magnetic field.

Principles of Magnetism (DeVry 22 min sd MP). Discusses polarity, lines of force, reluctance, and permeability; magnetic induction, uses of magnets; molecular theory of magnetism.

Principles of Electromagnetism (DeVry 22 min sd MP). Depicts electromagnetic phenomena; relationship between current and magnetic fields; coils and solenoids; transformers.

Electromagnetism (SVE FS). Deals with direction of electric current and electron movements, lines of force, magnetic fields, simple electromagnets, properties of a hollow coil.

Electrodynamics (EBF 10 min sd MP). Covers basic principles of electromagnetism and current electricity; presents magnetic fields about wire-carrying current and of a coil; electromagnets; magnetic hypothesis; alternating-current and direct-current generators; induction by an electric current.

Excursions in Science No. 1 (GE 10 min sd MP). Illustrates elementary principles of magnetism; shows the affinity different oils have for water; how the photocell is based upon the principles of the simple radiometer; a small model being driven by three photocells.

Excursions in Science No. 3 (GE 10 min sd MP). Presents two stories dealing with magnetism: one on the effect of strong magnets on weak magnets, and the electron theory of magnetism; the other on the effect of cold and heat on the Curie metal used in control devices with Alnico magnets.

CHAPTER 8—ELECTROMAGNETIC INDUCTION, TRANSFORMER ACTION, AND TRANSFORMERS

Electromagnetism (JH FS). Construction and use of the electromagnet; effects of the electromagnetic field, Oersted's experiment; strength of fields, the polarity of a solenoid; the telegraph; Faraday's experiment.

Principles of Current Generation (DeVry 22 min sd MP). Presents the principles involved in generating electrical power; correlated practical and theoretical phenomena of electromagnetic induction.

There's a Difference (GE 40 min sd MP). Story of development, modernization, and manufacture of electrical transformer.

The Operation and Use of Transformers (SVE FS). Shows principles and parts of the transformer; covers use of transformers in stepping down voltage for ordinary use.

Transformers (GE Slides). Shows various types of transformers; annealing furnace; winding disk coils; high-voltage testing machine for sheet insulation; legs and bottom yokes; interlocking legs and yoke laminations; large one- and two-core-type transformers.

CHAPTER 9—GENERATORS—DIRECT AND ALTERNATING CURRENT

The Generator (JH FS). Discusses principles of the generator, types, generating direct and alternating currents.

Alternating-current and Direct-current Generators (SVE FS). Shows a hydroelectric plant; answers many questions about generators.

CHAPTER 10—MOTORS—DIRECT AND ALTERNATING CURRENT

Motors (SVE FS). Principles of the electric motor; demonstrates parts and uses.

Electric Motors (JH FS). Principles of the motor; direct- and alternating-current motors; universal motors.

Principles of the Electric Motor (AMNH Slides). Magnets; electromagnets; commutator; electric motor; shunt-wound and series-wound motors.

Single-phase and Polyphase Circuits (USOE 17 min sd MP). Explains a single-phase synchronous generator, the use of sine curves to illustrate flow changes, a two-phase system and three-phase system; ways to simplify wiring in the two-phase and three-phase systems.

Rotating Magnetic Fields (USOE 13 min sd MP). Explains a rotating magnetic field pattern; traces the three-phase winding in a demonstration stator; shows the factors that cause rotation of the magnetic field; construction of polyphase motors.

Squirrel-cage Rotor Principles (USOE 10 min sd MP). Explains the fundamental law of magnetism; fundamental law of induced e.m.f.; electron flow in squirrel-cage rotor setting up magnetic poles that create torque, and construction of squirrel-cage rotors.

Split-phase Motor Principles (USOE 17 min sd MP). Explains the construction of stator and rotor; comparison of winding resistances and inductive reactances; use of capacitor to produce phase displacement.

Repulsion Motor Principles (USOE 18 min sd MP). Explains construction of repulsion motor; rotor circuits and effect of brush position; short-circuiting and brush-lifting mechanism; applications of repulsion motors.

Direct-current Controllers (USOE 15 min sd MP). Shows shunt motors and direct-current controllers in operation; direct-current faceplate controller connected to a shunt motor.

Across-the-line Starters (USOE 15 min sd MP). Explains the theory and operation of a manually operated thermal overload switch, a magnetically operated across-the-line starter, a drum reversing switch for a three-phase motor, and a magnetic reversing switch.

Reduced-voltage Starters (USOE 23 min sd MP). Principle of the transformer; mechanical operation of the manual starting compensator; electrical operation of the manual starting compensator; operation of the thermal overload relay; mechanical and electrical operation of an automatic starting compensator.

Wound-rotor Controllers (USOE 17 min sd MP). Explains wound-rotor motor principles; shows the operation of a face-plate controller, a drum-type nonreversing controller, drum-type reversing controller, and automatic magnetic starter for a wound-rotor motor.

GENERAL

Amperes, Volts, and Ohms (USN 8 min MP). Explains the meaning, relationship, and measurement of amperes, volts, and ohms. Correlated filmstrip, same title, 23 fr, also available.

Basic Electricity (USAF 20 min MP). An animated cartoon explaining the fundamentals of electricity, including voltage, current, resistance, magnetic fields, induction, primary and secondary coils, and series and parallel circuits.

Circuit Testing with Meters and Multimeters. Part 1: Theory (USA 30 min MP). Explains the theory and construction of meters and shows various types of meters used for circuit testing and associated external equipment.

Circuit Testing with Meters and Multimeters. Part 2: Practical Application (USA 37 min MP). Demonstrates how to use meters in testing transformers, capacitors, resistors, telephone loop circuits, etc.

Current and Electromotive Force (USN 11 min MP). Explains electron theory, the arrangement of molecules, building up of current, the nature of conductors, electromotive force, resistance, and chemical and mechanical sources of electromotive force. Correlated filmstrip, same title, 38 fr, also available.

D. C. Motor. Part 1: Mechanical Overhaul (USOE 20 min MP). How to test for electrical and mechanical faults, dismantle direct-current motor, turn commutator, repair and replace field coils, assemble motor, and adjust and make final tests. Correlated filmstrip, same title, 37 fr, also available.

D. C. Motor. Part 2: Rewinding (USOE 37 min MP). How to dismantle and clean an armature core, determine commutator pitch, reinsulate the core, insert coils, band an armature, shape coil ends, lay in and solder leads, balance and impregnate the armature, and turn a commutator. Correlated filmstrip, same title, 43 fr, also available.

Electrical Measurements, Part 4 (SVE FS). Power factor meters; frequency meters.

Electrical Measurements, Part 5 (SVE FS). The direct-reading wattmeter; the synchroscope; the thermammeter.

Electrochemistry (EBF 10 min sd MP). Shows the chemical reactions as dynamic processes; shows electrolytic decomposition of hydrogen chloride; storage battery integrates both processes.

Electrostatics (EBF 10 min sd MP). Shows the chemical reactions as dynamic processes; electrolytic.

Electrostatics, Part 1 (SVE FS). Explains the nature of positive and negative charges; defines conductors, nonconductors, and the function of insulators.

Electrostatics, Part 2 (SVE FS). Explains the nature of electrification produced by induction; shows how the electrophorus is used for generating electricity by induction.

Electrostatics, Part 3 (SVE FS). Illustrates two or more conductors separated by nonconducting material from a capacitor; how capacitors can hold much more powerful charges than can their elements independently; how charges attract and bind each other, reducing the scattering effect of the mutual repulsion of electrons, etc.

Inductance (USN 35 min MP). Shows how a magnetic force reacts around a coil, the nature of self-inductance, and how to increase the inductance of a coil. Correlated filmstrip, same title, 38 fr, also available.

Ohm's Law (USA 19 min MP). Explains the elements of electricity; electrical energy, its source, transmission, and use; composition of matter; use of force and energy; how Ohm's law functions; resistance; and the purpose and use of meters.

Principles of Electricity (GE 20 min MP). Explains the principles involved in the flow of current; defines volt, ampere, and ohm; and covers magnetism and magnetic fields as applied to motors.

Principles of Electrostatics (DeVry 22 min sd MP). Describes polarity, conductors, insulators, electrostatic induction, electron theory, distribution of charges, electric machines.

RCL: Resistance Capacitance (USN 34 min MP). Explains current and voltage in relation to time; voltage and current curves; the relationship of current and voltage; the measurement of voltage at source; the addition of phase components; and the effect of impedance on resonance.

Series and Parallel Circuits (USN 8 min MP). Illustrates series and parallel circuits, explaining current flow and voltage drop across each lamp. Correlated filmstrip, same title, 26 fr, also available.

Story of Electricity (UWF 10 min sd MP). Shows lodestone, magnetized iron, amber, the earth itself as a gigantic field, Franklin's kite, first motor, Morse telegraph, Edison lamp, commercial power plant, wireless, etc.

The Diode (USOE 17 min sd MP). Explains the principles of electron flow across a gap; basic features of the diode tube; control of electron flow in the tube; photoelectric cells; X-ray tubes; and the diode as a rectifier.

The Electric Cell (JH FS). Describes the change of chemical energy into electrical energy; primary and secondary cells.

The Triode: Amplification (USOE 14 min sd MP). Reviews the diode principle; explains the electric field in a diode; electric field in a triode; a triode amplifier circuit; amplification of direct-current voltage changes; amplification of alternating voltages; distortion; amplification of audio-frequency signals; reviews the triode principle.

Theory and Operation of the Four-pole Rotating Magnet (Bendix 42 min sd MP). Describes the operation of a particular type of "Scintilla" magneto.

Theory and Operation of the Eight-pole Rotating Magnet and Secondary Condenser (Bendix 27 min sd MP). Shows how a particular type of "Scintilla" aircraft magneto works.

Traveling Electric Waves (MIT 50 min si MP). Describes the behavior of electrical waves on a power transmission line; behavior of direct-current waves on an open line; behavior of direct-current waves on short-circuited and loaded lines.

West Lynn (GE 30 min sd c MP). Story of the watt-hour meter.

What Is Electricity? (Westinghouse 20 min sd MP). Shows movement of electrons, flow of current; basic facts of electricity; making and distribution.

SOURCES OF FILMS LISTED ABOVE

AMNH—American Museum of Natural History, 79th St. and Central Park West, New York 24.

*Army, USA—U.S. Dept. of the Army, Washington 25, D.C.

Bendix Aviation Corp., Fischer Bldg., Detroit.

Brandon Films, Inc., 1600 Broadway, New York 19.

DeVry Films, Inc., 1111 Armitage Ave., Chicago 14.

EBF—Encyclopaedia Britannica Films, Inc., Wilmette, Ill.

Edison, Thomas A., Inc., West Orange, N. J.

Edited Pictures System, 165 W. 46th St., New York 18.

GE—General Electric Co., Visual Instruction Section, 1 River Rd., Schenectady, N.Y.

*Films sold by United World Films, rented by many film libraries.

JH—Jam Handy Organization, 2821 E. Grand Blvd., Detroit 11.

MIT—Massachusetts Institute of Technology, Division of Visual Education, Cambridge, Mass.

*Navy, USN—U.S. Dept. of the Navy, Washington 25, D.C.

SVE—Society for Visual Education, 100 E. Ohio St., Chicago 11.

*USAF—U.S. Dept. of the Air Force, Washington 25, D.C.

*USOE—U.S. Office of Education, Washington 25, D.C.

UWF—United World Films, Inc., 1445 Park Ave., New York 29.

Westinghouse Electric Corp., 306 Fourth Ave., P.O. Box 1017, Pittsburgh 30.

* Films sold by United World Films, rented by many film libraries.

APPENDIX

BRIEF HISTORIES OF GREAT MEN IN ELECTRICAL SCIENCE AND IMPORTANT ELECTRICAL DEVELOPMENTS*

Luigi Galvani (1737–1798), Italian physiologist, the "father of galvanic electricity," discovered that legs, severed from a newly killed frog, contract when touched at different points by two dissimilar metals that also touch one another. The date of this discovery was about 1780.

Alessandro Volta (1745–1827) was professor of natural history at the University of Pavia, Italy. He invented the electrophorus in 1775 and discovered the effect, known as the *Volta effect*, which states that "when two dissimilar uncharged metals are placed in contact with each other, one becomes positively charged and the other negatively charged, and a difference of potential, depending on the nature of the metals, is set up between them. In 1779 he announced his construction of the *voltaic pile*, the first electric battery, which transforms chemical energy into electrical energy. Conversely, if an electric current is passed through water between platinum electrodes, oxygen is given off at one pole and hydrogen at the other.

Charles Augustin de Coulomb (1736–1806), French scientist, experimentally verified the inverse-square law for charges and for magnetic poles in 1785. Later, the *coulomb* unit of electrical quantity was named in his honor and defined as follows: "The international *coulomb* is the quantity of electricity which passes any section of an electric current in one second when the current in the circuit is one international ampere."

André Marie Ampère (1775–1836), French physicist, developed a terminology for electricity and published papers in 1820, explaining the nature of the electric current and its relation to magnetism. The famous solenoid was developed by him. The principles laid down by Ampère (and Oersted) established the science of measuring electricity by means of magnets. In recognition of Ampère's pioneer work, the *ampere*, the unit of electric current, was named in his honor.

Dominique François Jean Arago (1786–1853), French physicist, discovered in 1820 that a magnet can be made by placing an iron or steel bar in the center of one of Ampère's solenoids when a current is passing through the solenoid. In 1824 he caused a compass to rotate by rotating a copper disk near it. This is known as *Arago's disk* and consists of a horizontal nonmagnetic disk capable of being rotated rapidly. Suspended above its center is a magnetic needle,

*Excerpts taken from "A Chronological History of Electrical Development," published by the National Electrical Manufacturers Association, New York.

and when the disk is revolved, thc needle takes up the rotating motion. This is caused by the action on the needle of the induced current set up in the disk by the magnetism of the needle. *Arago's disk* was, therefore, the first elementary induction motor.

Michael Faraday (1791–1867), English chemist and physicist, working with Sir Humphry Davy in London, discovered magnetoelectricity in 1821 and produced rotation of a wire carrying a current around a pole (a crude electric motor). He established the theory that, when electrification is produced by friction, by induction, or by any other means, the positive and negative charges so produced are always equal. In 1831 he developed his disk dynamo and announced that an electromotive force is set up in a conducting wire when it is moved at right angles to a magnetic field. He and Joseph Henry are credited with developing the first experimental electric motors.

Faraday's law, or the law of electromagnetic induction, was enunciated in 1831 and states: "The electromotive force induced in a circuit is proportional to the time rate of change of flux of magnetic induction linked with a circuit. When the change in flux linkages is caused by the motion, relative to a magnetic field, of a conductor forming part of an electric circuit, the electromotive force induced in the circuit is proportional to the rate at which the conductor cuts the flux of magnetic induction."

Also in 1831, Faraday made the first transformer during his experiments on producing electricity by magnetism. The apparatus he used consisted of an iron ring wound with two coils of bare wire, one about 72 ft. and the other 60 ft. long, the turns being separated by twine and the layers separated by calico. The larger coil was connected to a primary battery, and a loop of the other passed over a magnetic needle. When the battery circuit was broken or closed, the needle was deflected one way or the other by the induced current set up.

In 1833 Faraday named the process of decomposition by electricity *electrolysis*. The wire carrying the current into the solution he called the *anode*, and the wire by which the current leaves, the *cathode*. The solution itself he termed the *electrolyte*. He also discovered the laws of electrochemical decomposition, which state: "The amount decomposed by an electric current is proportional to the current flowing and the time during which it flows; and when an electrolyte, or a series of electrolytes, is decomposed by an electric current, the components into which it is separated are always chemically equivalent."

The unit of electrical capacitance, the *farad*, is named in Faraday's honor and is defined as follows: "The international farad is the capacitance of a capacitor if a charge of one international coulomb produces a potential difference between the terminals of one international volt."

Hans Christian Oersted (1777–1851), a Danish scientist, professor at the University of Copenhagen, discovered in 1826 that (1) a compass is deflected when placed near a current-carrying wire, and (2) a magnet exerts a force on a wire carrying a current.

Georg Simon Ohm (1787–1854), a German physicist, announced in 1827 the law (later called *Ohm's law*) that in a given circuit the current in amperes is equal to the pressure in volts divided by the resistance in ohms. The *ohm* was named in his honor and is defined as "the resistance of a column of mercury of uniform cross section, having a length of 106.30 centimeters and a mass of 14.4521 grams, at the temperature of melting ice."

Joseph Henry (1797–1878), a teacher of physics at Albany Academy, Albany, N. Y., discovered in 1831 the electromotive force of self-inductance. He invented the first electric bell, was the first to insulate iron for a magnetic coil, and was first to work out the differing functions of two kinds of electromagnet, the one surrounded by numerous coils of no great length, the other surrounded by a continuous coil of very great length. He was able to increase the lifting power of an electromagnet from 9 lb. to 3,500 lb.

In 1893 the International Congress of Electricians in Chicago gave Henry's name to the unit of inductance, defining it as follows: "The *international henry* is the inductance which produces an electromotive force of one international volt when the current is changing at the rate of one international ampere per second."

Jean Charles Athanase Peltier (1785–1845), a French physicist, discovered, in 1834, the heating and cooling effect (the *Peltier effect*) of an electric current at the junction of two dissimilar metals. The Peltier effect is defined as follows: "When a current flows across a junction of two dissimilar metals, it causes either an absorption or a liberation of heat, depending on the direction of the current, at a rate directly proportional to the current."

Henri Frederic Emile Lenz (1804–1885), a Russian physicist, announced in 1834 his law on the direction of an induced current: "The current induced in a circuit as a result of its motion in a magnetic field is in such a direction as to exert a mechanical force opposing the motion."

Samuel Finley Breese Morse (1791–1872) made the first telegraph instrument in 1836 from an old picture frame and exhibited it in 1837 at the University of the City of New York.

Thomas Davenport (1802–1851), inventor, of Brandon, Vt., developed several types of electric motor in 1837 for industrial work and is generally credited with being the first to produce a commercially successful motor. His original machine is on exhibition at the Smithsonian Institution, Washington, D. C.

James Prescott Joule (1818–1889), an English physicist, formulated the law known as *Joule's law* in 1841. It states that "when a current of voltaic electricity is propagated along a metallic conductor, the heat evolved in a given time is proportional to the resistance of the conductor multiplied by the square of the electrical intensity." The *joule*, the unit of electrical energy named in his honor, is defined as "the energy required to transfer one international coulomb between two points having a potential difference of one international volt."

Gustav Robert Kirchhoff (1824–1887), German scientist, applied Ohm's law in 1849 to groups of circuits, making possible the determination of the electrical characteristics of circuit networks. These laws, known as *Kirchhoff's laws*, are (1) the algebraic sum of the currents flowing toward any point in a network is zero; (2) the algebraic sum of the products of the current and resistance in each of the conductors in any closed path in a network is equal to the algebraic sum of the electromotive forces in that path.

Gaston Planté (1834–1889), a French physicist of Paris, designed the first storage battery in 1859, using lead plates immersed in dilute sulfuric acid.

Thomas Alva Edison (1847–1931), an American electrician and inventor, is credited, among others, with the following important electrical contributions:

1874 The development of the quadruplex telegraph system, permitting the sending of four messages over one wire simultaneously, two in each direction.

1879 The development of the first incandescent lamp. This lamp consisted of a platinum wire spiral in a vacuum chamber. He first carbonized cotton filaments and on Oct. 21 produced a lamp that burned 40 hr.; later he carbonized Bristol board, and it burned several hundred hours.

1882 The opening of the first electric lighting plant in the United States, the Pearl Street Station of the Edison Electric Illuminating Company, New York, N. Y. Original equipment consisted of six dynamos, each lighting 800 incandescent lamps.

1882 The development of the three-wire system, generally known as the *Edison three-wire system.*

1883 The discovery that electric current can flow through space, from a filament to a plate in an incandescent light bulb. Later, this phenomenon was called the *Edison effect,* the basis of electronics.

1891 The invention of the kinetoscope for projection and the kinetographic camera for the production of motion pictures.

1896 The invention of the first fluorescent lamp.

1908 The development of the "nickel-iron-alkaline" storage battery, generally called the *Edison* battery.

Alexander Graham Bell (1847–1922), an American inventor, transmitted the first complete sentence by telephone on Mar. 10, 1876; it was "Mr. Watson, come here; I want you."

William Stanley (1858–1916), American engineer, demonstrated in 1886 the practicability of alternating-current distribution using transformers. The first commercial lighting system using alternating current was established at Great Barrington, Mass.

Heinrich Rudolph Hertz (1857–1894), German physicist, discovered in 1887 that certain metals give off electric energy under the influence of light. This is the principle of the "electric eye" wherein a beam of light strikes a metal plate in a phototube and produces an electric current.

Elihu Thomson (1853–1937), American electrician, operated the first radio set in history in 1875. In 1887 he built the first repulsion-induction motor.

Nikola Tesla (1856–1943), foreign-born American inventor, worked out the theory of the modern alternating-current induction motor in 1887.

G. Johnstone Stoney (1826–1911), Irish physicist and mathematician, gave the name *electrons* to the smallest negative particles of electricity in 1891.

Wilhelm Konrad Roentgen (1845–1923), German scientist, discovered rays that "emanate from the bombardment of a metallic plate by electrons in an evacuated tube" in 1895. Not understanding what these rays were, he called them *X rays.*

Guglielmo Marconi (1871–1937), Italian electrician, sent the first radio signal Oct. 12, 1901—the letter *S*—across the Atlantic Ocean from Poldhu, Cornwall, to St. Johns, Newfoundland.

Lee de Forest (1873–   ), American inventor, announced on Oct. 20, 1906, his first three-element vacuum tube, described as an amplifier of feeble electrical currents.

William David Coolidge (1873–   ), American scientist, made tungsten ductile for incandescent lamp filaments in 1910. In 1913 he produced a hot-cathode X-ray tube operating at 100,000 volts; these tubes have become invaluable in diagnosis and in the treatment of disease.

Radio broadcasting, through station KDKA, was started on a regularly scheduled program basis in 1920. The first broadcast was the election returns of the Harding-Cox presidential campaign, Nov. 2. The first broadcasting license was issued to station WLW, Cincinnati, Ohio, in 1922. The first chain broadcast was transmitted Jan. 4, 1923, between WEAF, New York, and WNAC, Boston.

Important electrical developments were originated as follows:

1886 The first direct-connected sewing-machine motor was invented by Philip Diehl.

1887 The first electric ceiling fan was placed in operation.

1892 The first rotary converter, nonarcing lightning arrester, and the polyphase system of alternating-current generation and distribution were developed.

1893 The first code covering the installation of electrical equipment was printed; this was the beginning of the National Electrical Code.

1896 The first electrically heated flatirons were introduced.

1900 The first escalator was exhibited at the Paris Exposition, Paris, France.

1904 Silicon steel was first used for transformer cores.

1914 The first completely automatic substation was placed in operation at Union, Ill., by the Detroit Edison Company.

1923 The first neon-tube advertising sign was installed in a theater in New York, N. Y.

1923 Permalloy, a new magnetic material, was introduced.

1925 The hermetically sealed domestic refrigerator was introduced.

1926 The first automatic toasters for home use were introduced.

1928 The first demonstration of home reception of television was made.

1929 The first artificial fever machine was developed.

1929 The first automatic waffle iron was developed.

1930 The first commercial electric shaver was developed.

1931 The *Alnico* permanent magnet was discovered by a Japanese named Mishima.

1933 The first sodium-vapor lamps, for highway lighting, were installed on Balltown Road, near Schenectady, N. Y.

1935 The first round-the-world telephone conversation by wire and radio was held in New York, N. Y.

1938 Fluorescent lamps were introduced.

1939 The electron microscope was developed.

1942 The largest water-wheel generator—108,000 kva.—for Grand Coulee was installed.

1943 New type of compass, the Gyro Flux Gate Compass, developed for aircraft use. It is unaffected by the plane's motion.
1944 Thermoplastic synthetic insulating materials developed.
1944 Development of first 2,000,000-volt X-ray unit. It can make radiographic inspections of steel up to 12 in. in thickness.
1945 All-electric torpedo developed for the U.S. Navy.
1945 Electric blankets developed for general use.
1945 World's largest refrigerator, a 15-acre storage cave in Kansas, went into operation for the Department of Agriculture.
1946 Largest single-cab all-electric locomotives, 5,000 hp., constructed for Great Northern Railway.
1947 Transformers installed and tested to study 500-kv. circuits.
1947 Largest automatic sequence calculator, Mark II, developed by Harvard University.
1947 Radio-relay towers installed for service between New York City and Schenectady, N.Y.
1948 First turbine operated at 1,050° F. installed in a steam-electric power plant of the New Jersey Public Service and Gas Co.
1948 Development of the *transistor* in Bell Telephone Laboratories.
1948 Development of the magnetically suspended moving-element watt-hour meter.
1949 Color television developed.
1949 First installation of a gas turbine in an Oklahoma Gas and Electric Company plant.
1949 Largest three-phase transformer, 145,000 kva., built by Westinghouse Electric Corporation.
1950 Three-dimensional television receiver developed in the Argonne National Laboratory
1950 First underwater transatlantic amplifier installed off the coast of Newfoundland.
1950 Largest reversing twin-drive unit installed in a 206-in. 4-high steel mill. Two 4,000-hp., 30/75-rpm, 600-volt reversing motors were used.
1951 Largest dry-type transformer, 12,500 kva., constructed.
1951 Largest motor, 65,000 hp., installed at Grand Coulee Dam.
1951 Transcontinental microwave-radio system installed.
1952 First 6-ft. fluorescent street-lighting units installed.
1952 Cosmotron, rated at 1.3 billion electron volts, developed at Brookhaven National Laboratory.
1953 Largest direct-current motors, 10,500 hp., installed in a U.S. Navy icebreaker.
1953 Largest motor, 83,000 hp., developed for supersonic wind-tunnel research.
1953 Microwave system for utility installations developed. Provides 30 voice and several service and alarm channels.
1953 First 330-kv. transformers installed. They have ratings of 150,000 kva., three-phase.

ANSWERS TO PROBLEMS

CHAPTER 2

1. (*a*) 2,500 ft.; (*b*) 1,250 turns **2.** (*a*) 9.65 ohms; (*b*) 11.75 ohms **3.** (*a*) 660 ohms per mil-ft.; (*b*) Nichrome **4.** 104 mils **5.** 17.8 ohms **6.** 1,280 ohms **7.** 10,240 ohms **8.** No. 6 A.w.g. **9.** No. 7, No. 8 A.w.g. **10.** 1,525 turns **11.** 34°C. **12.** 10,240 ohms

CHAPTER 3

1. (*a*) 144 ohms; (*b*) 22.1 ohms; (*c*) 9.3 ohms **2.** 11 ohms, 10.45 amp. **3.** (*b*) 300 ohms; (*c*) 0.5 amp., 2.0 amp. **4.** (*a*) 180 ohms, 2.0 amp., 240 watts; (*b*) 120 ohms, 3.0 amp., 540 watts; (*c*) 90 ohms, 4.0 amp., 960 watts; (*d*) 60 ohms, 6.0 amp., 2,160 watts **5.** (*a*) 18 amp.; (*b*) 144 volts; (*c*) 1,728 watts; (*d*) 2,592 watts **6.** (*a*) 80 volts; (*b*) 8 amp., 40 amp., 10 amp.; (*c*) 58 amp.; (*d*) 0.69 ohm; (*e*) 6,900 watts **7.** (*a*) 96 volts; (*b*) 6 watts; 768 watts **8.** (*a*) 10 ohms; (*b*) 12 amp.; (*c*) 6 amp.; (*d*) 216 watts **9.** (*a*) 0.833 amp., 66.6 watts; (*b*) 1.67 amp., 2.5 amp. **10.** 22,500 ohms **11.** 48 volts, 72 volts **12.** 44°C. **13.** 120 amp. **14.** 15 min., 30 ohms **15.** (*a*) 180 amp.; (*b*) 10 volts drop; (*c*) 240 volts **16.** 1,800 watts loss, 95.8% **17.** $5.35 **18.** $1,122.12 **19.** $1,044.12 **20.** 0.06 ohm **21.** 20 amp., 120 watts **22.** (*a*) 6 ohms; (*b*) 4 amp.; (*c*) 96 watts **23.** 235 ft. **24.** 49°C. rise **25.** (*a*) 0.016 ohm; (*b*) 500 watts

CHAPTER 4

1. (*a*) $I_F - I_E - I_B = 0$; (*b*) $E_B + I_C R_C + I_D R_D - I_F R_F - I_B R_B = 0$ **2.** (*a*) $I_L = 40$ amp., $I_A = 20$ amp., $I_B = 20$ amp.; (*b*) $V_L = 20$ volts; (*c*) $P_A = 800$ watts, $P_B = 480$ watts, $P_C = 520$ watts **3.** (*a*) 12 amp.; (*b*) 13 amp. **4.** 2.5 amp. **5.** 782 watts **6.** (*a*) $I_A = 16.8$ amp., $I_B = 25.2$ amp.; (*b*) $I_A = 15.2$ amp., $I_B = 22.8$ amp. **7.** (*a*) 240 watts; (*b*) 60 watts; (*c*) 15 watts **8.** $R_L = 90$ ohms, $P_L = 25.6$ watts **9.** $V_A = 226.8$ volts, $V_B = 231.6$ volts **10.** (*a*) 120 volts; (*b*) 24 volts **11.** 1.6 amp., from x to y **12.** (*a*) $I_1 = 80$ amp., $I_2 = 120$ amp.; (*b*) $E_A = 234$ volts, $E_B = 238$ volts **13.** (*a*) $E_A = 105.5$ volts, $E_B = 118.5$ volts, $E_C = 233$ volts; (*b*) $P_A = 5{,}275$ watts, $P_B = 3{,}555$ watts, $P_C = 4{,}460$ watts **14.** 20 amp. **15.** $I_A = 28$ amp., $I_B = 42$ amp. **16.** (*a*) 57.5 ohms; (*b*) 2 amp. **17.** (*a*) 10 ohms; (*b*) 36 volts; (*c*) 2 amp. **18.** (*a*) 0.8 ohm; (*b*) 180 watts, 50% **19.** (*a*) 0.4 ohm; (*b*) 90 watts, 16.67%

CHAPTER 5

1. 40 ohms, 20 ohms, 16.7 ohms, 80 ohms, 800 ohms **2.** 0.0167 sec., 0.04 sec., 0.02 sec. **3.** 8.5 amp., 162.6 volts **4.** 0.5 amp., 1.0 **5.** 4 milliamperes, 0.096 watt **6.** 6.7 milliamperes, 0.268 watt **7.** (*a*) 2.4 amp.; (*b*) 82.4 volts **8.** 0.675 **12.** $R = 33.4$ ohms, $L = 0.153$ henry **13.** 0.5 henry **14.** (*a*) 13 ohms; (*b*) 12 ohms; (*c*) 5 ohms; (*d*) 500 watts; (*e*) 0.384 **15.** 0.157 **16.** (*a*) 0.6; (*b*) 2.51 amp.; (*c*) 55.5 μf. **17.** (*a*) 11.5 amp.; (*b*) $E_R = 92$ volts, $E_L = 230$ volts, $E_C = 161$ volts; (*c*) 1,058 watts; (*d*) 0.8 **18.** 4,430 watts **19.** (*a*) 12.43 kw.; (*b*) 69.7 amp.; (*c*) 0.813 **20.** 26.6 ohms **21.** 164 μf. **22.** (*a*) 3 amp., 135 watts; (*b*) 63.6 volts

CHAPTER 6

4. 4,000 amp. turns **5.** (*a*) 2.5 amp., (*b*) 4.8 ohms **6.** 2,400 amp. turns **7.** 12 volts **9.** (*a*) 937 amp. turns; (*b*) 480 amp. turns **10.** 0.27 lb. repulsion **11.** 220 **12.** 1,250 **13.** 465 **14.** 12 **15.** 337.5 lb. **16.** 275 amp. turns, 250 lb. **17.** No. 23 A.w.g. **18.** 585 lb. **19.** (*a*) 13.7 watts; (*b*) 450 lb., 27.4 watts **20.** 648 lb. **21.** 400 lines per sq. in. **22.** Zero

CHAPTER 7

1. 8.47 dyne-cm. per degree **2.** 6% low **3.** (*a*) 0.05102 ohm; (*b*) 0.05 ohm **4.** 7,497.5 ohms **5.** 7,500 ohms **6.** (*a*) 0.02 amp.; (*b*) 24.98 amp. **7.** 75 volts **8.** (*a*) 2; (*b*) 4; (*c*) 3.4 **9.** 27,700 ohms tapped at 1,200 ohms and 14,700 ohms **10.** 154 volts **11.** 119 volts, 221 volts **12.** 278.5 volts **13.** (*a*) 42.5 ohms; (*b*) 51.8% deflection **14.** 35% deflection **15.** 1,682 ohms

CHAPTER 8

2. (*a*) 0.9 volt; (*b*) 225 volts **3.** 12.6 volts **4.** Zero **5.** 0.48 **6.** 0.00314 henry **7.** 5.02 volts **8.** 3.77 henrys **9.** 40 **11.** $I_p = 2.175$ amp., $I_s = 43.5$ amp. **12.** 10, 20, 50, 60, 70, 80 **13.** $I_p = 2.22$ amp., $I_s = 44.4$ amp. **14.** Power transformed = 1.6 kw., power conducted = 3.2 kw. **15.** $I_p = 41.1$ amp., $I_s = 20.5$ amp. **16.** $I_{L1} = 60$ amp., $I_{L2} = 70$ amp., $I_N = 10$ amp. **17.** (*a*) 14.95 kw.; (*b*) 13 amp. **18.** 2,300 volts **19.** 103.2 amp.

CHAPTER 9

1. 250 rpm, 200 rpm **2.** 10 **3.** Motor = 24 poles, alternator = 10 poles, 300 rpm **4.** 1,440 rpm, 1,080 rpm **5.** 210 amp. **6.** 7.5 kw. **7.** (*a*) 100 amp.; (*b*) 108 amp. **8.** 32.6 amp. **9.** 35.2 kw. **10.** (*a*) 136 watts; (*b*) 85 watts **11.** 360 watts **12.** 5,350 amp. turns per pole **13.** 0% **14.** (*a*) 140 volts; (*b*) 5.6 kw. **15.** (*a*) 0.12 ohm; (*b*) 11.9 ft. **16.** (*a*) Generator 1,210 kw., generator 2, 630 kw.;

(*b*) generator 1, 350 amp., generator 2, 1,050 amp. **17.** 230 volts
18. 268.5 volts **19.** 13.85 kw. **20.** (*a*) 230 volts, 25 kw.;
(*b*) P_A = 37.5 kw., P_B = 50 kw.; (*c*) P_A = 12.5 kw., P_B = 0

CHAPTER 10

1. (*a*) 4.62 lb.; (*b*) 18.5 in.-lb. **2.** 84 amp. **3.** 138.5 ft.-lb.
4. (*a*) 217.2 volts; (*b*) 8,688 watts **5.** (*a*) 1,262 rpm; (*b*) 5.17%
6. 800 rpm **7.** 512 watts **8.** (*a*) I_L = 19 amp., I_A = 17 amp.;
(*b*) P_{sh} = 440 watts, P_{se} = 28.9 watts **9.** 1.1 ohms **10.** 4.5 ohms
11. 797 amp. **12.** 12 hp. **13.** 18.5 ft.-lb. **14.** 10.4 ft.-lb. **15.** 1,530 rpm
16. 2,860 rpm **17.** 3,420 rpm, 1,710 rpm, 1,140 rpm, 855 rpm
18. (*a*) 0.643; (*b*) 4.17%; (*c*) 3.77%; (*d*) 54.8% **19.** 0.627, 62.2%
20. 128 amp. **21.** 300, 225, 720 rpm **22.** 1,800 and 900 rpm
23. 15.35 lb.-ft. **24.** 76.2 amp. **25.** 200 volts **26.** (*a*) 0.078;
(*b*) 8.07%; (*c*) 0.856; (*d*) 158 lb.-ft.; (*e*) 89.7%

INDEX